S0-AKF-119

WORKBOOK

Student Notes and Problems

MATHEMATICS 30-2
Alberta

CASTLE ROCK
RESEARCH CORP

© 2012–2017 by Castle Rock Research Corporation
All rights reserved. No part of this book covered by the copyright hereon
may be reproduced or used in any form or by any means graphic, electronic,
or mechanical, including photocopying, recording, taping, or information
storage and retrieval systems without the express permission of the
publisher.

Rao, Gautam, 1961 –
STUDENT NOTES AND PROBLEMS – Mathematics 30-2 Alberta
ISBN: 978-1-77044-380-8

1. Mathematics – Juvenile Literature. I. Title

Published by
Castle Rock Research Corp.
2000 First & Jasper
10065 Jasper Avenue
Edmonton, AB T5J 3B1

10 9 8 7 6 5 4

Publisher
Gautam Rao

Contributors
John Campbell
Victoria Garlitos
Kathleen McLennan
Sonya Witzman

Dedicated to the memory of Dr. V. S. Rao

STUDENT NOTES AND PROBLEMS WORKBOOKS

Student Notes and Problems (SNAP) workbooks are a series of support resources in mathematics for students in grades 3 to 12 and in science for students in grades 9 to 12. SNAP workbooks are 100% aligned with curriculum. The resources are designed to support classroom instructions and provide students with additional examples, practice exercises, and tests. SNAP workbooks are ideal for use all year long at school and at home.

The following is a summary of the key features of all SNAP workbooks.

UNIT OPENER PAGE

- Summarizes the curriculum outcomes addressed in the unit in age-appropriate language
- Identifies the lessons by title
- Lists the prerequisite knowledge and skills the student should know prior to beginning the unit

LESSONS

- Provide essential teaching pieces and explanations of the concepts
- Include example problems and questions with complete, detailed solutions that demonstrate the problem-solving process

NOTES BARS

- Contain key definitions, formulas, reminders, and important steps or procedures
- Provide space for students to add their own notes and helpful reminders

PRACTICE EXERCISES

- Include questions that relate to each of the curriculum outcomes for the unit
- Provide practice in applying the lesson concepts

REVIEW SUMMARY

- Provides a succinct review of the key concepts in the unit

PRACTICE TEST

- Assesses student learning of the unit concepts

ANSWERS AND SOLUTIONS

- Demonstrate the step-by-step process or problem-solving method used to arrive at the correct answer
- *Answers and solutions for the **odd-numbered questions** are provided in each student workbook.*

CONTENTS

Rational Expression and Equations

Logarithmic and Exponential Functions

Polynomial Functions

Sinusoidal Functions

Answers and Solutions

Appendices

LOGICAL REASONING AND PROBLEM STRATEGIES

When you are finished this unit, you will be able to…
- Identify the next element in a number or shape pattern that requires logical reasoning
- Use the rule in a number pattern to answer questions
- Use a variety of strategies to solve logical reasoning games
- Identify and correct errors in logical reasoning games
- Use a variety of strategies to play strategy games

PREREQUISITE SKILLS AND KNOWLEDGE

Prior to starting this unit, you should be able to…
- Know the rules of a variety of basic logical reasoning and strategy games:
  - Backgammon
  - Battleships
  - Bulls and Cows
  - Checkers
  - Kakuro
  - Logic puzzles
  - Minesweeper
  - Reversi
  - Spokes
  - Sudoku
- Rules for all of the listed games can be found in the Puzzle and Game Glossary.

Lesson 1 COMPLETING PATTERNS

NOTES

Patterns are regularities that can be used to solve problems. In visual patterns, elements may repeat at regular intervals or appear in different arrangements following a rule.

When extending or completing visual patterns, examine each element of the pattern to see how it changes from one figure to the next. Look for regularities that can be used to determine the elements of the missing figure. NOTE: When looking at complex visual patterns, different interpretations can sometimes be made about what is happening to change the pattern from term to term, and applying these different interpretations can result in identical predictions.

Example

What is the next figure in the given pattern?

Solution

Step 1

Look at the colours of the shapes.

In each figure, the circle is grey, the diamond is patterned, the triangle is white, and the square is black. The shapes in next figure in the pattern will probably have the same colours.

Step 2

Look at the order of the shapes.

The smallest shape of each figure becomes the largest shape of the following figure. Each of the other shapes decreases in size.

The smallest shape in the third figure is a patterned diamond, so that will be the largest shape in the next figure. Inside of the diamond will be the white triangle, followed by the black square, and the grey circle will be the smallest shape.

Copyright Protected

Class Exercise 1

What is the next figure in the given pattern?

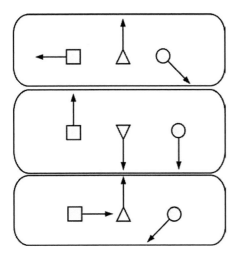

Number patterns often increase or decrease according to a rule involving number operations, but numbers can also form repeating or visual patterns. Just as with other visual patterns, visual number patterns can be extended by looking for regularities.

Example

The first four lines of a number pattern are given.

$$7 \times 9 = 63$$
$$77 \times 99 = 7623$$
$$777 \times 999 = 776223$$
$$7777 \times 9999 = 77762223$$

Apply the pattern to solve 777 777 × 999 999.

Solution
Step 1
Analyze the pattern.

In each row, an extra 7 is appended to the first multiplier, and an extra 9 is appended to the second multiplier. For each extra digit in each of the factors, an additional 7 is inserted at the beginning of the product, and an additional 2 is inserted before the 3.

In each row, if each of the factors has n digits, the product has $(n-1)$ 7s and $(n-1)$ 2s.

Step 2
Apply the pattern to solve 777 777 × 999 999.

Since there are six digits in each of the factors, the product will have five 7s and five 2s.

Therefore, the product is 777 776 222 223.

Class Exercise 2
The first four lines of a number pattern are given.

$$1089 \times 9 = 9801$$
$$10989 \times 9 = 98901$$
$$109989 \times 9 = 989901$$
$$1099989 \times 9 = 9899901$$

a) What is the next line in the pattern?

b) Without using a calculator, determine the product of 1 099 999 989 and 9.

PRACTICE EXERCISES

What is the fourth figure in each of the following patterns?

1.

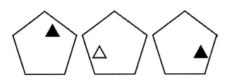

2.

3.

4.

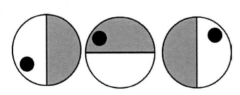

5.

Use the following information to answer the next question.

The perfect cube of any number, *n*, can be written as the sum of *n* consecutive odd numbers. Consider the following examples:

$$3^3 = 7 + 9 + 11$$
$$5^3 = 21 + 23 + 25 + 27 + 29$$
$$9^3 = 73 + 75 + 77 + 79 + 81 + 83 + 85 + 87 + 89$$

6. Express 7^3 as the sum of 7 consecutive odd numbers.

Use the following information to answer the next two questions.

The perfect squares of numbers composed entirely of 9s form a pattern:
$$9^2 = 81$$
$$99^2 = 9801$$
$$999^2 = 998001$$

7. According to the pattern, what is $9\,999^2$?

8. According to the pattern, what is $\sqrt{9\,999\,999\,800\,000\,001}$?

Use the following information to answer the next two questions.

A number pattern is given.

$$1 \times 9 + 2 = 11$$
$$12 \times 9 + 3 = 111$$
$$123 \times 9 + 4 = 1111$$

9. According to the pattern, what is $12\ 345 \times 9 + 6$?

10. If $x \times 9 + y = 11\ 111\ 111$, what is the value of y if the pattern continues?

Lesson 2 LOGICAL REASONING GAMES

NOTES

Logical reasoning games are puzzles (usually for one player) that can be solved using only logical reasoning. These games generally do not involve any specialized mathematical knowledge beyond basic counting and arithmetic.

LOOKING FOR A PATTERN

In some logical reasoning games, certain arrangements of numbers or other elements always produce the same results.

See the Puzzle and Game Glossary for a description of the rules of Minesweeper.

For example, in Minesweeper, if the numbers 2, 3, and 2 appear side by side on the edge of an empty area, then the adjacent spaces will always have the same configuration of mines, as shown. Mines are shown with flags, and empty spaces are shown with the letter E.

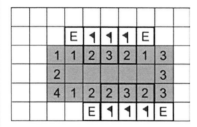

Example

In a Spokes puzzle on a triangular grid, whenever the number 4 appears on a hub on an edge of the triangle, it must be connected to all four adjacent hubs. Whenever the number 2 appears on a corner of the triangle, it must be connected to both adjacent hubs.

See the Puzzle and Game Glossary for a description of the rules of Spokes.

Use the given guidelines as a starting point to complete the following Spokes puzzle:

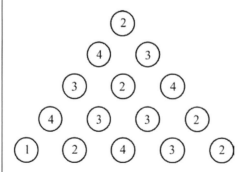

NOTES

Solution

Step 1

Join each of the 4s found along an edge to the four adjacent hubs.
Completed hubs are shaded.

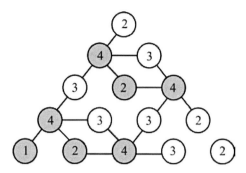

Step 2

Join each of the 2s found along an edge to the two adjacent hubs.
Completed hubs are shaded.

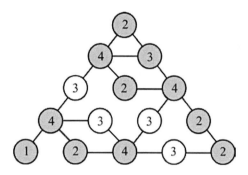

Step 3

Complete the remaining spokes.

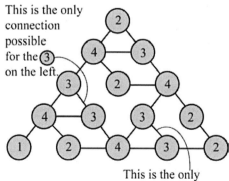

This is the only connection possible for the ③ on the left.

This is the only connection possible for the ③ on the bottom edge.

NOTES

DRAWING OR MODELLING

Drawing or *modelling* a problem involves creating a visual representation in order to help find the solution. Sometimes, drawing or modelling can lead directly to the solution of a problem or puzzle, and sometimes, it can suggest possible next steps.

Often, logic puzzles are solved using grids, where possibilities are checked off or eliminated according to certain clues. However, when logic puzzles involve visual elements, drawings or models may also be used.

See the Puzzle and Game Glossary for a description of logic puzzles.

Example

Suzie, Jonas, Olivia, and Simon are lined up to buy ice cream at an ice-cream truck. The following clues about their order are given:
1. They are in order from shortest to tallest, and the shortest person will be the first to get ice cream.
2. Olivia and Simon are both taller than Suzie is.
3. Simon will get his ice cream before Jonas does.
4. The two boys are not standing together.

What order are the children standing in?

Solution

Step 1
Analyze the first clue.

The first clue states that the children are lined up according to height. This gives general information about the situation but no specific information that can be used to order the children.

Step 2
Draw a model showing information from the second clue.

The second clue does not give information about the relative heights of Olivia and Simon, but you know that both of them are taller than Suzie.

Step 3
Draw a model including information from the third clue.

If Simon gets ice cream before Jonas, that means he must be shorter than Jonas. You already know that Simon is taller than Suzie, so draw a model showing Suzie, Simon, and Jonas.

Step 4
Analyze the last clue.

The two boys are not standing together, so one of the two girls must be between them. It cannot be Suzie because Suzie is shorter than both of the boys, so it must be Olivia.

NOTES

See the Puzzle and Game Glossary for a description of the rules of Sudoku.

ELIMINATING POSSIBILITIES

Eliminating possibilities is the process of narrowing many possible moves or choices down to a few.

Eliminating possibilities forms the basis for many logical reasoning games. In Sudoku, the simplest puzzles can be solved using this strategy alone.

Example

In this Sudoku puzzle, each row, column, and 2-by-3 box needs to contain each of the numbers 1 through 6.

				2	
4	2	6			
2			1		
			4	5	
5					
		1		6	

Use the process of elimination to find the location of all of the 2s.

Solution

Step 1
Fill in the missing 2 in the bottom left box.

The left and middle columns already contain 2s, so the only remaining option is for 2 to go in the empty square in the right-hand column. Arrows indicate rows or columns that already contain the number in question. The possibility that has not been eliminated is shown in the shaded square.

				2	
4	②	6			
②			1		
			4	5	
5		2			
		1		6	

Boxes refers to the smaller 2-by-3 grids that make up the puzzle. *Squares* refer to the individual spaces that each contains one number.

Step 2

Fill in the missing 2 in the middle box on the right.

The top row already contains the number 2, so the only place to put the number 2 is in the empty square on the bottom right.

					2
4	2	6			
②			1		▶
			4	5	2
5		2			
		1		6	

Step 3

Fill in the missing 2 in the box on the bottom right.

The only square that is in a row or column that does not already contain the number 2 is the bottom left square.

					2
4	2	6			
2			1		
			4	5	②
5		②			▶
		1	2	6	▼

Another way to use the process of elimination in a Sudoku puzzle is to look at an individual square and find the number that goes in that square by eliminating other possibilities.

Example

				2	
4	2	6			
2			1	★	
			4	5	2
5		2			
		1		6	

Use the process of elimination to determine which number goes in the starred square.

Solution

The starred square cannot contain the numbers 1, 2, 4, or 5, because the box containing the star already contains those numbers. It also cannot contain the number 6 because there is already a number 6 in that row.

See Puzzle Solutions at the back of the book for the completed puzzle.

See the Puzzle and Game Glossary for a description of the rules of Bulls and Cows.

See Puzzle Solutions for an explanation of how these guesses can be used to determine which four digits form the secret number.

The only possibility remaining is the number 3.

					2
4	2	6			
2			1	3	
			4	5	2
5		2			
		1		6	

In Bulls and Cows, a player first needs to identify which digits are included in a four-digit number and then determine the order of the digits.
The process of elimination is one way to determine the order of the digits.

Class Exercise 1

Trevor is playing a game of Bulls and Cows. After the sixth move, he correctly determines that the digits in the four-digit secret number are 1, 2, 4, and 5. His guesses are shown:

	Guess	Bulls	Cows
1	1234	0	3
2	2345	0	3
3	3456	1	1
4	4572	0	3
5	5728	2	0
6	7289	0	1

Use the process of elimination to determine the order of the digits in the secret number.

TRIAL AND ERROR

Trial and error is a method of finding a solution that involves attempting a variety of methods or possibilities until a successful one is found.
Trial and error should involve as little random guessing as possible.
Attempts should be made using all of the given information, and the outcome of each trial should result in better informed subsequent tries.

Trial and error can sometimes be used to determine the solution in logical reasoning games. The use of logical reasoning techniques may lead to a choice between two or three possibilities. In this case, choose one option, and test it to see if it results in a solution. If it does not, choose another option.

Copyright Protected

Example

The partial solution to a Sudoku puzzle is shown.

2		4	1	8	9	3	5	6
8	1	3	5		6	4		9
	6	9	3		4	1		
1	3		8	4	7	6	9	
	8			3			4	1
	4		2		1	5	3	8
6		8		1	3			4
3	2	7	4	6	8	9	1	5
4		1				8	6	3

Use trial and error to fill in the empty squares in the circled box.

Solution

Step 1
Determine which numbers can go in the empty boxes.

The bottom right-hand box has only two empty squares.
Since the two numbers missing from that box are the numbers 2 and 7, each empty square must contain either 2 or 7.

Step 2
Use trial and error to determine the correct locations of the numbers.

If 7 is placed in the left-hand square, then 2 will go in the right-hand square. In this case, there is no place to put the number 7 in the box above.

2		4	1	8	9	3	5	6
8	1	3	5		6	4		9
	6	9			4	1		
1	3		8	4	7	6	9	
	8			3			4	1
	4		2		1	5	3	8
6		8		1	3	7	2	4
3	2	7	4	6	8	9	1	5
4		1				8	6	3

This square cannot contain a number 7, because there is already a 7 in the same row.

This square cannot contain a number 7, because there is already a 7 in the same column.

See Puzzle Solutions at the back of the book for the completed puzzle.

NOTES

Putting the number 7 on the left led to contradictions, so the number 7 must be in the right-hand square.

2		4	1	8	9	3	5	6
8	1	3	5		2	4		9
	6	9				1		
1	3		8	4	7	6	9	2
	8			3		7	4	1
	4		2		1	5	3	8
6		8		1	3	2	7	4
3	2	7	4	6	8	9	1	5
4		1				8	6	3

Class Exercise 2

Four puzzle pieces must be arranged to form a 3-by-3 grid so that two identical shapes are never vertically or horizontally adjacent. The pieces may not be rotated.

Use trial and error to determine the arrangement of the pieces.

MAKE A SYSTEMATIC LIST

A *systematic list* is a way to organize information in an orderly way to make it easier to determine what information is still needed. Systematic lists can also be helpful in eliminating possibilities or applying other logical reasoning strategies.

In some logical reasoning games that involve filling in a grid, the numbers that may go in each space in the grid can be listed. Often, listing the possibilities leads to a logical solution.

Example

One corner of a Kakuro puzzle is shown.

NOTES

See the Puzzle and Game Glossary for a description of the rules of Kakuro.

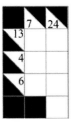

Because the only three numbers that have a sum of 7 are 1, 2, and 4, it is possible to make a systematic list of the possibilities for the empty squares in the column on the left.

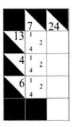

Use the ordered list to complete this portion of the Kakuro puzzle.

Solution
Step 1

Fill in the first row.

One of the numbers 1, 2, or 4 needs to be added to another number to total 13. Make another ordered list showing the sums using these three numbers.

- $\underline{1} + 12 = 13$
- $\underline{2} + 11 = 13$
- $\underline{4} + 9 = 13$

The rules of Kakuro state that only single-digit numbers may be used, so the only possible sum is $4 + 9$.

Because there is already a 4 in the first column, the two remaining squares must contain the numbers 1 and 2.

Step 2

Fill in the second row.

The only two remaining possibilities for the middle square on the left are 1 and 2. Make a list of sums with a total of 4:

- $1 + 3 = 4$
- $2 + 2 = 4$

Since it is not permitted to have the same number twice in one row or column, the only possible sum is $1 + 3$.

Step 3

Fill in the third row.

The only possibility remaining for the square on the left is 2. The square on the right must contain the number 4 because $2 + 4 = 6$.

Step 4

Fill in the remaining squares.

The sum of the numbers in the right column is 24. The sum of 9, 3, and 4 is 16, so the number in the empty square must be $24 - 16 = 8$.

 Copyright Protected

Class Exercise 3

The partial solution to a Sudoku puzzle is shown.

5	1	7		2	3	8	9	6
2	4	6	8	1	9	7	5	3
8	9	3		5	7	4	2	1
4	6	8	2	7	1	9	3	5
3	2	5	9			1	7	4
1	7	9	5	3	4	6	8	2
9		2		4		5	1	7
6	5	1	7	9	2	3	4	8
7		4	1			2	6	9

Use an ordered list to determine which numbers go in the empty squares in the circled box.

SIMPLIFYING THE ORIGINAL PROBLEM

Often, an entire puzzle or game board is too large or too complex to be analyzed all at one time. When this is the case, it can be advantageous to focus on only one small portion of the puzzle.

Example

This Kakuro puzzle is on a 9-by-10 grid, but there are six smaller sections that are connected to the rest of the puzzle with only one square.

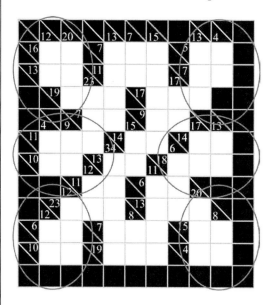

Each of these squares can be solved on its own to make the entire puzzle easier to solve.

Determine the numbers that belong in the five squares in the top left.

Solution

The sum of the rows inside the circled box is equal to the sum of the columns inside the circled box. This means that the number that will go into the starred square must be equal to the difference between the sum 12 + 20 = 32 and the sum 16 + 13 = 29.
32 – 29 = 3

The number 3 must go in the starred square.

 Copyright Protected

NOTES

The problem can now be simplified even further. The sum of the three numbers in the column on the right is 20, so the sum of the numbers in the two empty squares must be 20 – 3 = 17.

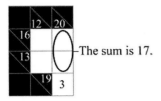 —The sum is 17.

The only two one-digit numbers with a sum of 17 are 8 and 9, so each of the empty squares in the column on the right is either 8 or 9.

The sum of the two numbers in the top row is 16. The only two pairs of one-digit numbers with a sum of 16 are 7 + 9 and 8 + 8. Since the rules of Kakuro do not allow a number to be repeated in a sum, each of the numbers in the top row must be either 7 or 9.

The only number that can be included in both the top row and the right-hand column is 9, so the number in the top right-hand square must be 9.

All of the other squares in this section of the puzzle can be completed using subtraction.

All of the other circled portions in the original puzzle can be completed in the same way, which will lead to the solution to the entire puzzle.

See Puzzle Solutions at the back of the book for the completed puzzle.

DEVELOPING ALTERNATIVE APPROACHES

Often in logical reasoning games, different strategies must be used in turn to solve one puzzle.

Example

In this version of Sudoku, the digits 1 through 5 need to appear once in every row, column, and outlined shape.

Use a variety of strategies to find the solution to the puzzle.

Solution

Step 1

Use the process of elimination to fill in the numbers in the outlined shape at the top left and in the top row.

In the outlined shape in the top left, the empty squares must contain the numbers 2 and 5. The empty square in the top row cannot contain the number 2. Therefore, the digit 2 is in the second row, and the digit 5 is in the top row.

The last remaining square in the top row cannot be 1, 2, 3, or 5, because the row already has those numbers. The only possibility is that it is 4.

Step 2

Make an ordered list of the numbers that can go in the empty squares in the second column.

      22   Copyright Protected

The numbers 1 and 4 must go into the two squares that fall inside the bottom left box, because 1 and 4 are already in the left column.

The remaining empty square in the second column cannot be 2 or 5 because the column already contains those numbers. It must be 1, 3, or 4.

There is only one square in the column that can contain the number 3.

Step 3
Use trial and error to complete the remaining squares in the second column.

Try putting 4 in the upper square and 1 in the lower square.

If 4 goes in the upper square, then there will be no possible place to put 4 in the outlined shape immediately to the right. Therefore, this guess is incorrect, and the locations of 4 and 1 must be reversed.

Recall that arrows indicate rows or columns that already contain the number in question. The possibility that has not been eliminated is indicated with a shaded square.

Step 4

Use the process of elimination to fill in the remainder of the puzzle.

Fill in the missing 4s.

Fill in the missing 3s

Fill in the top middle box.

The two empty squares must be 1 and 5. The digit 1 can go in the upper box only, because the third row already contains the digit 1.

Fill in the missing 5s.

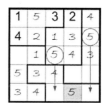

Step 5

Fill in the last remaining squares in columns 1, 3, and 4.

Step 6

Fill in the last remaining squares in the fourth and fifth rows.

1	5	3	2	4
4	2	1	3	5
2	1	5	4	3
5	3	4	1	2
3	4	2	5	1

PRACTICE EXERCISES

Use the following information to answer the next two questions.

The rules of a logic puzzle state that each of the letters A, B, C, D, and E must appear exactly once in each row, column, and string of five circles on a 5-by-5 grid.

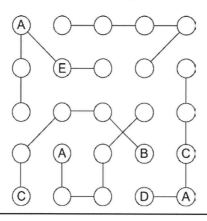

1. Make ordered lists of the letters that can go in each of the circles in the middle row.

2. Determine which letter goes in each of the circles in the middle row.

Use the following information to answer the next question.

A 3-by-3 grid must be filled in using nine distinct pictures. There are three of each of the following shapes: triangles, squares, and circles. Each shape may be black, grey, or spotted. A partially completed grid is given. White shapes indicate missing colours, and stars indicate missing shapes.

Samia says that it is impossible to determine the shape that belongs in the top left square, because only one other black shape is given.

3. Explain why Samia is correct or incorrect.

Use the following information to answer the next question.

A 4-by-4 grid contains the numbers 1 through 4. Squares must be crossed out so that no numbers are repeated in any row or column. To correctly solve the puzzle, the fewest possible squares should be eliminated.

2	3	1	3
1	3	4	2
3	3	4	4
2	4	2	2

4. In the circled column, which 3 should **not** be eliminated?

Use the following information to answer the next question.

A 5-by-5 grid must be filled in with the numbers 1 through 25 so that consecutive numbers are vertically, horizontally, or diagonally adjacent. The row, column, or diagonal where each number is found is given in the clues around the outside of the puzzle.

The number 1 is given. Lucy fills in the numbers 2 and 3 by following the clues, but she makes at least one error.

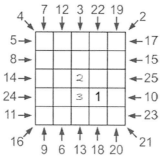

5. Explain what Lucy did wrong.

Use the following information to answer the next question.

A 6-by-6 grid must be completed so that each of the numbers 1 through 6 appears once in each row, column, and 2-by-3 box. Wherever two squares are separated by a dotted line, the numbers in those squares are consecutive.

6. Fill in the remainder of the grid.

Lesson 3 STRATEGY GAMES

A strategy game is a multiplayer game whose outcome relies on the strategic thinking of the opponents. Although some strategy games have a small element of luck, in true strategy games, players with stronger strategic reasoning skills generally win.

TRIAL AND ERROR

Strategy games, such as Battleships, are based on trial and error. Players begin by randomly trying out possible solutions. On subsequent turns, they use feedback about their attempts in order to make better guesses until a solution is found.

NOTES

See the Puzzle and Game Glossary for a description of the rules of Battleships.

Example

In a game of Battleships, a player's first three turns are misses, but the fourth turn is a hit, as shown. Misses are shown with white pegs, and hits are shown with shaded pegs.

	1	2	3	4	5	6	7	8	9	10
A										
B								●		
C										
D				O						
E										
F							O			
G										
H										
I		O								
J										

What are the player's best options for the next guess?

Solution

Since every ship has at least two pegs, there has to be another hit in at least one of the squares A8, B7, B9, and C8.

	1	2	3	4	5	6	7	8	9	10
A								↑		
B							← ● →			
C								↓		
D				O						
E										
F							O			
G										
H										
I		O								
J										

Ships cannot be placed diagonally, so although it is possible that there is a hit on a different ship in one of squares A7, A9, C7, and C9, the squares that are horizontally or vertically adjacent to B8 are better guesses.

See the Puzzle and Game Glossary for a description of the rules of Checkers and Reversi.

The player should guess those squares until a second hit is made. If the hit was made on a ship with more than two pegs, the player should continue guessing adjacent squares until the ship is sunk.

On the first three turns, the player had to make random guesses, because there was no information about the locations of the ships. However, once a hit was scored, better informed decisions about the locations of future hits could be made.

In other strategy games, such as Checkers or Reversi, players may attempt new strategies. If the strategy fails, the player may lose the game, but this should result in better plays in the future.

LOOKING FOR A PATTERN

In strategy games, players may either seek or avoid certain patterns of pieces. For example, in the game of Four in a Row, the goal is to form a vertical, horizontal, or diagonal row of four pieces. A player who can place three pieces in a row without an opponent's piece on either end will win the game. In the game board shown, white will win because the opponent has no move that can prevent him or her from making a row of four on the following turn.

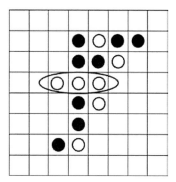

In Checkers, players avoid arranging their pieces in the following pattern, because it allows the opponent to capture multiple pieces in one turn:

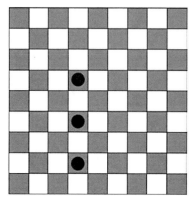

A player who sees that some of the opponent's pieces are arranged in this pattern should begin to manoeuvre into a position to capture these pieces.

ELIMINATING POSSIBILITES

In strategy games, there are often many possible moves at any time. Different moves can be eliminated based on the specific strategy that a player has chosen to use or by predicting the result that a given move may have.

Example

In Reversi, the most valuable spaces to control are generally considered to be the corners, and after that, the edges. For this reason, the squares that are diagonally adjacent to each of the corners should be avoided, because they provide the opponent the opportunity to control the corners. In this diagram, desirable squares are marked with happy faces, and undesirable squares are marked with sad faces.

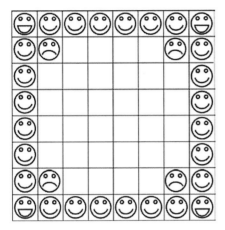

In the game shown, it is white's turn to play. Potential moves are numbered 1 though 4.

According to the given information, which move is the least desirable?

Solution

If white places a piece in square 1, then two black pieces will be captured. Any other move will capture only one black piece. However, square 1 is diagonally adjacent to the corner, and placing a piece in that square may allow the opponent eventual control of the corner or edge squares. For this reason, square 1 is not a desirable move, giving the player only three possible moves to choose from.

It is also worth noting that in Reversi, it is not necessarily advantageous to control the majority of the squares early in the game, so decisions based on position are especially important.

NOTES

Class Exercise 1

Adam and Carrie are playing checkers. Adam is playing white, and it is his move. The white pieces that have a legal move are numbered 1 through 7.

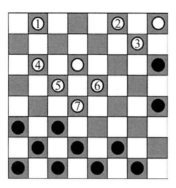

Adam does not want to allow Carrie to capture any more of his pieces, even if it results in an exchange.

Use the process of elimination to determine which pieces Adam can move.

DEVELOPING ALTERNATIVE APPROACHES

In many cases, one strategy is not sufficient to win a game or solve a puzzle. A successful player should be comfortable with a wide variety of approaches.

In strategy games, this often involves knowing several different strategies and applying them at different points in the game as appropriate. The approach that should be used can depend on the strategy that the opponent is using or on the current layout of the game board. Some strategies are more suitable at different stages of the game.

See the Puzzle and Game Glossary for a description of the rules of Backgammon.

Example

In the game of Backgammon, one strategy is to leave checkers in your opponent's home board, and another strategy is to try to clear your checkers out of your opponent's home board. Each of these two opposing strategies can be adopted depending on the point in the game and whether your pieces are more advanced than your opponent's.

In general, if most of your checkers are more advanced than those of your opponent, it is a good idea to move your checkers out of the opponent's home board. On this game board, black has eight checkers in the home board and five more that can be moved in with one roll. Black should probably move the two checkers remaining out of white's home board as soon as possible.

White home board

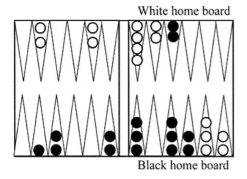

Black home board

On the other hand, if the opponent is winning, the opposite strategy can be used. In the following situation, white's pieces are much more advanced than black's pieces, and black has five pieces in white's home board.

White home board

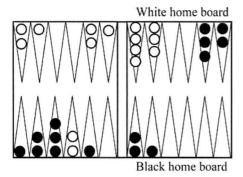

Black home board

Black may want to keep the checkers in white's home board to try to block the play and possibly knock off some white checkers as they move into the home board. This strategy is called the back game.

Playing the back game is not always advantageous, even if your opponent is winning. In the following board, black's checkers are in exactly the same position as in the previous situation, but white's pieces are distributed differently.

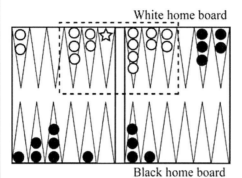

If white can cover the starred square with two checkers, it will form a *prime*, or a wall of six points. If white does this, then black will be unable to escape white's home board until the prime is broken. In this situation, black should try to get the checkers out as soon as possible rather than play the back game.

When playing strategy games, it is important to be able to evaluate, select, and apply a variety of strategies.

Copyright Protected

PRACTICE EXERCISES

Use the following information to answer the next two questions.

The object of a strategy game played with white and black checkers on a 7-by-7 grid is to capture all of the opponent's checkers. Checkers may move one space horizontally, vertically, or diagonally into any vacant adjacent space. When a player moves a checker into a space adjacent to an opponent's checker, that checker is captured, along with all of the opponent's checkers that fall on the capturing checker's line of movement. Only checkers that form a continuous line are captured.

In the situation shown, when the black checker moves into the space shown, all three starred white checkers are captured and removed from the board. The white checker in the top row is not captured because it is separated from the rest of the white pieces by a black checker. The two white checkers in a horizontal row are not captured because they do not fall along the line of movement.

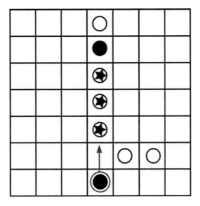

In the game shown, it is white's move. The white player sees that there are two rows of four white checkers that black could capture on the next move.

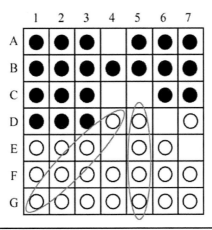

1. Find a move that white can make to prevent black from capturing either row of four checkers.

Use the following additional information to answer the next question.

Another way to capture is by withdrawal. A checker that is adjacent to an opponent's checker may capture that piece by moving away from it. This capture also includes all of the opponent's checkers in a continuous row along the line of movement. In the situation shown, the two starred white checkers are captured.

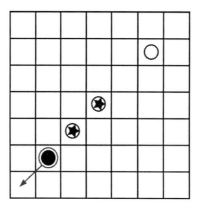

A move is considered good if it captures more pieces than will be lost on the opponent's turn.

On the board shown, it is white's turn.

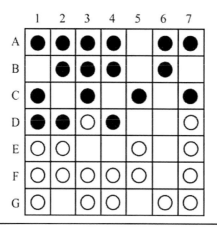

2.   What is white's **best** possible move?

Use the following information to answer the next question.

Tamia and Genevieve are playing a game in which the objective is to join four letters in a vertical, horizontal, or diagonal line. Each girl uses her initial to show her moves. The girls have to leave a game partway through, and when they come back later, they cannot remember whose turn it is.

	1	2	3	4	5	6
A			T			T
B					T	
C			G	G	T	G
D			G	T	G	G
E						T
F						

Tamia says that it does not matter who takes the next turn, but Genevieve says that it does matter because whoever goes next can win the game.

3. Explain why Genevieve is correct or incorrect.

Use the following information to answer the next two questions.

The goal of a particular strategy game is to draw lines from one point to another point following a set of simple rules:

- A line may be straight or curved, but it cannot cross any other line.
- A line may go from one point to another point, or it may form a loop that starts and ends at the same point.
- When a player draws a line, he or she must also draw a point that falls somewhere on that line.
- Any point may have a maximum of three lines attached to it. A loop counts as two lines coming out of a point.

Any player who cannot draw a legal line loses the game.

The first three moves of a game are shown. The game starts with two points already drawn. Player 1 makes dotted lines, and player 2 makes solid lines. Points with three lines already attached are coloured black.

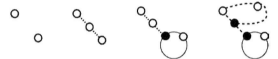

4.   What line can player 2 draw to win the game?

Use the following additional information to answer the next question.

In a variation on the previous game, the last player to draw a legal line loses the game. The first three moves of a game are shown.

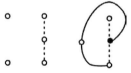

5.   Where can player 1 draw a line to win the game?

REVIEW SUMMARY

- When extending or completing visual patterns, examine each element of the pattern to see how it changes from one figure to the next. Look for regularities that can be used to determine subsequent elements.
- Visual patterns may involve shapes, pictures, or numbers.
- Logical reasoning games are puzzles (usually for one person) that can be solved using only logical reasoning. They generally do not involve any specialized mathematical knowledge beyond basic counting and arithmetic.
- A strategy game is a multiplayer game whose outcome relies on the strategic thinking of the players.
- There are several strategies that can be used in logical reasoning and strategy games.
- Look for a pattern: certain arrangements of numbers or other elements always produce the same results.
  - Draw or model: create a visual representation in order to help find the solution.
  - Eliminate possibilities: narrow many possible moves or choices down to a few.
  - Trial and error: attempt a variety of methods or possibilities until a successful one is found.
  - Systematic lists: create an ordered list showing possibilities or other information related to the puzzle.
  - Simplify the original problem: focus on solving a portion of the puzzle or controlling a portion of the game board.
- It is usually necessary to use a variety of approaches when solving a single logical reasoning game or playing a single strategy game.

PRACTICE TEST

Use the following information to answer the next question.

The first four lines of a number pattern are given.
$$999\ 999 \times 1 = 999\ 999$$
$$999\ 999 \times 2 = 1\ 999\ 998$$
$$999\ 999 \times 3 = 2\ 999\ 997$$
$$999\ 999 \times 4 = 3\ 999\ 996$$

1. If the pattern continues, what needs to be multiplied by 999 999 to result in a product of 6 999 993?

Determine the fourth figure in each of the following patterns.

2.

3.

Use the following information to answer the next question.

To solve a small Kakuro puzzle, Alice starts by making lists of the possible addends for each of the numbers in the puzzle. Then, she fills in the first column with a list of the numbers that can be used to add up to 22.

$$8 = (1+2+5), (1+3+4)$$
$$9 = (2+3+4), (1+3+5), (1+2+6)$$
$$11 = (2+9), (3+8), (4+7), (5+6)$$
$$14 = (5+9), (6+8)$$
$$20 = (5+7+8), (5+6+9), (4+7+9), (3+8+9)$$
$$22 = (6+7+9), (5+8+9)$$

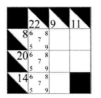

4. Use the lists to fill in the remainder of the puzzle.

Use the following information to answer the next question.

A 4-by-4 grid must be filled in using 16 distinct pictures. There are four each of the following shapes: hearts, diamonds, clubs, and spades. Each shape may be black, grey, spotted, or hatched. A partially completed grid is given. White shapes represent missing colours, and stars represent missing shapes.

5. What picture should go in the square that contains a white star?

Use the following information to answer the next two questions.

A 4-by-4 grid contains the numbers 1 through 4. Numbers must be circled so that the circled numbers in each row and column add up to the totals given along the right side and the bottom of the grid.

2	3	3	1	4
4	1	3	2	5
1	2	4	2	7
1	3	2	4	8
6	6	7	5	

6. In which row or column is there only one way to circle numbers to reach the desired sum?

Use the following additional information to answer the next question.

Darcy begins to solve the puzzle, but his partial solution contains one error.

2	③	3	①	4
④	1	3	2	5
①	2	4	2	7
①	③	2	④	8
6	6	7	5	

7. Find and correct Darcy's error.

 Copyright Protected

Use the following information to answer the next question.

A 5-by-5 grid needs to be partitioned into square- and rectangular-shaped sections. Each number in the grid gives the number of squares in that section. Each section contains only one number, and there are no sections without a number.

Two of the sections in this grid are given.

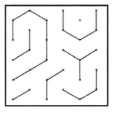

8. Partition the grid according the given rules.

Use the following information to answer the next question.

Tyler and Matt are playing a game in which the goal is to complete equilateral triangles on dot paper. On each player's turn, that player connects two adjacent dots. Any player who completes a triangle writes his initial inside that triangle and then takes another turn.

Moves can be rated based on the number of triangles completed or given up. For example, completing 4 triangles in one turn gets a rating of 4. Drawing a line that allows the opponent to complete 2 triangles on his turn gets a rating of –2. A move that neither completes a triangle nor allows an opponent to complete a triangle gets a rating of 0.

9. It is Tyler's turn. What is the rating of his **best** move?

Use the following information to answer the next question.

In a particular strategy game, the goal is to capture all of the opponent's pieces. On a player's turn, that player moves a piece one spot in any direction following the lines. If a player forms a row of three pieces along a line, then that player may remove one of the opponent's pieces from the board.

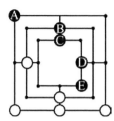

In this game, white has just formed a row of three pieces and may now remove one of the black pieces.

10. Which piece is **best** black piece for white to remove?

SET THEORY

When you are finished this unit, you will be able to…
- Define a set using a verbal description, roster form, or set notation
- Define a single set in more than one way
- Identify and define the empty set, the universal set, subsets, unions, intersections, and disjoint sets
- Understand and apply set theory notation, including the symbols $\in$, $\subset$, $\varnothing$, $\cup$, and $\cap$
- Determine the intersection or the union of two or three sets
- Count the elements in a set
- Represent up to three sets using a Venn diagram or a Carroll diagram
- Use logical operators AND, OR, and NOT to define sets
- Solve problems involving sets

Lesson	Page	Completed on
1. Understanding Sets and Set Notation	46	
2. Solving Problems Involving Sets	61	
Review Summary	75	
Practice Test	76	
Answers and Solutions	at the back of the book	

PREREQUISITE SKILLS AND KNOWLEDGE

Prior to starting this unit, you should be able to…
- Read and interpret Venn diagrams
- Sort sets of numbers, objects, and other groups into Venn diagrams with up to three circles
- Recognize various number systems, including natural numbers, whole numbers, rational numbers, and real numbers
- Understand and apply basic number relationships, such as factors and multiples
- Understand and apply basic number properties, such as prime numbers, composite numbers, perfect squares, and perfect cubes

Lesson 1 *UNDERSTANDING SETS AND SET NOTATION*

NOTES

A **set** is a collection of distinct objects, such as people, items, numbers, or other sets. Anything that belongs to a set is called an **element** of that set. For example, if set A contains the number 3, then the number 3 is an element of A. This is denoted $3 \in A$.

DEFINING SETS IN ROSTER FORM

A set may be defined by listing all of the elements of the set. Generally, the name of the set is given, followed by a pair of curly brackets containing a list of the elements of the set separated by commas. This is called listing a set in **roster form**.

For example, set B, containing the letters in the word TEN, is given in roster form as $B = \{T, E, N\}$.

Repeated elements within a set are considered irrelevant, and two sets with identical elements are the same set. Therefore, the sets of letters in the words TEEN {T, E, N} and NET {N, E, T} are also set B.

Set C, containing the even integers between 1 and 9, is given in roster form as $C = \{2, 4, 6, 8\}$.

Roster form can also be used to define sets with a large number of elements or with an infinite number of elements, as long as those elements are numbers that continue in a predictable pattern. An ellipsis (…) is used to replace any number of elements in the set.

Example

List the elements of M in roster form, where M is the set of positive multiples of 10 up to and including 500.

Solution

This set has 50 elements. It would be possible to list all of the elements in roster form, but it would take a lot of space and time. Instead, begin the roster with three elements, replace all of the middle elements with an ellipsis, and then end with the largest number in the set.

$M = \{10, 20, 30, \ldots, 500\}$

Class Exercise 1

Set D is the set of days in one week. Define D in roster form.

Copyright Protected

Class Exercise 2

Define P in roster form, where P is the set of all positive integers.

DEFINING SETS USING VERBAL DESCRIPTIONS

A set may also be defined using a verbal description. For example, the set {M, A, T, H} can be defined as the set of letters contained in the word MATH.

Example

Set A is defined in roster form as {11, 13, 15, 17, 19}. Define A using a verbal description.

Solution

Step 1

Establish what the elements of the set have in common.

The numbers 11, 13, 15, 17, and 19 are all odd numbers, and they are all greater than 10 and less than 20.

Step 2

Define the set.

Set A is the set of odd numbers between 10 and 20.

DEFINING SETS USING SET BUILDER NOTATION

Sets containing only numbers can be defined using **set builder notation**. Set builder notation is shorthand mathematical notation used to describe a set according to the properties of its elements.

Like roster form, curly brackets are used in set builder notation. The elements of a set are defined using a variable followed by a colon or a vertical line, followed by a list of any restrictions on the elements.

Consider the elements of set $P = \{1, 2, 3, ...\}$. The elements can have any value, as long as that value is a positive integer. In other words, P contains all values of x such that x is an integer and x is greater than 0. Given in set notation, this is $P = \{x : x \text{ is an integer}, x > 0\}$, or

$P = \{x \mid x \text{ is an integer}, x > 0\}$.

The phrase "x is an integer" can be written more formally as $x \in I$, which means that x is an element of the set of all integers.

NOTES

Sometimes, formulas are used to help define the kinds of numbers that belong in a given set.

Example

Define set $C = \{2, 4, 6, 8\}$ using set builder notation.

Solution

Step 1
Assign a variable to the elements of the set.

Any variable may be assigned. In this case, use k.

Step 2
Use a formula to define k.

All of the possible values of k are even numbers. Every even number is a multiple of 2, so every value of k is 2 multiplied by another number, n, as long as n is an integer. Therefore, $k = 2n$.

The variable n must be an integer, because if it is not, then k will not be an even number. For example, if $n = 1.5$, then $k = 2(1.5) = 3$.

Step 3
List any other restrictions on n.

All of the values of k are from 2 to 8, inclusive. Since $k = 2n$, the values of n must be from 1 to 4, inclusive.

Step 4
Express $C = \{2, 4, 6, 8\}$ using set builder notation.

Set C contains all the values of k such that $k = 2n$, where n is an integer with a value from 1 to 4, inclusive.
$C = \{k : k = 2n, n \text{ is an integer}, 1 \le n \le 4\}$

Another form of set builder notation only uses one variable; this set would be defined as
$C = \begin{Bmatrix} 2n : n \text{ is an integer,} \\ 1 \le n \le 4 \end{Bmatrix}$.

Class Exercise 3

Define $M = \{10, 20, 30, \ldots, 500\}$ using set builder notation.

Class Exercise 4

Set $F = \{p : p = x^3, x \text{ is an integer}, x \le -1\}$. Define F in roster form.

THE EMPTY SET

The set containing no elements is called the **empty set**, denoted {} or Ø. Sets with identical elements are considered to be the same set. For this reason, there is only one empty set.

Example

Determine whether each of the following phrases describes the empty set:
- Set K contains all of the presidents of Canada.
- Set L contains all even prime numbers.
- Set M contains all of the negative perfect squares.
- Set N contains all insects with eight legs.

Solution

Examine each description. If there are no elements in the set described, then it is the empty set.
- Canada does not have any presidents, so $K = Ø$.
- The number 2 is an even prime number, so $L \neq Ø$.
- All perfect squares are positive, so $M = Ø$.
- All insects have exactly six legs, so $N = Ø$.

Therefore, K, M, and N all describe the empty set, and $K = M = N = Ø$.

THE UNIVERSAL SET

The **universal set** is the larger, inclusive set from which elements can be considered. For example, the set of vowel letters is $V = \{A, E, I, O, U\}$ only if the universal set is letters of the English language. If the universal set is letters of the Russian language, then $V = \{А, Я, О, Ё, Э, Е, У, Ю, Ы, И\}$.

In a Venn diagram, a set is represented as a circle contained within a rectangular universe. This diagram shows set A contained within universe U.

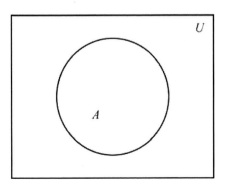

Some sets are common in set theory, and many of these sets are identified by special symbols. The empty set is one of these common sets. The following sets are also identified by special symbols:

Natural numbers ($\mathbb{N}$)

Integers (I or $\mathbb{Z}$)

Rational numbers ($\mathbb{Q}$)

Real numbers ($\mathbb{R}$)

Example

In the following diagram, set S contains only perfect squares less than 100, and the universal set O consists of all odd integers.

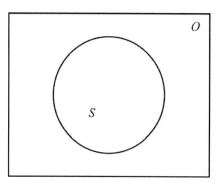

List the elements of set S in roster form.

Solution

Step 1
List all perfect squares less than 100.

The perfect squares less than 100 are 1, 4, 9, 16, 25, 36, 49, 64, and 81.

Step 2
List the elements of set S.

Set S is in universe O, which contains only odd numbers. None of the even perfect squares (4, 16, 36, and 64) exist in the universe, so they are not contained in set S. Therefore, $S = \{1, 9, 25, 49, 81\}$.

Class Exercise 5

Universal set C consists of all Canadian coins with a value equal to or less than 10¢. Set D, contained in universe C, contains only coins whose value is not divisible by 2¢. List the elements of D in roster form.

NOTES

THE COMPLEMENT OF A SET

The **complement** of a set within a given universe contains all of the elements in the universe that are not elements of the set. For example, the complement of set A is denoted A' or $\overline{A}$ and is given by the shaded region in the following Venn diagram.

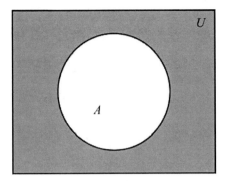

Example

If the universal set, U, is the set of all integers, and $Q = \{-3,\ -2,\ -1,\ 0,\ 1,\ 2,\ 3\}$, then what is Q'?

Solution

The complement of a set contains all of the elements in the universe that are not also contained in that set. The universal set contains all integers, and set Q contains the integers from –3 to 3, inclusive, so Q' contains all integers less than –3 and greater than 3.

This is expressed in roster form as $Q' = \{\ldots\ -6,\ -5,\ -4,\ 4,\ 5,\ 6,\ \ldots\}$ or in set builder notation as $Q' = \{x : x \text{ is an integer}, x < -3, x > 3\}$.

Class Exercise 6

Universal set P, containing all one-digit positive integers, contains set C, where $C = \{2,\ 4,\ 6,\ 8\}$. List the elements of C' in roster form.

NOTES

The empty set is a subset of every other set.

A set that is completely contained within another set is a proper subset. For example, if $M = \{2, 4, 6\}$ and $N = \{2, 4, 6, 8\}$, then M is a proper subset of N. If $O = \{2, 4, 6, 8\}$, it is not a proper subset of N because both sets have exactly the same elements. In this book, the word *subset* always refers to a proper subset.

SUBSETS

It is possible for one set to be completely contained within another set. If set A is contained within set B, then A is a **subset** of B. This is denoted $A \subset B$.

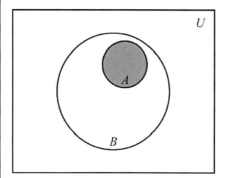

Example

Set N is the set containing all North American countries. Determine whether each of the following sets is a subset of N:

a) The set of countries in the Commonwealth

Solution

Examine each of the sets described. Sets containing only North American countries are subsets of N.
   a) The Commonwealth includes countries on all continents except Antarctica; therefore, it is not a subset of N.

b) The set containing only Canada

Solution

   b) Canada is a North American country, so the set containing only Canada is a subset of N.

c) The set of countries bordering the Arctic Circle

Solution

   c) Norway, Sweden, Finland, Russia, Canada, the United States, Greenland, and Iceland all border the Arctic Circle. Only two of these countries are in North America, so this is not a subset of N.

Class Exercise 7

Set W contains only the numbers 1, 2, and 3. Define four sets that are subsets of W.

UNIONS

The **union** of sets A and B, denoted $A \cup B$, consists of all of the elements found in set A or set B. The shaded region of the given diagram shows $A \cup B$.

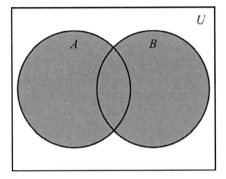

In everyday language, the word *or* usually means one or the other. For example, you can have fries or a salad, but not both. In set theory, the word *or* has an expanded meaning. For example, fries or salad might mean only fries, only salad, or fries and salad.

Example

Two sets are given:
Set V contains the months whose names begin with a vowel.

Set S contains the months when high school students generally have summer vacation.

Determine $V \cup S$.

Solution

Step 1
List the elements of each of the two sets.

V = {April, August, October}
S = {July, August}

Step 2
Determine $V \cup S$.

The union of two sets contains all of the elements found in either set. Elements found in both sets are not repeated.
$V \cup S$ = {April, July, August, October}

Class Exercise 8

Three sets are given:
$V = \{1, 2, 3\}$
$W = \{1, 3, 5\}$
$X = \{3, 4, 6\}$

Determine the union of each pair of sets.
Which union has the smallest number of elements?
What is $V \cup W \cup X$ in roster form?

INTERSECTIONS

The **intersection** of sets A and B, denoted $A \cap B$, consists of all of the elements found in both A and B. The shaded region of the given diagram shows $A \cap B$.

If the intersection of two sets is equal to one of the sets, then that set is a subset. In other words, if $C \cap D = C$, then $C \subset D$.

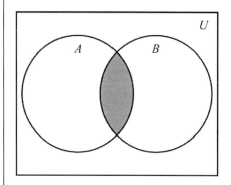

Example

Two sets are given.
Set F contains all integers from -10 to 10, inclusive.
Set G contains all non-negative multiples of 3.

How many elements are contained in $F \cap G$?

Solution
Step 1
List the elements of each of the two sets.
$F = \{-10, -9, -8, -7, -6, -5, -4, -3, -2, -1, 0, 1, 2, 3, 4, 5, 6, 7, 8, 9, 10\}$
$G = \{0, 3, 6, 9, 12, ...\}$

54   Copyright Protected

NOTES

Step 2

Count the elements in $F \cap G$.

The intersection of two sets contains all of the elements that are common to both sets.

$F \cap G = \{0, 3, 6, 9\}$

Therefore, $F \cap G$ has 4 elements.

Class Exercise 9

The set of Canadian cities that have hosted the Olympic Games is O, and the set of all cities in Alberta is A. Determine $O \cap A$.

DISJOINT SETS

If two sets, A and B, have no common elements, then those sets are **disjoint**. This is denoted $A \cap B = \varnothing$ and is indicated on a Venn diagram as two circles with no overlapping region.

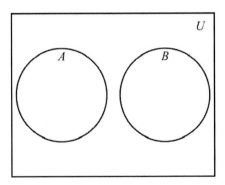

Example

Consider the following three sets:

• Set H consists of all multiples of 3.
• Set I consists of all negative multiples of 4.
• Set J consists of all positive multiple of 5.

Which of the given sets is disjoint?

Solution

Sets are disjoint if their intersection is the empty set. Examine each pair of sets. If they share even one element, then the sets are not disjoint.

Step 1

Determine if $H \cap I$ is the empty set.

The number -12 is a multiple of 3, so $-12 \in H$. It is also a negative multiple of 4, so $-12 \in I$. Therefore, $-12 \in H \cap I$, and sets H and I are not disjoint.

Step 2

Determine if $H \cap J$ is the empty set.

The number 15 is a multiple of 3, so $15 \in H$. It is also a positive multiple of 5, so $15 \in J$. Therefore, $15 \in H \cap J$, and sets H and J are not disjoint.

Step 3

Determine if $I \cap J$ is the empty set.

There is no number that is both positive and negative, so sets I and J do not share any common elements, and $I \cap J = \varnothing$. Therefore, I and J are disjoint sets.

Class Exercise 10

The following three sets of animals are given:
- Set S is the set of animals that can swim.
- Set M is the set of all mammals.
- Set V is the set of animals without vertebrae.

Which pair of sets is disjoint?

PRACTICE EXERCISES

Use the following information to answer the next question.

Josie Jay, Kaleidoscope, Leather Land, and Magnifique are four stores found in the same strip mall. Sets J, K, L, and M are defined according to the items that are sold at each of the stores:
- Set J contains the kinds of items that are sold at Josie Jay: {shirts, pants, jackets, skirts, belts}.
- Set K contains the kinds of items that are sold at Kaleidoscope: {jewellery, shoes, belts, hats, bags}.
- Set L contains the kinds of items that are sold at Leather Land: {jackets, pants, belts, bags}.
- Set M contains the kinds of items that are sold at Magnifique: {shoes, bags}.

The universal set contains all of the kinds of items that are sold at any of the four stores.

1. **a)** How many elements are contained in the universal set?

    b) Determine K'.

    c) Determine $J \cup L$.

    d) Determine $(J \cup L)'$.

    e) Determine $J \cap L$.

    f) Determine $K \cap L \cap M$.

    g) Which set is a subset of another set?

Use the following information to answer the next question.

This Venn diagram shows the relationship between sets E, F, G, and H within universe U.

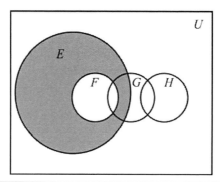

2. Explain why each of the following statements is true or false.

   a) $E \subset F$

   b) $(F \cap G) \subset E$

   c) $(F \cup G) \subset E$

   d) $F \cap H = \varnothing$

   e) The shaded region represents F'.

Use the following information to answer the next seven questions.

Four sets are given.

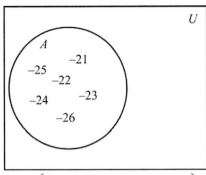

$$B = \left\{ \ldots, \ -\frac{2}{5}, \ -\frac{1}{5}, \ \frac{0}{5}, \ \frac{1}{5}, \ \frac{2}{5}, \ \ldots \right\}$$

C is the set of all numbers from 0 to 1, inclusive.

$$D = \left\{ k : k = 3n, \ n \text{ is an integer}, \ -12 \le n \le -6 \right\}$$

3. Define the following sets using roster form:

   a) *A*

   b) *D*

4. Define the following sets using a description:

   a) *A*

   b) *B*

   c) *D*

5. Define the following sets using set builder notation:

    a) A

    b) B

    c) C

6. Explain why set C cannot be defined using roster form.

7. Determine $B \cap C$.

8. Determine $A \cup D$.

9. Which pairs of sets are disjoint?

Lesson 2 SOLVING PROBLEMS INVOLVING SETS

REPRESENTING DATA USING VISUAL ORGANIZERS

Set theory can be useful when working with data involving overlapping categories. The data can be organized into sets that can then be manipulated and worked with as needed.

Consider the following table. It contains the answers given by 15 students who were asked if they had spent time reading or watching TV the previous evening.

Student	Reading	TV
1	✓	✓
2	✓	
3		✓
4		✓
5		
6	✓	✓
7		
8		✓
9		✓
10	✓	✓
11	✓	
12		✓
13	✓	✓
14		✓
15	✓	

A frequency table showing the given data looks like this:

Reading	7
TV	10

Although the information in this table is correct, it does not accurately reflect the information because it does not account for the 4 students who spent time doing both activities or the 2 students who did not do either activity. The data can also be shown in the following table:

Reading	7
TV	10
Reading and TV	4
Neither	2

This table is also accurate, and it is more representative of the information than the previous table. However, this table is still misleading because it appears as though 23 students were surveyed.

NOTES

The data in these Venn and Carroll diagrams are entered as frequencies. For example, the number 4 in the section where the circles overlap does not mean that student number 4 both read and watched TV, but rather that a total of 4 students both read and watched TV.

Venn diagrams and Carroll diagrams are two ways to represent this data more clearly:

Venn Diagram

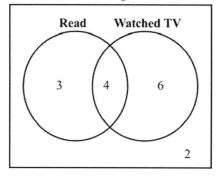

Carroll Diagram

	Read	Did Not Read
Watched TV	4	6
Did not watch TV	3	2

Both diagrams show the same information:
- 4 students read and watched TV
- 6 students watched TV but did not read
- 3 students read but did not watch TV
- 2 students did not read and did not watch TV

The sum of the numbers in all of the regions is equal to the number of students surveyed, and this is the number of elements in the universal set.

The advantage of using graphic organizers like Venn and Carroll diagrams is that it makes it easy to answer a variety of questions. For example, the number of people who spent time reading (7) can easily be calculated by adding the numbers in the appropriate circle in the Venn diagram or the appropriate column in the Carroll diagram.

Venn Diagram

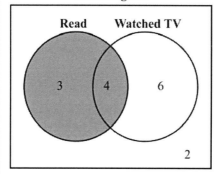

	Read	Did Not Read
Watched TV	4	6
Did not watch TV	3	2

Example

A class of 30 Grade 12 students were asked how they access the Internet outside of school. Their responses are given in the following table:

Computer	23
Smartphone	12
Computer and smartphone	9
Neither	4

a) Calculate the number of students who access the Internet only on a computer.

Solution

According to the table, 23 students use computers to access the Internet. Of these, 9 students also use smartphones.
Therefore, $23 - 9 = 14$ students use a computer but not a smartphone.

b) Calculate the number of students who access the Internet only on a smartphone.

Solution

According to the table, 12 students use phones to access the Internet. Of these, 9 students also use computers. Therefore, $12 - 9 = 3$ students use a smartphone but not a computer.

c) Organize the given information using a Carroll diagram.

Solution
Step 1
Draw the diagram.

Students can access the Internet using a computer or using a smartphone. Draw a two-way table with the following column and row headings:

	Computer	No Computer
Smartphone		
No smartphone		

Step 2
Fill in the table with the given data.

Each of the blank squares can be completed using information either from the given table or from calculations that were completed in parts A and B.
- Computer and smartphone: 9
- Computer and no smartphone: 14
- Smartphone and no computer: 3
- No smartphone and no computer: 4

	Computer	No Computer
Smartphone	9	3
No smartphone	14	4

d) Organize the given information using a Venn diagram.

Solution
Step 1
Draw the diagram.

Students can access the Internet using a computer or using a smartphone. Draw a rectangle to represent the universal set of 30 students who were surveyed, as well as two overlapping circles labelled as follows:

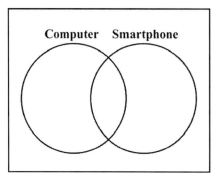

Step 2
Fill in the diagram with the given data.

The data is the same data that was used to complete the Carroll diagram. In this diagram, the number 4 represents students who do not use a computer or a smartphone to access the Internet. It is located in the bottom right corner of the diagram, but it can go anywhere inside the rectangle and outside of the overlapping circles.

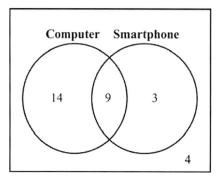

Class Exercise 1

Country Wagon Cars offers convenience, safety, and entertainment options on all of their new cars. They are planning to upgrade their options packages, so the manager tracks the popularity of different kinds of options over the course of one month. Of the 129 cars that were sold, the following options were purchased:

Type of Option	Number of Buyers
Convenience	67
Safety	57
Entertainment	46
Convenience and safety only	16
Convenience and entertainment only	11
Safety and entertainment only	9
All three options	18
No options	31

At the end of the month, the manager organizes the data into the following Venn diagram:

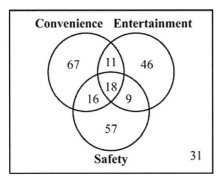

a) What is indicated by the difference between the number of elements in the universal set of the given Venn diagram and the number of cars that were sold in one month?

b) Find and correct the errors in the Venn diagram.

c) Explain why a Carroll diagram is **not** a suitable representation for this data.

65

These operators are used in Boolean searches to broaden or limit search results.

LOGICAL OPERATORS

Often, the logical operators AND, OR, and NOT are used in questions about sets. Each of these terms corresponds to one of the set operations.

• "*A* OR *B*" refers to the union of sets *A* and *B*, or $A \cup B$.

• "*A* AND *B*" refers to the intersection of sets *A* and *B*, or $A \cap B$.

• "NOT *A*" refers to the complement of set *A*, or A'.

The word *not* can be used in conjunction with another term that must appear. The search query "*A* NOT *B*" refers to the intersection of *A* and the complement of *B*, or $A \cap B'$, as represented by the shaded region in this Venn diagram:

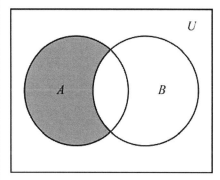

When solving problems that involve one or more logical operators, it can be helpful to rephrase the problem in terms of set theory.

Example

The counselling department at a Lethbridge high school received a grant to allow them to expand one of their existing programs. The department surveyed 75 students who had used one or more programs offered, asking which of the two most popular programs they had accessed in the past six months. The results are summarized in the following Venn diagram. The circle on the left represents the set of students who accessed post-secondary information services, and the circle on the right represents the set of students who accessed personal counselling services.

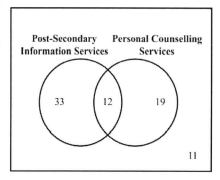

a) How many of the surveyed students used the post-secondary information services or personal counselling services?

Solution

The number of students who used the post-secondary information services or the personal counselling services corresponds to the union between the two sets. This can be calculated by finding the sum of the numbers in the shaded regions.

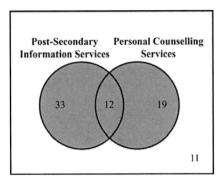

$33 + 12 + 19 = 64$

Therefore, a total of 64 students used the post-secondary information services or personal counselling services.

b) How many of the surveyed students used the post-secondary information services and personal counselling services?

Solution

The number of students who used post-secondary information services and the personal counselling services corresponds to the intersection between the two sets. This is equal to the number in the shaded region.

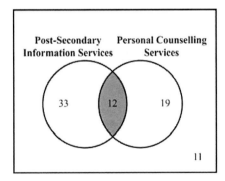

Therefore, a total of 12 students used the post-secondary information services and personal counselling services.

c) How many of the surveyed students did not use post-secondary information services?

Solution

The number of students who did not use post-secondary information services corresponds to the complement of that set. This can be calculated by finding the sum of the numbers in the shaded regions.

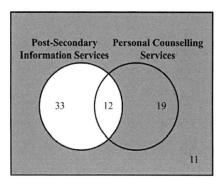

$19 + 11 = 30$

Therefore, a total of 30 students did not use post-secondary information services.

d) How many of the surveyed students used personal counselling services and not post-secondary information services?

Solution

The number of students who used personal counselling services and not post-secondary information services corresponds to the intersection between the set of students who used personal counselling services and the complement of the set of students who used post-secondary information services. This is equal to the number in the shaded region.

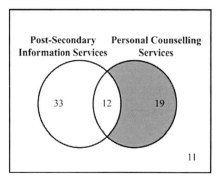

Therefore, a total of 19 students used personal counselling services and not post-secondary information services.

 Copyright Protected

Class Exercise 2

A survey given to 100 people exiting a popular mall asked respondents to identify if they had spent money on shopping or food while at the mall. The results are given in the following Carroll diagram.

	Spent Money Shopping	Did Not Spend Money Shopping
Spent money on food	28	32
Did not spend money on food	26	14

a) How many people spent money shopping or on food?

b) How many people spent money shopping and on food?

c) How many people did not spend money shopping?

d) How many people spent money shopping but not on food?

Class Exercise 3

Do you think it is easier to answer this kind of question when the data is given in a Venn diagram or a Carroll diagram? Explain.

PRACTICE EXERCISES

Use the following information to answer the next question.

Christa has a collection of 47 Christmas ornaments. She has 28 glass ornaments, of which 5 ornaments are angels. She also has an additional 10 angel ornaments that are not glass.

1. Organize the given information using a Venn diagram.

Use the following information to answer the next question.

A survey asked 12 students if they were planning on participating in any outdoor activities over the summer. Their responses are given in a table. Names of students who were not planning to do any outdoor activity are not shown.

Camping	Hiking
Trudy	Trudy
Simon	Liam
Liam	Sandy
Sandy	Haruki
Kendra	Eli
Haruki	Julianna
	Owen

2. Organize the given data using a Carroll diagram.

 Copyright Protected

Use the following information to answer the next question.

In order to decide where to hold their graduation dinner, the grad committee provided a survey to all of the graduating students. The survey gave the choice of booking a restaurant, getting a catered dinner in a hotel, or eating buffet-style in the school gym. Students were encouraged to check off as many options as they wanted. A total of 77 students handed in the surveys, with the following results:

- 47 students checked off booking a restaurant
- 58 students checked off getting dinner catered in a hotel
- 33 students checked off eating buffet-style in the gym
- 23 students checked off restaurant or gym
- 33 students checked off restaurant or hotel
- 26 students checked off hotel or gym
- 18 students checked off all three options
- 3 students did not check off any options

3. Organize the given information using a Venn diagram.

Use the following information to answer the next question.

Tina organized all of her books according to whether they are fiction or non-fiction and hardcover or softcover. Her results are shown in the following Carroll diagram.

	Fiction	Non-Fiction
Hardcover	7	4
Softcover	16	9

4. a) How many books are fiction or hardcover?

   b) How many books are fiction and softcover?

Use the following information to answer the next question.

Universe *A* contains sets *B* and *C*, as shown in the given Venn diagram.

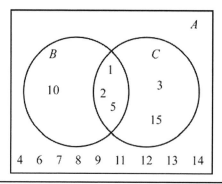

5. List the elements contained in the following sets:

a) *B*

b) NOT *C*

c) *B* AND NOT *C*

d) *B* OR NOT *C*

e) NOT *B* AND NOT *C*

f) NOT (NOT *B*)

g) *B* AND *C*

h) NOT (*B* AND *C*)

i) *B* OR *C*

j) NOT (*B* OR *C*)

Use the following information to answer the next question.

Natasha surveyed some of her classmates to find out which sports they watched on TV. She summarized her results in the following Venn diagram.

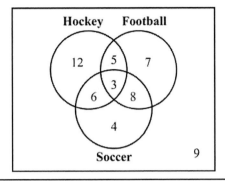

6. **a)** How many people did Natasha survey?

    b) How many people do not watch hockey?

    c) How many people watch hockey but not soccer?

    d) How many people watch football and soccer or football and hockey?

Use the following information to answer the next question.

At a model UN conference for high school students, students had to attend at least one committee session. A total of 46 students attended only the morning session, 61 students attended only the afternoon session, and 32 students attended both sessions.

7. How many students attended the morning session?

Use the following information to answer the next question.

In a group of 40 students, 18 students are skateboarders, 20 students are snowboarders, and 15 students do not skateboard or snowboard.

8. How many students are both skateboarders and snowboarders?

REVIEW SUMMARY

- A **set** is a collection of distinct objects, such as people, items, numbers, or other sets. A set may be defined with a verbal description, using roster form, or using set builder notation.
- The order of elements in a set is irrelevant, and identical elements are not repeated.
- The set containing no elements is called the **empty set**, denoted {} or ∅.
- The **universal set** is the larger, inclusive set from which elements can be considered. In a Venn diagram, the universal set is represented with a rectangle enclosing other sets.
- The **complement** of a set within a given universe contains all of the elements in the universe that are not elements of that set. The complement of A is denoted A' or $\overline{A}$.
- If set A is completely contained within set B, then A is a **subset** of B. This is denoted $A \subset B$.
- The **union** of two sets contains all of the elements found in either of the two sets. The union of A and B is denoted $A \cup B$.
- The **intersection** of two sets contains only the elements that are found in both sets. The intersection of A and B is denoted $A \cap B$.
- Two sets that share no common elements are **disjoint** sets. If $A \cap B = \varnothing$, then A and B are disjoint.
- Data containing overlapping categories can be represented using graphic organizers, such as Venn diagrams and Carroll diagrams. In these diagrams, the data is usually given as frequencies.
- In a Venn diagram representing data, the rectangle represents the universal set and contains exactly the number of data points being considered. Each circular set represents one category of data. Data with two or three categories can be easily represented using a Venn diagram.
- A Carroll diagram is a two-way table with columns indicating membership or non-membership in one category and rows indicating membership or non-membership in the other. Only data with two categories can be represented in a Carroll diagram.
- The logical operators AND, OR, and NOT can be used to solve problems involving sets.
  - "A OR B" refers to the union of A and B, or $A \cup B$.
  - "A AND B" refers to the intersection of A and B, or $A \cap B$.
  - "NOT A" refers to the complement of A, or A'.

PRACTICE TEST

Use the following information to answer the next question.

The universal set U contains the elements $\{-4, -2, 5, 7, 11, 15, 20\}$. Set B, contained within U, is defined as $B = \{-4, 5, 11, 15\}$.

1. Determine the complement of B.

Use the following information to answer the next question.

Consider the following two sets:

$$A = \{-12, -5, 0, 1, 7\}$$
$$B = \{-17, -5, 0, 2, 7, 9\}$$

2. a) Determine $A \cup B$.

b) Determine $A \cap B$.

Use the following information to answer the next question.

Consider the following two sets:
$$A = \{x : 3n, n \text{ is an integer}, 0 \le n \le 5\}$$
$$B = \{x : 2n+1, n \text{ is an integer}, -2 \le n \le 4\}$$

3. **a)** Determine $A \cup B$.

b) Determine $A \cap B$.

Use the following information to answer the next question.

Each region on this Venn diagram is labelled with one of the numbers 1 through 8.

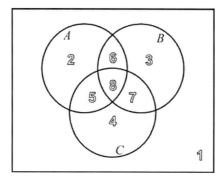

4. State the region or regions of the given Venn diagram that corresponds to each of the following sets.

a) A

b) A'

c) $A \cup B$

d) $(A \cup B)'$

e) $B \cap C$

f) $B \cap C'$

g) $A \cup B \cup C$

h) $A \cap B \cap C$

i) $(A \cup B) \cap C$

Use the following information to answer the next question.

The universal set U consists of all regular polygons. Set A, contained in U, is the set of polygons with fewer than seven sides.

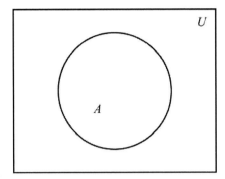

5. Explain why each of the following sets is or is not a subset of A.

a)

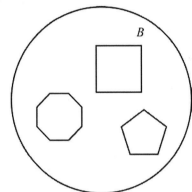

b)

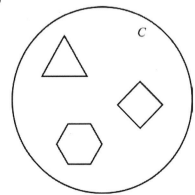

c)

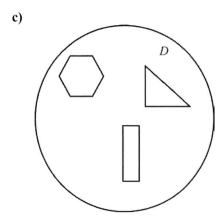

Use the following information to answer the next question.

In a particular class of Grade 12 students, 18 students are taking chemistry, 15 students are taking physics, 8 students are taking chemistry and physics, and 7 students are not taking either course.

6. How many students are in the class?

Use the following information to answer the next question.

A survey of 25 local gyms shows that 16 gyms offer free classes with membership, 6 gyms offer free classes and towel service, and 4 gyms offer neither.

7. How many gyms offer towel service?

 Copyright Protected

Use the following information to answer the next question.

Of 80 competitors at a track-and-field competition, 36 competitors are participating in long-distance events, 41 competitors are participating in sprints, and 29 competitors are not participating in either class of running event.

8. How many competitors are participating in both long-distance events and sprints?

Use the following information to answer the next question.

A group of 50 high school students were surveyed about the major sources of stress in their lives. The survey had the following results:

- 18 students said that schoolwork was their only source of stress
- 10 students said that their home life was their only source of stress
- 13 students said that both schoolwork and home life were sources of stress
- 9 students said that their stress came from sources other than schoolwork and home life

9. a) How many students said that schoolwork was a source of stress?

b) How many students said that schoolwork or home life was a source of stress?

c) How many students did **not** say that home life was a source of stress?

Use the following information to answer the next question.

Five sets are defined according to the colours found on various national flags. Each set is named according to the first initial of the country whose flag contains those colours. The universal set contains all of the colours that appear on at least one of the five flags.

 Canada: C = {red, white}

 India: I = {blue, green, orange, white}

 Jamaica: J = {black, green, yellow}

 Philippines: P = {blue, red, white, yellow}

 South Africa: S = {black, blue, green, red, white, yellow}

10. a) Determine $C \cup I$.

b) Determine $I \cap P$.

c) Determine J'.

d) Determine $J' \cap S$.

e) Determine $C \cap I \cap P$.

f) Determine $(I \cap S) \cup (J \cap P)$.

g) Which set is **not** a subset of S?

h) Which two sets are disjoint?

Use the following additional information to answer the next question.

Three of the five sets, labelled *x*, *y*, and *z*, are represented in a Venn diagram.

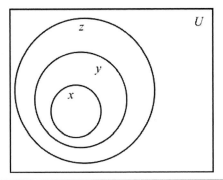

11. Identify the sets represented by *x*, *y*, and *z*.

Use the following information to answer the next question.

A survey of 150 high school students asked what meals they had eaten for breakfast during the previous five days. The results of the survey are shown in the following table:

Cereal	66
Toast	76
Oatmeal	48
Cereal and toast	31
Toast and oatmeal	20
Cereal and oatmeal	16
Toast, cereal, and oatmeal	9

The following Venn diagram incorrectly sorts the given data:

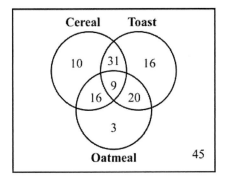

12. a) Correct the errors in the Venn diagram.

b) How many students had not eaten toast?

c) How many students had eaten cereal or toast?

d) How many students had eaten cereal and toast?

e) How many students had eaten cereal or oatmeal, but not toast?

Copyright Protected

Use the following information to answer the next three questions.

Tamia is doing research at the local library for a social studies paper about Francophone nationalism outside of Québec. She decides that the most relevant search terms are *French*, *nationalism*, and *Québec*.

The given Venn diagram shows the number of results Tamia gets when she searches the database at the library. The universal set contains all of the searchable records in the database.

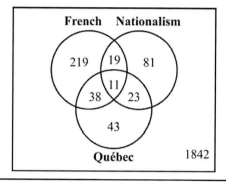

13. How many searchable records are there in the database that Tamia is using?

14. How many search results will Tamia get for each of the following searches?

   a) French OR nationalism

   b) Nationalism NOT Québec

   c) (French OR nationalism) NOT Québec

15. Which terms should Tamia search in order to obtain the results indicated by the shaded regions of the following Venn diagrams?

a)

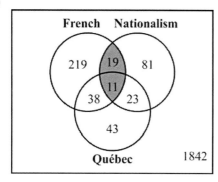

b)

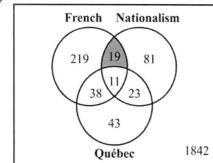

Copyright Protected

PROBABILITY

When you are finished this unit, you will be able to…
- Calculate the probability and the odds in favour or odds against a simple event
- Convert between odds and probability statements
- Determine the sample space for compound events
- Distinguish between mutually exclusive and non-mutually exclusive events
- Calculate the probability of mutually exclusive and non-mutually exclusive events
- Identify complementary events
- Calculate the probability of complementary events
- Represent mutually exclusive, non-mutually exclusive, and complementary events using a Venn diagram
- Distinguish between dependent and independent events
- Calculate the probability of dependent and independent events
- Apply probability formulas in a variety of situations

PREREQUISITE SKILLS AND KNOWLEDGE

- Prior to starting this unit, you should be able to
- Identify the outcomes for a simple probability experiment
- Calculate the probability of a simple event
- Express probabilities as ratios, fractions, and percentages
- Identify disjoint sets
- Use set notation to represent the union and the intersection of sets
- Isolate the variable in an equation

Lesson 1 ODDS AND PROBABILITY

Uncertainty is a feature of everyday life. What are the chances of winning the lottery? Will your favourite hockey team make it to the playoffs? The answers to these questions can be given using probability and odds statements.

PROBABILITY

Probability expresses the likelihood of a particular event happening. The sample space of a probability experiment is the set of possible outcomes for that experiment. For example, if a probability experiment consists of tossing a coin, then the sample space is {heads, tails}.

The probability of an event is the ratio of favourable outcomes to the size of the sample space. This is often given by the formula

$$P(E) = \frac{\text{number of favourable outcomes}}{\text{total number of possible outcomes}}.$$

When calculating probability, it is important that each of the possible outcomes has the same probability. Spinning the following spinner has only three possible results: 1, 2, or 3.

However, it would be incorrect to say that there are 3 outcomes in the sample space, and therefore, the probability of spinning 2 is $\frac{1}{3}$. In order to correctly calculate the probability of spinning 2, the list of possible outcomes must be adjusted to account for the fact that it is twice as likely to spin 1 as it is to spin 2 or 3.

On this amended spinner, each of the outcomes has an equal probability. The experiment has 4 equally probable outcomes, and the probability of spinning 2 is correctly calculated as $\frac{1}{4}$, or 25%.

NOTES

When the probability of an event is given as a fraction, the numerator does not always represent the exact number of favourable outcomes, and the denominator does not always represent the exact number of possible outcomes. For example, the probability of rolling an even number using a standard six-sided die is $\frac{1}{2}$, although there are 3 favourable outcomes and 6 possible outcomes.

Probabilities can be expressed as fractions, decimals, or percentages. For example, the probability of flipping heads on a coin toss can be expressed as $\frac{1}{2}$, 0.5, or 50%.

The probability of an event is always a value between 0 and 1; the probability of an impossible event is 0, and the probability of an event that is certain is 1.

 Copyright Protected

Example

A group of students is conducting a probability experiment that involves rolling a special six-sided die that has colours rather than numbers. Three of the sides are blue, two sides are red, and one side is yellow.

a) Make a list of equally probable outcomes for this probability experiment.

Solution

Rolling the die has three possible results, but each of the results has a different probability. To make a list of equally probable outcomes, list the outcome for each side separately. Use subscripted numbers to differentiate results that are the same, such as the three sides that result in a roll of blue.

The list of equally probable outcomes is {$blue_1$, $blue_2$, $blue_3$, red_1, red_2, yellow}.

b) Express the probability of rolling yellow as a decimal.

Solution

The die has only one yellow side, so there is 1 favourable outcome out of 6 possible outcomes. Therefore, the probability of rolling yellow is $\frac{1}{6}$. Written as a decimal, this is $0.1\overline{6}$.

A compound event involves two or more simple events. For example, tossing heads twice in a row is a compound event because the coin must be tossed twice. It is possible to use graphic organizers, such as tables and tree diagrams, to determine the sample space of a compound event.

Example

A probability experiment involves rolling a four-sided die and spinning a spinner with four equal segments that are red, blue, green, and yellow.

a) Use a tree diagram to determine the sample space for the experiment.

Solution

Step 1
Identify the sample space of each separate event:
Rolling the die: {1, 2, 3, 4}
Spinning the spinner: {red, blue, green, yellow}

Step 2
Draw a tree diagram to represent the possible outcomes of both actions.

NOTES

Odds statements can also be given as fractions. The odds of drawing a penny from Jacqueline's change purse can be expressed as $\frac{3}{4}$.

On the left side of the diagram, list the outcome of rolling the die. Draw one branch from each of these outcomes for each of the outcomes of spinning the spinner. Because the spinner has four outcomes, each of the die rolls will have four branches. Use the initials R, B, G, and Y to represent each of the colours. For example, 1R means rolling 1 on the die and spinning red on the spinner.

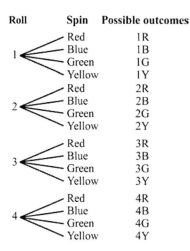

Step 3
List the possible outcomes.

S = {1R, 1B, 1G, 1Y, 2R, 2B, 2G, 2Y, 3R, 3B, 3G, 3Y, 4R, 4B, 4G, 4Y}

b) Use a table to determine the sample space for the experiment.

Solution
Step 1
Identify the sample space of each separate event:
Rolling the die: {1,2,3,4}
Spinning the spinner: {red, blue, green, yellow}

Step 2
Draw a two-way table to represent the possible outcomes of both actions.

Along the top of the table, list the outcomes for rolling the die. Along the left, list the outcomes for the spinner. In each empty space in the table, use the column and row headings to list one outcome for each action. Use the initials R, B, G, and Y to represent each of the colours. For example, 1R means rolling 1 on the die and spinning red on the spinner.

	1	2	3	4
Red	1R	2R	3R	4R
Blue	1B	2B	3B	4B
Green	1G	2G	3G	4G
Yellow	1Y	2Y	3Y	4Y

Step 3

List the possible outcomes.

S = {1R, 1B,1G, 1Y, 2R, 2B,2G, 2Y, 3R, 3B, 3G, 3Y, 4R, 4B,4G, 4Y}

c) Express the probability of rolling 3 and spinning green as a percentage.

Solution

The only favourable outcome for rolling a 3 and spinning green is 3G. The sample space contains 16 elements, so there are 16 possible outcomes. Therefore, the probability is $\frac{1}{16}$, or 6.25%.

Class Exercise 1

In a probability experiment, students first draw one marble at random out of a bag containing 2 purple marbles and 1 orange marble, and then they roll a standard six-sided die.

a) Use a table or tree diagram to make a list of equally probable outcomes for the experiment.

b) Calculate the probability of drawing a purple marble and then rolling 5.

ODDS

An alternative way to express the likelihood of an event is using an odds statement. The odds in favour of an event are the ratio of favourable outcomes to unfavourable outcomes. Conversely, the odds against an event are the ratio of the number of unfavourable outcomes to the number of favourable outcomes.

Likelihoods are often expressed as odds statements rather than probabilities in contexts involving sporting events. Generally, the likelihood is given as odds against statements. For example, if the odds are 5:1 that a horse will win a race, there is a 5 times greater chance that the horse will lose than that it will win.

NOTES

Example

Jacqueline has the following coins in her change purse. She reaches in and pulls out one coin at random.

a) What are the odds in favour of Jacqueline pulling out a penny?

Solution

Jacqueline has 3 pennies, so there are 3 favourable outcomes. She has 4 coins that are not pennies, so there are 4 unfavourable outcomes. Therefore, the odds in favour of pulling out a penny are 3:4.

b) What are the odds against pulling out the toonie?

Solution

Jacqueline has 6 coins that are not toonies, so there are 6 unfavourable outcomes. She has 1 toonie, so there is 1 favourable outcome. Therefore, the odds against pulling out a toonie are 6:1.

Class Exercise 2

The following spinner has eight equal spaces showing the numbers 1 through 4.

a) What are the odds in favour of spinning 4?

b) What are the odds against spinning 3?

Odds statements can be converted from odds in favour to odds against or from odds against to odds in favour simply by reversing the order of the terms.

Example

The odds in favour of the Yarmouth High School basketball team making it to the playoffs are 2:5. What are the odds against the team making it to the playoffs?

Solution

To change the statement from odds in favour to odds against, reverse the order of the terms. The odds against the team making it to the playoffs are 5:2.

CONVERTING BETWEEN ODDS AND PROBABILITY STATEMENTS

Odds statements can be converted to probability statements, and vice versa. An odds statement contains information about the ratio of favourable to unfavourable outcomes. This information can be used to determine the total possible outcomes.

Example

The odds against an event are 15:4. What is the probability of this event?

Solution

In this event, for every 15 unfavourable outcomes, there are 4 favourable outcomes. This means that for every 4 favourable outcomes, there are $4 + 15 = 19$ possible outcomes.

Therefore, the probability of this event is $\dfrac{4}{19}$.

Similarly, the information about the ratio of favourable outcomes to total number of outcomes in a probability statement can be used to determine the unfavourable outcomes.

Example

The probability of an event is $\dfrac{2}{5}$. What are the odds against this event?

Solution

The odds against an event are the ratio of unfavourable to favourable outcomes. In this event, for every 5 possible outcomes, there are 2 favourable outcomes. This means that for every 5 possible outcomes, there are $5 - 2 = 3$ unfavourable outcomes. Therefore, the ratio of unfavourable to favourable outcomes is 3:2.

The terms in an odds statement do not necessarily represent an actual number of favourable and unfavourable outcomes. The numbers 2 and 5 in the given example do not mean that there are 2 favourable outcomes and 5 unfavourable outcomes for a total of 7 possible outcomes. However, when working with odds and probability statements, it is often useful to think in these terms.

Probability is almost always given as the probability in favour of an event, unless otherwise stated.

Class Exercise 3

The odds in favour of drawing a blue marble from a bag full of marbles are 3:7. The probability of drawing a red marble from the same bag is $\frac{1}{4}$.

a) What is the probability of drawing a blue marble?

b) What are the odds in favour of drawing a red marble?

c) Oliver says that the given situation is impossible because the total number of marbles in the bag is different in parts **(a)** and **(b)**. Explain why Oliver's statement is false.

PRACTICE EXERCISES

For each of the following experiments, state the probability that the outcome will be a multiple of 3.

1. Rolling a standard six-sided die

2. Rolling a special six-sided die with three sides showing the number 3, one side showing the number 8, and two sides showing the number 12

For each of the following experiments, state the odds in favour and the odds against an outcome of red.

3. Rolling a four-sided die with the colours yellow, blue, red, and black

4. Spinning a spinner with five equal sections labelled yellow, yellow, red, red, and black

5. Drawing a red marble out of a bag containing 3 red marbles, 5 purple marbles, and 7 orange marbles

Use the following information to answer the next three questions.

In a probability experiment, students use the given spinner. The section with the circle is $\frac{1}{2}$ of the circle, the section with the square is $\frac{1}{4}$ of the circle, and the sections with the triangle and hexagon are each $\frac{1}{8}$ of the circle.

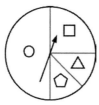

6. What is the probability that the pointer will land on a square?

7. What are the odds in favour of spinning a circle?

8. What are the odds against spinning a triangle?

Use the following information to answer the next two questions.

Teachers at Nakiskaw High School nominate one student from each of the grades 10, 11, and 12 to participate in a committee on improving local schools. Teachers at Middleside High School also nominate one student from each of the grades 10, 11, and 12 to participate on the committee. The leadership of the committee is determined by randomly selecting one of the three Nakiskaw students and one of the three Middleside students.

9. Use a table to determine how many ways the two students who will lead the committee can be selected.

10. Determine the probability that the committee will be led by a Grade 11 student and a Grade 12 student.

Use the following information to answer the next two questions.

Jake is playing a game in which each move's distance and direction are determined using a bag of marbles and a coin. The bag contains 1 green marble, 2 yellow marbles, and 2 red marbles. Drawing a green marble means the player must move 3 spaces, a player drawing yellow moves 2 spaces, and a player drawing red moves 1 space. If the result of the coin toss is heads, the player moves to the left, and if the result is tails, the player moves to the right. In order to win the game, Jake needs to move 2 or more spaces to the left.

11. Use a tree diagram to determine all the equally probable outcomes for drawing a marble and flipping a coin.

12. Determine the odds against Jake winning the game on his next move.

Express each of the following odds statements as a probability statement.

13. The odds in favour of winning a door prize at a school-sponsored event are 2:7.

14 The odds against drawing a white marble from a bag of marbles are 22:3.

For each probability statement, write the odds in favour of that event occurring.

15. The probability of rolling a sum of 6 when two standard six-sided dice are rolled is $\dfrac{5}{36}$.

16. The probability of rain on a certain day is 40%.

Lesson 2   *MUTUALLY EXCLUSIVE AND NON-MUTUALLY EXCLUSIVE EVENTS*

NOTES

IDENTIFYING MUTUALLY EXCLUSIVE AND NON-MUTUALLY EXCLUSIVE EVENTS

In probability, an event is a subset of a given sample space.

For example, when rolling a standard six-sided die, the sample space, S, is {1, 2, 3, 4, 5, 6}. Event A is rolling 1. This event has only one favourable outcome: {1}. Event B is rolling a number greater than 3. This event has three favourable outcomes: {4, 5, 6}.

This can be represented using set notation as $A \cap B = \varnothing$.

The sample space, *S*, and events *A* and *B* can be represented on the following
Venn diagram, where *A* and *B* are disjoint sets.

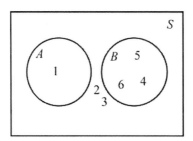

When two or more events have no common outcomes, they are mutually exclusive events. Events *A* and *B* are mutually exclusive events because there is no outcome that is both the number 1 and a number greater than 3.

This can be represented using set notation as $B \cap C \neq \varnothing$.

Events that share at least one outcome are non-mutually exclusive events. The following Venn diagram represents event *B* (rolling a number greater than 3) and event *C*, which is rolling an odd number.

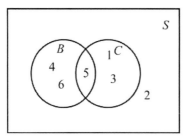

The circles in this diagram overlap because rolling 5 is an outcome of both events. Therefore, *B* and *C* are non-mutually exclusive events.

98   Copyright Protected

NOTES

Example

Determine if each of the following pairs of events is mutually exclusive or non-mutually exclusive when a standard six-sided die is rolled once.

a) Rolling an even number and rolling an odd number

Solution

These events do not have any common outcomes because there is no number that is both even and odd. Therefore, they are mutually exclusive events.

b) Rolling a multiple of 3 and rolling a multiple of 2

Solution

The set of favourable outcomes for rolling a multiple of 3 is {3, 6}, and the set for rolling a multiple of 2 is {2, 4, 6}. Rolling 6 is an outcome of both events, so they are non-mutually exclusive.

c) Rolling a prime number and rolling a number less than 4

Solution

The set of favourable outcomes for rolling a prime number is {2, 3, 5}, and the set for rolling a number less than 4 is {1, 2, 3}. Rolling 2 and rolling 3 are outcomes of both events, so they are non-mutually exclusive.

d) Rolling a perfect square and rolling a number greater than 4

Solution

The set of favourable outcomes for rolling a perfect square is {1, 4} and the set for rolling a number greater than 4 is {5, 6}. There are no common outcomes for these events, so they are mutually exclusive.

Class Exercise 1

A bag contains the following set of cards showing different shapes and colours. In a probability experiment, the cards are turned facedown, and one card is chosen at random.

Determine if each of the following pairs of events is mutually exclusive or non-mutually exclusive.

a) Choosing a circle and choosing a square

b) Choosing a black shape and choosing a triangle

c) Choosing a grey shape and choosing a white shape

d) Choosing a grey shape and choosing a circle

COMPLEMENTARY EVENTS

The complement of an event A, denoted A' or $\overline{A}$, is the set of all of the outcomes in the sample space that are not elements of A.

Consider an experiment involving the given spinner, with a sample space S, where S = {red, blue, green, yellow, orange}.

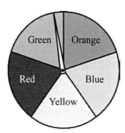

If event C is spinning a primary colour, then C = {red, blue, yellow}. The colours belonging to the complement of C, or C', are all of the colours in the sample space that are not elements of C. Therefore C' = {green, orange}.

Two events are complementary if they are mutually exclusive and the sum of their probabilities is 1. In the given example, C and C' are mutually exclusive because colours are either primary or not primary. Their sum is
$$P(C) + P(C') = \frac{3}{5} + \frac{2}{5} = 1.$$

Example

Melanie has a collection of buttons of various shapes and colours.

Determine if the following pairs of events are complementary.

a) Selecting a round button and selecting a square button

Solution
There is no button that is both round and square, so the events are mutually exclusive.

Copyright Protected

However, the probability of selecting a round button is $\frac{4}{7}$, and the probability of selecting a square button is $\frac{1}{7}$. The sum of the probabilities is $\frac{5}{7}$. This is not equal to 1, so the events are non-mutually exclusive.

b) Selecting a heart-shaped button and selecting a button with two holes

Solution
There is no heart-shaped button with two holes, so the events are mutually exclusive. The probability of selecting a heart-shaped button is $\frac{2}{7}$, and the probability of selecting a button with two holes is $\frac{5}{7}$, so the sum of the two probabilities is $\frac{7}{7}$, or 1. Therefore, these two events are complementary.

It is possible to determine that these events are not complementary simply by examining the set. If they were complementary, then every button that was not round would be square. There are buttons that are neither round nor square, so selecting a round button cannot be the complement of selecting a square button.

Example
The probability of an event T is 0.72. What is the probability of T'?

Solution
The sum of the probabilities of an event and its complement is always 1.
$$P(T) + P(T') = 1$$
$$0.72 + P(T') = 1$$
$$P(T') = 0.28$$

Therefore, the probability of T' is 0.28.

It would be possible to imagine a set of buttons in which selecting a heart-shaped button and selecting a button with two holes were not complementary events. However, in this particular set, every button that is not heart-shaped has two holes, and vice versa.

Class Exercise 2
A 10-sided die shows the numbers 1 through 10. A probability experiment involves rolling the die once. Event A is rolling an even number, and event B is rolling a multiple of 5.

a) Sort the outcomes in the sample space into a Venn diagram showing A and B.

b) List the outcomes that are elements of B'.

c) List the outcomes that are elements of (A or B').

PROBABILITY OF MUTUALLY EXCLUSIVE EVENTS

To calculate the probability that at least one of two mutually exclusive events will occur, find the sum of the probability of each separate event. This is represented by the formula $P(A \text{ or } B) = P(A) + P(B)$, where A and B are mutually exclusive events

Example

Calculate the probability of rolling either 1 or a number greater than 3 on a standard six-sided die.

Solution

Step 1

Determine the probability of each separate event.

Event A is the probability of rolling 1. There is 1 favourable outcome out of a total of 6 possible outcomes. Therefore, $P(A) = \dfrac{1}{6}$.

Event B is the probability of rolling a number greater than 3. There are 3 favourable outcomes out of a total of 6 possible outcomes.

Therefore, $P(B) = \dfrac{3}{6}$.

$P(A \text{ or } B)$ represents the probability of the union of event A and event B. Therefore, the formula can also be given as $P(A \cup B) = P(A) + P(B)$, $A \cap B = \varnothing$

Step 2

Apply the formula $P(A \cup B) = P(A) + P(B)$.

$P(A \cup B) = P(A) + P(B)$

$P(A \cup B) = \dfrac{1}{6} + \dfrac{3}{6}$

$P(A \cup B) = \dfrac{4}{6}$

$P(A \cup B) = \dfrac{2}{3}$

Therefore, the probability of rolling either 1 or a number greater than 3 is $\dfrac{2}{3}$.

Even though it is faster to get the answer by noticing that 4 of the 6 numbers on a standard die are either 1 or greater than 3, it is calculated this way here to demonstrate the formula.

Class Exercise 3

A bag of marbles contains red, yellow, white, and green marbles. The probability of drawing a red marble is 0.35, and the probability of drawing a yellow marble is 0.45.

a) What is the probability of drawing a red marble or a yellow marble?

b) If the probability of drawing a red marble or a white marble is 0.5, then what is the probability of drawing a white marble?

 Copyright Protected

PROBABILITY OF NON-MUTUALLY EXCLUSIVE EVENTS

When events are non-mutually exclusive, the probability that at least one of the two events will occur cannot be calculated simply by adding the separate probabilities.

Consider the probability of rolling an even number or rolling a number less than 5 on a standard six-sided die. If rolling an even number is event A, and rolling a number less than 5 is event B, then $P(A) = \dfrac{3}{6}$ and $P(B) = \dfrac{4}{6}$.

The sum of these events is $P(A) + P(B) = \dfrac{3}{6} + \dfrac{4}{6} = \dfrac{7}{6}$. This must be incorrect, because a probability is always a number between 0 and 1.

The problem with the calculation is that A and B are non-mutually exclusive events. Rolling 2 and rolling 4 are elements of both sets, so when $P(A)$ and $P(B)$ are added together, these outcomes are counted twice.

P(A and *B)* represents the intersection of event A and event B. Therefore, the formula can also be given as $P(A \cup B)$
$$= P(A) + P(B)$$
$$- P(A \cap B)$$

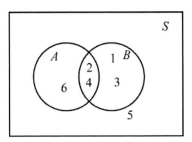

To calculate the probability of non-mutually exclusive events, it is necessary to subtract the probability of the events in the area of overlap to prevent them from being counted twice. This is given in the formula $P(A \text{ or } B) = P(A) + P(B) - P(A \text{ and } B)$, where A and B are non-mutually exclusive events.

Example

Each letter of the alphabet is written on a card. Then, all 26 cards are shuffled together and placed facedown on a table. One card will be drawn from the set of cards. Event L is drawing one of the letters in the word LETHBRIDGE, and event M is drawing one of the letters in the words MEDICINE HAT. What is the probability of drawing a letter that is in at least one of these two place names?

Solution

There are letters that are contained in the names of both places, so L and M are non-mutually exclusive events. Use the formula $P(L \cup M) = P(L) + P(M) - P(L \cap M)$.

Step 1

Determine $P(L)$, $P(M)$, and $P(L \cap M)$.

The word LETHBRIDGE has 10 letters, but the letter E is repeated, so there are only 9 different letters. There are 26 letters in the bag, so

$$P(L) = \frac{9}{26}.$$

The words MEDICINE HAT have 11 letters, but one E and one I are repeated, so it also has 9 different letters. Therefore, $P(M) = \frac{9}{26}.$

The letters D, E, H, I, and T are found in both place names. Therefore, $P(L \cap M) = \frac{5}{26}.$

Step 2

Apply the formula $P(L \cup M) = P(L) + P(M) - P(L \cap M).$

$$P(L \cup M) = P(L) + P(M) - P(L \cap M)$$
$$P(L \cup M) = \frac{9}{26} + \frac{9}{26} - \frac{5}{26}$$
$$P(L \cup M) = \frac{13}{26}$$
$$P(L \cup M) = 50\%$$

Therefore, the probability of drawing a letter that is found in one of the two place names is 50%.

Class Exercise 4

A box of assorted candy has chocolates with a variety of coatings and fillings. Call the probability that a chocolate chosen at random will have nuts $P(N)$, the probability that it will have caramel $P(C)$, and the probability that it will have dark chocolate $P(D)$.

a) If $\frac{1}{4}$ of the chocolates have caramel, $\frac{1}{2}$ of them have dark chocolate, and $\frac{1}{12}$ have caramel and dark chocolate, then what is the probability of choosing a chocolate that has caramel or dark chocolate?

b) If $\frac{2}{3}$ of the chocolates have dark chocolate or nuts, $\frac{1}{2}$ of the chocolates have dark chocolate, and $\frac{1}{3}$ of the chocolates have nuts, then what is the probability of choosing a chocolate with dark chocolate and nuts?

Copyright Protected

PRACTICE EXERCISES

Use the following information to answer the next question.

A probability experiment involves spinning the following spinner.

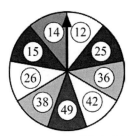

1. Classify each of the following pairs of events as mutually exclusive, non-mutually exclusive, or mutually exclusive and complementary, and explain your reasoning.

    a) Spinning white and spinning grey

    b) Spinning a multiple of 2 and spinning a multiple of 3

    c) Spinning white and spinning a perfect square

    d) Spinning an even number and spinning black

    c) Spinning grey and spinning a number containing the digit 4

Use the following information to answer the next six questions.

Hannah puts number tiles showing each of the numbers 1 through 20 into a bag and then draws one tile at random. Event *A* is drawing a perfect square, and event *B* is drawing a multiple of 5.

2. Draw a Venn diagram to represent events *A* and *B*.

3. List the elements in A'.

4. List the elements in $A \cup B$.

Use the following additional information to answer the next three questions.

Event *C* is drawing a prime number, and event *D* is drawing an odd number.

5. Draw a Venn diagram to represent events *C* and *D*.

6. List the elements in C'.

7. List the elements in $(C \cup D)'$.

Use the following information to answer the next four questions.

A box of pattern blocks contains coloured hexagons, trapezoids, triangles, squares, and large and small rhombuses. The probabilities of drawing some of these shapes when one tile is drawn at random from the box are as follows:
- $P(\text{hexagon}) = 0.24$
- $P(\text{square}) = 0.20$
- $P(\text{triangle}) = 0.08$
- $P(\text{triangle or trapezoid}) = 0.40$

8. What is the probability of drawing a hexagon or a square?

9. What is the probability of drawing a trapezoid?

10. What is the probability of drawing a shape that is not a hexagon?

Copyright Protected

11. What is the probability of drawing a shape that is not a square or a triangle?

Use the following information to answer the next three questions.

A bag contains three sizes of marble (S, M, L) that are blue (B), yellow (Y), or red (R).
The probabilities of drawing some of these marbles when one marble is drawn at random from the bag are as follows:

$$P(B) = \frac{5}{9}$$

$$P(R) = \frac{5}{18}$$

$$P(L) = \frac{13}{18}$$

$$P(B \cap L) = \frac{7}{18}$$

$$P(B \cap S) = \frac{1}{9}$$

$$P(B \cup S) = \frac{11}{18}$$

12. What is the probability of drawing a marble that is blue or large?

13. What is the probability of drawing a small marble?

Use the following additional information to answer the next question.

Muna notices that the probability of drawing a red marble and the probability of drawing a large marble have a sum of 1. She says that drawing a red marble and drawing a large marble must be complementary events.

14. Explain why Muna's statement is false.

Use the following information to answer the next two questions.

A survey of students at an Edmonton high school determined that 77% of the students regularly do homework at home. Another 36% of students do their homework at the library, and 25% of students do homework at both locations.

15. What is the probability that a student selected at random does not do homework at home or at the library?

16. Organize the given information using a Venn diagram.

Lesson 3 *DEPENDENT AND INDEPENDENT EVENTS*

IDENTIFYING DEPENDENT AND INDEPENDENT EVENTS

Compound events, or events involving two or more simple events, can involve one action being repeated, such as tossing a coin twice, or different actions, such as rolling a die and then spinning a spinner.

In independent events, the occurrence of one event does not affect the probability of the second event. For example, if a coin is tossed twice, the probability of heads on the second toss is 50%, regardless of the outcome of the first toss.

In dependent events, the occurrence of the first event changes the sample space for any event that follows. For example, if two cards are drawn without replacement from a standard deck of playing cards, then the first draw has a sample space of
52 cards, and the second draw has a sample space of only 51 cards. Also, the elements of the sample space for the second draw depend on what was drawn with the first card.

NOTE:

The words "without replacement" are a clue that events are probably dependent, because removing an element from the sample space necessarily changes that sample space.

Example

Four groups of students are doing probability experiments involving drawing two marbles at random from bags containing red and blue marbles. In each experiment, one event is choosing a blue marble on the first draw, and the other event is choosing a red marble on the second draw. Explain whether the two events are dependent or independent in each of the following experiments.

a) One marble is drawn from a bag, and a second marble is immediately drawn from the same bag.

Solution
Because the first marble is not put back in the bag before the second marble is drawn, the result of the first draw affects the probability of choosing a red marble on the second draw. Therefore, the events are dependent.

b) One marble is drawn from a bag and replaced before the second marble is drawn from the same bag.

Solution
Because the first marble is replaced in the bag before the second marble is drawn, the result of the first draw does not affect the possible outcomes for the second draw. Therefore, the events are independent.

c) Two bags contain identical sets of marbles. The first marble is drawn from one bag, and a second marble is drawn from the other bag.

Solution
The marbles are being drawn from different bags, so the result of the first draw will not have any effect on the possible outcomes for the second draw. Therefore, the events are independent.

d) Two bags contain different sets of marbles. The first marble is drawn from one bag, and a second marble is drawn from the other bag.

Solution

The marbles are being drawn from different bags, so even though the bags do not have identical sets of marbles, the result of the first draw will not have any effect on the possible outcomes for the second draw. Therefore, the events are independent.

Class Exercise 1

For each of the following pairs of events, determine if A and B are dependent or independent events.

a) Event A is drawing a black card from a standard deck of cards, and event B is drawing another black card from the same deck if the first card drawn is not replaced.

b) Event A is rolling 3 on a standard six-sided die, and event B is spinning blue on a spinner with four sections.

c) Event A is rolling 3 on the first roll of a standard six-sided die, and event B is rolling 3 on the second roll of the same die.

d) Event A is selecting a girl at random from a class, and event B is selecting a boy at random from the remaining students in the class.

PROBABILITY THAT TWO INDEPENDENT EVENTS WILL BOTH OCCUR

$P(A$ and $B)$ represents the intersection of event A and event B.
Therefore, the formula can also be given as
$P(A \cap B) = P(A) \times P(B)$.

To calculate the probability that two independent events will both occur, find the product of the probability of each separate event. This is represented by the formula $P(A$ and $B) = P(A) \times P(B)$, where A and B are independent events.

Example

Calculate the probability of rolling a number greater than 2 and then a multiple of 3 when a standard six-sided die is rolled twice.

Solution
Step 1
Determine the probability of each separate event.

Event A is the probability of rolling a number greater than 2. There are 4 favourable outcomes out of a total of 6 possible outcomes.

Therefore, $P(A) = \dfrac{4}{6}$.

Event B is the probability of rolling a multiple of 3. There are 2 favourable outcomes out of a total of 6 possible outcomes. Therefore, $P(B) = \dfrac{2}{6}$.

Step 2
Apply the formula $P(A \cap B) = P(A) \times P(B)$.

$P(A \cap B) = P(A) \times P(B)$

$P(A \cap B) = \dfrac{4}{6} \times \dfrac{2}{6}$

$P(A \cap B) = \dfrac{8}{36}$

$P(A \cap B) = \dfrac{2}{9}$

Therefore, the probability of rolling a number greater than 2 and then a multiple of 3 is $\dfrac{2}{9}$.

Class Exercise 2

A spinner has the numbers 1 through 4 on unequally sized sections. The probability of spinning 1 is 0.13, and the probability of spinning 2 is 0.36.

a) If the spinner is spun twice, what is the probability of spinning 1 and then 2, expressed as a decimal to the nearest ten thousandth?

b) If the probability of spinning a 2 and then a 3 is 0.1044, then what is the probability of spinning 3, expressed as a decimal to the nearest hundredth?

NOTES

When the order of the events is not specified, you need to calculate the probability for each ordering separately and then add them together.

Example

Shawna has two bags containing coloured marbles. Bag 1 contains 1 white marble and 2 green marbles. Bag 2 contains 3 white marbles, 4 red marbles, and 5 green marbles. If Shawna draws one marble at random from each bag, what is the probability that she draws 1 white marble and 1 green marble?

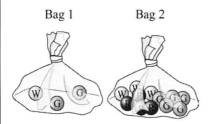

Bag 1   Bag 2

Solution

Step 1

Determine which formula to use.

There are two ways that Shawna can draw a white marble and a green marble: green from the first bag and white from the second bag, or white from the first bag and green from the second bag. Find the probability of each possibility, and then add them together.

Call event G_1 drawing a green marble from bag 1, G_2 drawing a green marble from bag 2, W_1 drawing a white marble from bag 1, and W_2 drawing a white marble from bag 2.

When two marbles are drawn from different bags, the outcome of one draw has no effect on the probability of the second draw, so these are independent events. To determine the probability of drawing a green marble and a white marble, calculate the probability of drawing the green marble first, and then add that to the probability of drawing a green marble second, as follows:

$$P\left(G \cap W\right) = \left[P\left(G_1\right) \times P\left(W_2\right)\right] + \left[P\left(W_1\right) \times P\left(G_2\right)\right]$$

Step 2

Calculate each separate probability.

Bag 1 has 1 white marble and 2 green marbles, so $P\left(W_1\right) = \dfrac{1}{3}$, and $P\left(G_1\right) = \dfrac{2}{3}$.

Bag 2 has 3 white marbles, 5 green marble, and 4 red marbles, so $P\left(W_2\right) = \dfrac{3}{12} = \dfrac{1}{4}$, and $P\left(G_2\right) = \dfrac{5}{12}$.

$P(A$ and $B)$ represents the intersection of event A and event B. Therefore, the formula can also be given as

$$P\left(A \cap B\right) = P\left(A\right) \times P\left(B \mid A\right)$$

Copyright Protected

Step 3

Apply the formula $P(G \cap W) = \left[P(G_1) \times P(W_2) \right] + \left[P(W_1) \times P(G_2) \right]$.

$$P(G \cap W) = \left[P(G_1) \times P(W_2) \right] + \left[P(W_1) \times P(G_2) \right]$$

$$P(G \cap W) = \left[\frac{2}{3} \times \frac{1}{4} \right] + \left[\frac{1}{3} \times \frac{5}{12} \right]$$

$$P(G \cap W) = \frac{1}{6} + \frac{5}{36}$$

$$P(G \cap W) = \frac{11}{36}$$

Therefore, the probability that Shawna will draw a green marble and a white marble is $\frac{11}{36}$.

Class Exercise 3

When two standard six-sided dice are rolled, what is the probability of rolling 4 on one die and a multiple of 3 on the other die?

PROBABILITY THAT TWO DEPENDENT EVENTS WILL BOTH OCCUR

Calculating the probability that two dependent events will both occur also involves multiplying the probability of each separate event. However, because the probability of the second event depends on the outcome of the first event, a different formula is needed.

In the formula $P(A \text{ and } B) = P(A) \times P(B \mid A)$, where A and B are dependent events, $P(B \mid A)$ is the probability that B will occur if A has already occurred.

Example

Each letter in the words RED DEER are written on a separate piece of paper and dropped into a hat. What is the probability of drawing 2 E's if the first paper is not replaced before the second letter is drawn?

Solution

Since the first paper is not replaced before the second paper is drawn, the possible outcomes for the second event are different from the possible outcomes for the first event, and the events are dependent.

Use the formula $P(A \cap B) = P(A) \times P(B \mid A)$.

Step 1

Determine the probability of each event.

If E_1 is drawing a letter E on the first draw, then $P(E_1) = \frac{3}{7}$.

After a letter E is already drawn, then there are 6 letters remaining in the hat, of which 2 are E's. If E_2 is drawing a letter E on the second draw, then

$$P(E_2 \mid E_1) = \frac{2}{6} = \frac{1}{3}.$$

Step 2

Apply the formula $P(E_1 \cap E_2) = P(E_1) \times P(E_2 \mid E_1)$.

$$P(E_1 \cap E_2) = P(E_1) \times P(E_2 \mid E_1)$$

$$P(E_1 \cap E_2) = \frac{3}{7} \times \frac{1}{3}$$

$$P(E_1 \cap E_2) = \frac{1}{7}$$

Therefore, the probability of drawing 2 E's is $\frac{1}{7}$.

Class Exercise 4

If two cards are drawn out of a standard deck of playing cards without replacement, what is the probability of drawing a red card and then a spade?

Example

In a class of 28 students, 4 students have names with five letters, and 3 students have names with seven letters. If the name of each student in the class is written on a slip of paper and put into a hat, and two names are drawn without replacement, what is the probability that one of the names will have five letters and the other name will have seven letters?

Solution

Step 1

Determine which formula to use.

There are two ways that the names can be drawn: the name with five letters could be drawn first, and the name with seven letters could be drawn second, or the name with seven letters could be drawn first, and the name with five letters could be drawn second. Find the probability of each possibility, and then add them together.

Call event F_1 drawing a name with five letters on the first draw, F_2 drawing a name with five letters on the second draw, S_1 drawing a name with seven letters on the first draw, and S_2 drawing a name with seven letters on the second draw.

Since the second name is drawn without replacing the first name, the sample space for the second event is different from the sample space for the first event, and the events are dependent. Use the formula

$$P(F \cap S) = \left[P(F_1) \times P(S_2 \mid F_1) \right] + \left[P(S_1) \times P(F_2 \mid S_1) \right].$$

 Copyright Protected

Step 2

Calculate each separate probability.

There are 28 names in the bag to start out with, so $P(F_1) = \dfrac{4}{28} = \dfrac{1}{7}$,

and $P(S_1) = \dfrac{3}{28}$.

NOTES

If a name with five letters is drawn first, then there will be 27 names left, including 3 names with seven letters. Therefore,

$P(S_2 \mid F_1) = \dfrac{3}{27} = \dfrac{1}{9}$.

When calculating the probability of two events that occur simultaneously, treat them as though one event occurred first and the other event occurred second without replacement.

If a name with seven letters is drawn first, then there will be 27 names left, including 4 names with five letters. Therefore, $P(F_2 \mid S_1) = \dfrac{4}{27}$.

Step 3

Apply the formula

$P(F \cap S) = \left[P(F_1) \times P(S_2 \mid F_1) \right] + \left[P(S_1) \times P(F_2 \mid S_1) \right]$.

$P(F \cap S) = \left[P(F_1) \times P(S_2 \mid F_1) \right] + \left[P(S_1) \times P(F_2 \mid S_1) \right]$

$P(F \cap S) = \left(\dfrac{1}{7} \times \dfrac{1}{9} \right) + \left(\dfrac{3}{28} \times \dfrac{4}{27} \right)$

$P(F \cap S) = \dfrac{1}{63} + \dfrac{1}{63}$

$P(F \cap S) = \dfrac{2}{63}$

Therefore, the probability of drawing a name with five letters and a name with seven letters is $\dfrac{2}{63}$.

Class Exercise 5

Stephan writes each letter of his name on an index card and then places all of the index cards facedown on the table. If he flips over 2 cards at random, what is the probability that he will flip over a vowel and a consonant?

PRACTICE EXERCISES

Use the following information to answer the next question.

Kwon sorts a set of 26 alphabet tiles into a pile of vowel tiles and a pile of consonant tiles. He puts the 5 vowel tiles into one bag and the 21 consonant tiles into another bag. He plans a series of probability experiments that involve drawing two of the tiles.

Classify each of the following pairs of events in Kwon's probability experiments as dependent or independent.

1. **a)** The first experiment is drawing a letter from the vowel bag, replacing it, and then drawing another letter from the same bag. One event is drawing an A, and the other event is drawing an E.

   b) The second experiment is drawing a letter from the vowel bag, not replacing it, and then drawing another letter from the same bag. One event is drawing an A, and the other event is drawing an E.

   c) The third experiment is drawing a letter from the vowel bag, not replacing it, and then drawing a letter from the consonant bag. One event is drawing an A, and the other event is drawing a B.

   d) The fourth experiment is drawing two letters simultaneously from the consonant bag. One event is drawing a B, and the other event is drawing a C.

   e) The fifth experiment is simultaneously drawing one letter from the vowel bag and one letter from the consonant bag. One event is drawing an A, and the other event is drawing a C.

 Copyright Protected

Use the following information to answer the next three questions.

A special 12-sided die has only the numbers 1 through 4 in different distributions.
The probabilities of some rolls are listed as follows:

The probability of rolling 1 is $\dfrac{1}{12}$.

The probability of rolling 2 is $\dfrac{1}{6}$.

When the die is rolled twice, the probability of rolling 1 and then 3 is $\dfrac{1}{36}$.

2. If the die is rolled twice, what is the probability of rolling 1 both times?

3. What is the probability of rolling 3?

4. If the die is rolled twice, what is the probability that the rolls will have a sum of 3?

Use the following information to answer the next three questions.

A bag contains 2 red marbles, 3 purple marbles, and 4 black marbles. Two marbles are drawn from the bag without replacement.

5. What is the probability of drawing a red marble on the second draw if a purple marble is drawn first?

6. What is the probability of drawing a red marble on the second draw if a black marble is drawn first?

7. What is the probability of drawing a red marble on the second draw if a red marble is drawn first?

Use the following information to answer the next five questions.

Ali writes the numbers 1 through 25 onto slips of paper and puts them into a bag.

8. When one slip is drawn at random and replaced before a second slip is drawn, what is the probability of drawing an even number both times?

9. When one slip is drawn at random and replaced before a second slip is drawn, what is the probability of drawing an even number and then a multiple of 5?

10. When one slip is drawn at random and not replaced before a second slip is drawn, what is the probability of drawing an even number both times?

11. When one slip is drawn at random and not replaced before a second slip is drawn, what is the probability that one of the slips will have an even number, and the other slip will have an odd number?

Use the following additional information to answer the next question.

Ali says that if the two slips are drawn without replacement, the probability of drawing an even number and then a multiple of 5 is equal to $\dfrac{12}{25} \times \dfrac{5}{24}$.

12. Explain why Ali's calculation is incorrect.

REVIEW SUMMARY

- Probability is the ratio of favourable outcomes of an event to the total number of possible outcomes in the sample space.
- When calculating the number of outcomes of an event, each possible outcome must have the same probability.
- The number of outcomes for compound events can be determined using graphic organizers, such as tree diagrams and two-way tables.
- The odds in favour of an event are the ratio of favourable to unfavourable outcomes. The odds against an event are the ratio of unfavourable to favourable outcomes.
- Events are mutually exclusive when they have no common outcomes. The probability that one or both of
  two mutually exclusive events, A and B, occur can be determined using the formula
  $P(A \cup B) = P(A) + P(B), A \cap B = \varnothing$.
- Events are non-mutually exclusive when they share at least one outcome. The probability that one or both of two non-mutually exclusive events, A and B, occur can be determined using the formula
  $P(A \cup B) = P(A) + P(B) - P(A \cap B)$.
- The complement of an event A, denoted A' or $\overline{A}$, is the set of all of the outcomes in the sample space that
  are not elements of A. Complementary events are always mutually exclusive, and the sum of their probabilities is 1.
- In independent events, the result of one of the events does not affect the probability of the other event or events. If two events, A and B, are independent, then the probability that both of them will occur is calculated using the formula $P(A \cap B) = P(A) \times P(B)$.
- In dependent events, the result of the first event affects the probability of the other event or events. If two events, A and B, are dependent, then the probability that both of them will occur is calculated using the formula $P(A \cap B) = P(A) \times P(B \mid A)$, where $P(B|A)$ is the probability of B if A has occurred.

PRACTICE TEST

Use the following information to answer the next three questions.

In a probability experiment, each letter in the word MATH is written on a separate card, and the cards are then placed in a box. One card is drawn at random from the box.

1. Determine the sample space for the experiment.

2. What is the probability that the letter on the card is M?

3. What are the odds against drawing a vowel?

Use the following information to answer the next two questions.

A spinner has orange, red, and green sections that are the same size and a blue section that is twice as large as each of the other three sections.

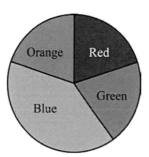

4. What is the probability of spinning green on this spinner? Express the answer as a decimal.

120 Copyright Protected

5. What is the probability of spinning a colour other than green?

Use the following information to answer the next question.

Aiden and Victor want to calculate the probability of spinning 3 and then 2 using the following spinner.

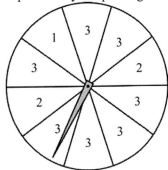

Aiden says that they should use a two-way table to determine the number of outcomes.
They would count the number of favourable outcomes and the total number of outcomes, and then use the probability formula to find the probability.

Victor says that they should use the probability formula to determine the probability of spinning 3 and the probability of spinning 2, and then multiply those probabilities together.

6. Use a table or a tree diagram to determine the number of equally probable outcomes for a probability experiment that involves spinning the given spinner and then flipping a coin.

7. Calculate the probability of spinning 3 and then 2 using each method.

Use the following information to answer the next three questions.

Two competing fast-food chains, Duke of Burgers and Cluck-King, each have a promotion in which everyone who buys a meal deal is entered into a contest. The odds in favour of winning a prize at Duke of Burgers are 2:13, and the probability of winning a prize at Cluck-King is $\frac{1}{7}$.

8. What is the probability of winning a prize at Duke of Burgers?

9. What are the odds in favour of winning a prize at Cluck-King?

10. Which chain offers a greater likelihood of winning a prize?

Use the following information to answer the next question.

On her way to the airport to pick up a friend, Carlene hears on the news that because of a storm, 30% of flights arriving in the next three hours will be delayed.

11. What is the probability that Carlene's friend's flight will be early or on time?

Use the following information to answer the next question.

A group of students from all over Alberta is gathered for a conference on ways to combat poverty. One of the students in attendance will be selected at random to participate in one of the panel discussions. For every 50 students at the conference, 15 students are from Calgary, 26 students are from Edmonton or Calgary, and 1 student is from Grande Prairie.

12. What is the probability that the student selected will be from Edmonton or Grande Prairie?

Use the following information to answer the next two questions.

In a probability experiment involving a 10-sided die with the numbers 1 through 10, event A is defined as rolling an odd number, and event B is defined as rolling a perfect square.

13. What is the probability of $A \cup B$?

14. What is the probability of $(A \cup B)'$?

Use the following information to answer the next question.

The following Venn diagram shows the number of students taking a computer course (C), the number of students taking a data management course (D), the number of students taking both courses, and the number of students taking neither course.

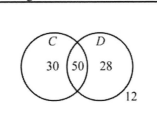

Amber uses the Venn diagram to make the following calculations regarding the likelihood that a student chosen at random is enrolled in these courses:

$$P(C) = \frac{2}{3}$$

$$P(D) = \frac{7}{20}$$

$$P(C \cap D) = \frac{9}{10}$$

$$P(C \cup D)' = \frac{1}{10}$$

15. Correct any errors that Amber made.

Use the following information to answer the next questions.

A bag of beads contains round and square beads of various colours. If *R* is drawing a round bead at random from the bag, and *G* is drawing a green bead, then $P(R) = 0.47$, $P(G) = 0.31$, and $P(R \text{ and } G) = 0.22$.

16. What is the probability of drawing a bead that is round or green?

Use the following additional information to answer the next two questions.

If *W* is drawing a white bead at random from the bag, then $P(R \text{ or } W) = 0.67$, and $P(R \text{ and } W) = 0.08$.

17. What is the probability of drawing a white bead?

18. How many white beads should there be if the bag contains 200 beads?

Use the following information to answer the next question.

The probability that Xavier will pass Grade 12 math this semester is 0.82, and the probability that he will pass chemistry is 0.78.

19. If passing math and passing chemistry are independent events, what is the probability that Xavier will pass math but not chemistry? Round the answer to the nearest hundredth.

Use the following information to answer the next three questions.

During a game of basketball, Brayden and Carter each take a foul shot. The probability that Brayden will score a point is $\frac{7}{10}$, and the probability that Carter will score a point is $\frac{3}{5}$.

20. What is the probability that both boys will score a point?

21. What is the probability that at least one of the boys will score a point?

22. What is the probability that neither boy will score a point?

Use the following information to answer the next question.

Margaret writes the letters of the word TORONTO on separate slips of paper, folds them, and places them in a hat. She mixes them and pulls two slips randomly from the hat, one after the other without replacement.

23. What is the probability that the second letter Margaret chooses is O, given that the first letter she chose was O?

Use the following information to answer the next four questions.

A card player successively draws two cards at random from a standard deck of playing cards.

24. Determine the following probabilities with and without replacement of the first card before the second draw.

25. Both cards are black.

26. The first card is a queen, and the second card is a king.

27. One of the cards is a queen, and the other card is a king.

126 Copyright Protected

THE FUNDAMENTAL COUNTING PRINCIPLE, PERMUTATIONS, AND COMBINATIONS

When you are finished this unit, you will be able to…
- Use the fundamental counting principle to solve a counting problem
- Use factorial notation where appropriate to write, simplify, or evaluate expressions
- Recognize and classify problems as permutations or combinations
- Determine the number of permutations of n objects taken r at a time
- Determine the number of permutations of n non-objects taken n at a time
- Determine the number of combinations of n distinct objects taken r at a time
- Solve an equation that involves $_nP_r$ or $_nC_r$ notation
- Apply permutations and combinations to problems involving probability

PREREQUISITE SKILLS AND KNOWLEDGE

Prior to starting this unit, you should be able to…
- Perform operations on polynomials
- Factor and solve a quadratic equation
- Apply exponent laws
- Read problems carefully to interpret the correct meaning
- Be flexible in the approaches to problem solving
- Find the probability of an event and its complementary event

Lesson 1   THE FUNDAMENTAL COUNTING PRINCIPLE

NOTES

A certain task may require you to count how many ways a task can be accomplished. For example, you may be curious about the number of possible arrangements of three friends sitting next to each other on a sofa or the number of possible choices for numbers on a raffle ticket. One way of solving these kinds of counting problems is to list all of the possible arrangements and then count the number of arrangements. A graphic organizer such as a list or tree diagram can help you determine all of the possible arrangements.

Example

In a school cafeteria, students must select one entrée and one side dish for lunch.

The students have the following choices:

Entrées	Side Dishes
Beef	Fries
Chicken	Pasta
Pork	Salad
Tofu	

a) List all the possible lunch meals using a graphic organizer.

Solution

Method 1:
List all the possible meals in pairs in which the first element in each pair is the entrée, and the second element is the side dish.

{Beef, Fries}   {Chicken, Fries}

{Beef, Pasta}   {Chicken, Pasta}

{Beef, Salad}   {Chicken Salad}

{Pork, Fries}   {Tofu, Fries}

{Pork, Pasta}   {Tofu, Pasta}

{Pork, Salad}   {Tofu, Salad}

128 Copyright Protected

Method 2:

Make a tree diagram with the entrée options on the far left-hand side, and then make a branch that corresponds to each side dish.

Entrée	Side dish	Possible Meals
Beef	Fries	Beef, Fries
	Pasta	Beef, Pasta
	Salad	Beef, Salad
Chicken	Fries	Chicken, Fries
	Pasta	Chicken, Pasta
	Salad	Chicken, Salad
Pork	Fries	Pork, Fries
	Pasta	Pork, Pasta
	Salad	Pork, Salad
Tofu	Fries	Tofu, Fries
	Pasta	Tofu, Pasta
	Salad	Tofu, Salad

Start ◂

b) How many different lunch meals are possible?

Solution

Count the number of lunch meals obtained in each method from part **a)**. Both methods show that that there are 12 possible lunch meals.

Class Exercise 1

A television game show asks participants to choose a door and then choose a curtain behind the door. There are 5 doors and 3 curtains behind each door.

a) List all possible outcomes using a tree diagram.

b) How many different choices are possible?

A tree diagram is a useful method of visually representing all the possible ways of completing a task. Another method of finding out how many ways a task can be completed is the **fundamental counting principle**. According to this principle, you can calculate how many ways a task can be completed by multiplying the number of options for each step of the task.

Example

A certain bike lock combination consists of three digits. If the digits 0 to 9 can be used, how many possible codes are there?

a) List the stages of making a three-digit bike lock combination.

Solution

The task is to make a three-digit bike lock combination. This task has three stages:
1. Pick the first digit. Since there are 10 digits to pick from (any digit from 0 to 9), there are 10 ways to pick the first digit.
2. Pick the second digit. Since there are 10 digits to pick from, there are 10 ways to pick the second digit.
3. Pick the third digit. Since there are 10 digits to pick from, there are 10 ways to pick the third digit.

b) Determine the number of possible combinations.

Solution

Apply the fundamental counting principle. Multiply the number of options for each digit in the combination.
$10 \times 10 \times 10 = 1000$

Therefore, there are 1 000 possible combinations.

In general, the **fundamental counting principle** states that if a task is made up of several stages in which there are m ways to accomplish stage 1, n ways to accomplish stage 2, p ways to accomplish stage 3, and so on, then the total ways that the entire task can be accomplished (stage 1, 2, 3, and so on) is $m \times n \times p \times \dots$.

 Copyright Protected

Example

Natalie, Matthew, Vickie, Tyler, and Trina are lining up for a group photo. How many different arrangements are possible if Vickie and Tyler insist on standing on opposite ends of the line?

a) List the stages of taking a group photo.

Solution

The task is to take a group photo in which Vickie and Tyler are on opposite ends of the photo. There are five spots in the photo. This task has five stages:
1. Assign the first spot. Either Vickie or Tyler must stand in the first spot, so there are 2 ways to assign the first spot.
2. Assign the second spot. Natalie, Matthew, or Trina can stand in the second spot, so there are 3 ways to assign the second spot.
3. Assign the third spot. Once a spot has been assigned in stage 2, there are only 2 remaining people who can stand in the third spot. This means there are 2 ways to assign the third spot.
4. Assign the fourth spot. Once people have been designated in stages 2 and 3, there will only be 1 person remaining to stand in the fourth spot. Therefore, there is 1 way to assign the fourth spot.
5. Assign the fifth spot. Either Vickie or Tyler must stand on the far right. One of them has been assigned in the first stage. Therefore, there is 1 way to assign the spot on the far right.

b) Determine the number of possible arrangements for the group photo.

Solution

Apply the fundamental counting principle. Multiply the number of arrangements of each spot in the group photo.
$2 \times 3 \times 2 \times 1 \times 1 = 12$

The number of possible arrangements for the group photo is 12.

Class Exercise 2

A certain province has particular rules for its licence plates. Each license plate has 5 characters. The first 3 characters must be letters such that the first and third letters are consonants, and the second letter is a vowel. The next two characters must be odd digits that cannot be the same. If there are 21 consonants and 5 vowels in the alphabet, how many different licence plates are possible?

PRACTICE EXERCISES

Use the following information to answer the next three questions.

Rental packages including a pair of skis and boots can be purchased at a local ski hill. In the rental shop, there are standard, deluxe, or professional skis and economy, regular, or insulated ski boots. Any type of ski can be adjusted to fit any type of boot.

1. Draw a tree diagram to represent the number of different rental packages.

2. How many different rental packages consisting of deluxe skis and one pair of boots are possible?

3. How many different rental packages are possible?

Use the following information to answer the next two questions.

A bank machine code consists of four digits, and the first digit cannot be 0.

4. How many different codes are possible if the digits must all be different?

 Copyright Protected

5. How many different codes are possible if repetitions are allowed?

6. How many different seating arrangements of 4 boys and 4 girls sitting in a row are possible if the boys and girls sit in alternate positions and the seating arrangement starts with a girl?

7. How many different even five-digit whole numbers beginning with a 7 or an 8 are possible?

8. How many three-digit numbers either start with the digit 3 or have no 3s?

9. If there are 26 letters in the alphabet, how many three-letter arrangements begin with the letter L and end with the letter P if there are no repetitions?

10. Jessica rides her bicycle to work every day. On the way to work, she always stops for coffee at a café. There are 4 different bicycle paths she can to take from her house to the cafe. If there are twice as many bicycle paths from the café to work than there are from her house to the café, how many different routes can Jessica take to get to work from her house?

Lesson 2   FACTORIAL NOTATION

NOTES

Factorial notation is a shorthand mathematical notation for multiplying descending sequences. The symbol $n!$, where n is a positive integer, is read as n factorial and is defined as $n! = n \times (n-1) \times (n-2) \times ... \times 2 \times 1$.

For example, the factorial 7! can be written as $7 \times 6 \times 5 \times 4 \times 3 \times 2 \times 1$.

Factorials are not defined for negative integers or for non-integers. For example, (–5)! is not defined. By definition, $0! = 1$.

Example

Evaluate $\dfrac{5!}{2}$.

Solution
Rewrite 5! as a product, and evaluate.

$$\frac{5!}{2}$$
$$= \frac{5 \times 4 \times 3 \times 2 \times 1}{2}$$
$$= \frac{120}{2}$$
$$= 60$$

Therefore, the value of $\dfrac{5!}{2}$ is 60.

A useful property of factorials is that many of the individual numbers (or factors) will divide out (or cancel) when the factorials are divided.

For example, writing $\dfrac{6!}{4!}$ as products gives the expression

$\dfrac{6 \times 5 \times 4 \times 3 \times 2 \times 1}{4 \times 3 \times 2 \times 1}$. Since both the numerator and the denominator include the expression $4 \times 3 \times 2 \times 1$, these factors can be grouped together and cancelled out.

$$\frac{6 \times 5 \times 4 \times 3 \times 2 \times 1}{4 \times 3 \times 2 \times 1}$$
$$= \frac{6 \times 5 \times (4 \times 3 \times 2 \times 1)}{(4 \times 3 \times 2 \times 1)}$$
$$= \frac{6 \times 5 \times \cancel{(4 \times 3 \times 2 \times 1)}}{\cancel{(4 \times 3 \times 2 \times 1)}}$$
$$= 6 \times 5$$

This leaves a relatively simple expression to evaluate.
$6 \times 5 = 30$

Therefore, to determine which factors can cancel out, rewrite the factorials as products, and then cancel out the common factors in the numerator and denominator.

Example

Evaluate $\dfrac{8!}{5!}$.

Solution

Step 1
Rewrite the factorials as products.
$$\frac{8!}{5!} = \frac{8 \times 7 \times 6 \times 5 \times 4 \times 3 \times 2 \times 1}{5 \times 4 \times 3 \times 2 \times 1}$$

Step 2
Cancel out the common factors in the numerator and denominator, and evaluate.

$$\frac{8 \times 7 \times 6 \times 5 \times 4 \times 3 \times 2 \times 1}{5 \times 4 \times 3 \times 2 \times 1}$$
$$= \frac{8 \times 7 \times 6 \times \left(5 \times 4 \times 3 \times 2 \times 1\right)}{\left(5 \times 4 \times 3 \times 2 \times 1\right)}$$
$$= 8 \times 7 \times 6$$
$$= 336$$

Therefore $\dfrac{8!}{5!} = 336$.

Class Exercise 1

Evaluate $\dfrac{9!}{3!}$.

EVALUATING FACTORIALS USING TECHNOLOGY

You can also use a graphing calculator to calculate factorials.

For example, to evaluate 6! using a TI-83 or similar calculator, press $\boxed{6}$ $\boxed{\text{MATH}}$ $\boxed{\triangleleft}$ to access the PRB menu. Select 4:!, and then press $\boxed{\text{ENTER}}$ twice. The result is 720.

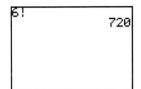

Example

Evaluate $\dfrac{18!}{14!}$.

Solution

Step 1
Enter the numerator.
Press $\boxed{1}$ $\boxed{8}$ $\boxed{\text{MATH}}$ $\boxed{\triangleleft}$, and select 4:!.

```
18!


```

Step 2
Enter the denominator.
Press $\boxed{\div}$ $\boxed{1}$ $\boxed{4}$ $\boxed{\text{MATH}}$ $\boxed{\triangleleft}$, and select 4:!.

```
18!/14!


```

Step 3
Press $\boxed{\text{ENTER}}$.

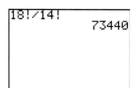

```
18!/14!
          73440

```

Therefore, $\dfrac{18!}{14!} = 73\,440$.

Class Exercise 2

Evaluate $\dfrac{21!}{16!}$ using technology.

SIMPLIFYING EXPRESSIONS INVOLVING FACTORIALS

You can simplify algebraic expressions involving n factorial by applying the formal definition $n! = n \times (n-1) \times (n-2) \times ... \times 2 \times 1$.

Example

Express $\dfrac{(n+1)!}{(n-1)!}$ in simplified form.

NOTES

Solution

Step 1

Rewrite the factorials as products.

$$\frac{(n+1)!}{(n-1)!}$$

$$= \frac{(n+1) \times n \times (n-1) \times (n-2) \times (n-3) \times ... \times 2 \times 1}{(n-1) \times (n-2) \times (n-3) \times ... \times 2 \times 1}$$

The second term in the expression $(n+1)!$ is $(n+1)-1 = n$. The third term is $(n-1)$, the fourth term is $(n-1)-1 = (n-2)$, and so on.

Step 2

Cancel out the common factors in the numerator and denominator.

$$\frac{(n+1)!}{(n-1)!}$$

$$= \frac{(n+1) \times n \times (n-1) \times (n-2) \times (n-3) \times ... \times 2 \times 1}{(n-1) \times (n-2) \times (n-3) \times ... \times 2 \times 1}$$

$$= (n+1) \times n$$

Step 3

Expand.

$$(n+1) \times n$$
$$= n^2 + n$$

Therefore, $\dfrac{(n+1)!}{(n-1)!} = n^2 + n$.

Sometimes, rewriting the factorial as a product can be a time-consuming process, especially if the factorial is a large sequence of numbers. In this case, expand the larger factorial until there is a common factor that can be cancelled out.

The larger factorial is the expression that has the most factors.

For example, instead of rewriting the expression $\dfrac{10!}{2!}$ as

$\dfrac{10 \times 9 \times 8 \times 7 \times 6 \times 5 \times 4 \times 3 \times 2 \times 1}{7 \times 6 \times 5 \times 4 \times 3 \times 2 \times 1}$, expand the larger factorial (10!) so that

the expression becomes $\dfrac{10 \times 9 \times 8 \times 7!}{7!}$. You can then proceed to cancel

out the common factor 7!, which will give a result of $10 \times 9 \times 8 = 720$.

NOTES

Example

Simplify $\dfrac{(n-15)!}{(n-13)!}$.

In the given expression, the larger factorial is $(n-13)!$. Therefore, expand the expression $(n-13)!$ until there is a common factor with the numerator $(n-15)!$.

Solution
Step 1
Rewrite the denominator as $(n-13)(n-14)(n-15)!$.

$$\frac{(n-15)!}{(n-13)!} = \frac{(n-15)!}{(n-13)(n-14)(n-15)!}$$

Step 2
Cancel out the common factors in the numerator and denominator.

$$\frac{(n-15)!}{(n-13)(n-14)(n-15)!}$$
$$= \frac{1}{(n-13)(n-14)}$$

It is not necessary to expand the simplified form of an expression.

Therefore, the simplified form of $\dfrac{(n-15)!}{(n-12)!}$ is $\dfrac{1}{(n-13)(n-14)}$.

Class Exercise 3

Simplify $\dfrac{(n-34)!}{(n-36)!}$.

SOLVING EQUATIONS INVOLVING FACTORIALS
You can solve an equation involving factorial notation.

Example

Determine the value of n in the equation $\dfrac{(n+5)!}{(n+3)!} = 56$.

Solution
The largest factorial in the expression is $(n+5)!$. Therefore, expand $(n+5)!$ until there is a common a factor with the denominator $(n+3)!$.

 Copyright Protected

Step 1

Rewrite the numerator as $(n+5)(n+4)(n+3)!$.

$$\frac{(n+5)!}{(n+3)!} = 56$$

$$\frac{(n+5)(n+4)(n+3)!}{(n+3)!} = 56$$

Step 2

Cancel out the common factors, and expand.

$$\frac{(n+5)(n+4)(n+3)!}{(n+3)!} = 56$$

$$(n+5)(n+4) = 56$$

$$n^2 + 9n + 20 = 56$$

Step 3

Bring all terms to one side, and factor the trinomial.

$$n^2 + 9n + 20 = 56$$

$$n^2 + 9n - 36 = 0$$

$$(n+12)(n-3) = 0$$

Step 4

Solve for n.

$$(n+12)(n-3) = 0$$

$$n+12 = 0 \qquad n-3 = 0$$

$$n = -12 \qquad n = 3$$

Since n cannot be a negative integer, the value of n is 3.

Class Exercise 4

Solve for n in the equation $90(n-4)! = (n-2)!$.

PRACTICE EXERCISES

Evaluate the following expressions without using technology.

1. $\dfrac{6!}{9!}$

2. $\dfrac{7!}{10!}$

3. $\dfrac{26!}{24!} - 17$

4. $\dfrac{5!}{0!} + \dfrac{14!}{16!}$

Simplify the following expressions.

5. $\dfrac{(n+1)!}{n!}$

6. $\dfrac{(n+3)!}{n!}$

7. $\dfrac{(n+1)!}{(n-2)!}$

8. $\dfrac{n!(n+1)!}{(n-1)!(n-1)!}$

Solve for n in the following equations.

9. $(n+9)! = 342(n+7)!$

10. $\dfrac{(n+2)!}{n!} = 42$

 Copyright Protected

Lesson 3 PERMUTATIONS

Many counting problems refer to a set of objects. These problems often describe how some or all of the objects could be arranged.

In some situations, the order in which objects are arranged is important. For example, if you are filling 3 chairs in a row with 3 people, the order in which the chairs are filled matters because any change in the order results in a different arrangement of people. The arrangement of a set of objects in a particular order is called a **permutation**.

There are three different types of permutation problems:
- Permutations of *n* distinct objects taken *n* at time
- Permutations of *n* distinct objects taken *r* at a time
- Permutations of non-distinct objects

NOTES
Common sets of objects include numbers, letters in the alphabet, and groups of people.

PERMUTATIONS OF *n* DISTINCT OBJECTS

The permutation of *n* distinct objects is the arrangement of all given objects.

Example

Five people want to sit together in a row.

Determine the number of different seating arrangements of 5 people in a row.

Solution

There are 5 people that all need to be seated. Since you are required to find the number of arrangements of seating 5 people, the order in which they are arranged matters.

Step 1

List the stages of seating the 5 people. The process of seating the 5 people consists of five stages.
1. Fill the first chair. There are 5 people to seat, so there are 5 ways to fill the first chair.
2. Fill the second chair. Once 1 person has been seated in the first chair, there are only 4 people left to be seated. There are 4 ways to fill the second chair.
3. Fill the third chair. Since there are 3 people left to be seated, there are 3 ways to fill the third chair.

NOTES

4. Fill the fourth chair. There are only 2 people left, so there are 2 ways to fill the fourth chair.
5. Fill the fifth chair. There is only 1 person left to be seated, so there is 1 way to fill the fifth chair.

Step 2
Determine the number of possible seating arrangements.
By the fundamental counting principle, the solution is determined by multiplying the number of choices for accomplishing each stage.
$5 \times 4 \times 3 \times 2 \times 1 = 120$

Therefore, there are 120 possible seating arrangements for all 5 people.

Example
Determine the number of different seating arrangements of n people in a row.
Solution
Step 1
List the stages of seating n people. The process of seating the n people consists of n stages:
1. There are n different people who can sit in the first chair.
2. There are $(n-1)$ different people who can sit in the second chair.
3. There are $(n-2)$ different people who can sit in the third chair. The seating process continues until there is only 1 person left to be seated in the nth chair.

In the second last stage, there are 2 different people left to be seated in the $(n-1)^{th}$ chair. In the last stage, there is only 1 person left to be seated in n^{th} chair.

Step 2
Determine the number of seating arrangements of n people in a row. To complete the task of seating all n people, all the stages must be completed. That is, a person must be placed in the first chair, second chair, third chair, $(n-1)^{th}$ chair, and n^{th} chair. Therefore, the total number of possible arrangements is as follows:
$n \times (n-1) \times (n-2) \times ... \times 2 \times 1 = n!$

In general, $n! = n \times (n-1) \times (n-2) \times ... \times 2 \times 1$ represents the number of permutations of n distinct objects.

Class Exercise 1

There are 11 different acts lined up for a school talent show. The acts are going on one after another in the show. How many different arrangements are possible for the 11 acts? Express your answer in factorial notation.

PERMUTATIONS OF NON-DISTINCT OBJECTS

Permutations of non-distinct objects occur when there is a set of objects in which some of the objects are identical.

Consider the number of fruit arrangements in a row using a pear, a banana, and two identical apples. Number the two apples.

When the apples are treated as two distinct objects, the following two arrangements are possible:

However, when the apples are treated as two identical objects, the two arrangements count as one arrangement.

Since the apples are treated as identical, there are duplications in the list of fruit arrangements that can be assembled. Therefore, there are fewer permutations with identical pieces of fruit than there are when all the fruits are distinct.

If all the pieces of fruit were distinct, the number of permutations would be 4!, or 24. Because of the two identical apples, divide 4! by 2!.

$$\frac{4!}{2!}$$
$$= \frac{24}{2!}$$
$$= 12$$

Therefore, 12 different arrangements of fruit can be made using a pear, a banana, and two identical apples.

Example

How many different 5-letter arrangements can be made using all the letters from the word POPPY?

Solution

Start by treating the three P's as if they were distinct. Label them P_1, P_2, and P_3. Therefore, one possible word is $P_1OP_2P_3Y$.

If all 5 letters are distinct, there are $5! = 120$ permutations. Instead of listing all 120 words, examine only those that begin with the letters OY.

If the O and Y are fixed in the first and second positions, it is necessary to arrange only the 3 distinct P's. There are 3!, or 6, arrangements for the 3 distinct P's. However, if the designations P_1, P_2, and P_3 are ignored, and the P's become non-distinct, the 6 permutations all become the same. Thus, only one word (OYPPP) is possible. The same result will occur for every other situation in which the O and Y are in certain positions, such as OPYPP and POPYP.

If all 5 letters were distinct, there would be 5! permutations. However, since there are 3 identical P's, 5! must be divided by 3!, or 6.

$$\frac{5!}{3!}$$
$$= \frac{120}{6}$$
$$= 20$$

Therefore, there are 20 different five-letter arrangements that can be made.

In general, when some of the objects to be arranged are identical, the number of permutations of the *n* objects can be calculated using the formula $\frac{n!}{a!b!c!...}$, where *a* objects are one kind, *b* objects are a second kind, *c* objects are a third kind, and so on.

The numerator *n*! is the number of permutations if all *n* objects are distinct. The denominator *a*!, *b*!, *c*! … accounts for the various permutations of the repeated objects.

Class Exercise 2

Kathleen wants to plant a row of 10 trees in front of her farmhouse. She has 3 identical pine trees, 4 identical elm trees, 2 identical birch trees, and 1 willow tree. How many different arrangements are possible for planting the trees in a row?

 Copyright Protected

PERMUTATIONS OF *n* DISTINCT OBJECTS TAKEN *r* AT A TIME

The permutation of *n* objects taken *r* at a time is the arrangement of some and not all of the objects.

Example

A teacher must form an executive committee consisting of a president, a vice-president, a treasurer, and a secretary. There are 16 available student council members. Determine the number of different executive committees that the teacher can form.

Solution

There are 16 available student council members and four positions on the executive committee. Since you are required to determine the number of different executive committees that the teacher can form, the order in which the students are chosen matters.

Step 1

List the stages of forming an executive committee. The process of forming an executive committee consists of four stages.
1. Appoint a president. There are 16 possible choices for the president.
2. Appoint a vice-president. Once the president has been appointed, there are only 15 council members left. There are 15 possible choices for the vice-president.
3. Appoint a treasurer. Since there are 14 council members left, there are 14 possible choices for the treasurer.
4. Appoint a secretary. There are 13 council members left, so there are 13 possible choices for the secretary.

Step 2

Determine the number of different executive committees that the teacher can form.

By the fundamental counting principle, the required result can be determined by multiplying the number of possible appointees for each position on the committee.
$16 \times 15 \times 14 \times 13 = 43\,680$

Therefore, there are 43 680 different executive committees that the teacher can form.

In the previous example, there is a sequence of numbers in descending order that are multiplied together. Although the numbers get smaller, they do not reach 1. Consider if the product of numbers in descending order continued all the way to 1. The result would be that the product of the *n* numbers could be simplified to the expression *n*!. However, if the product were extended to 1, some values would be multiplied unnecessarily. Therefore, the unnecessary product must be divided out.

Example

Express the product $6 \times 5 \times 4 \times 3$ using factorial notation.

Solution

Express the solution as a fraction in which the numerator is the product of descending whole number values starting at 6 and ending at 1, and the denominator is the product of any of the unnecessary values from the numerator.

$$6 \times 5 \times 4 \times 3$$
$$= \frac{6 \times 5 \times 4 \times 3 \times (2 \times 1)}{(2 \times 1)}$$

The expression $\dfrac{6 \times 5 \times 4 \times 3 \times (2 \times 1)}{(2 \times 1)}$ is equivalent to $\dfrac{6!}{2!} = \dfrac{6!}{(6-4)!}$.

In general, the number of permutations of n distinct objects taken r at a time, which is denoted $_nP_r$, is defined by the formula $_nP_r = \dfrac{n!}{(n-r)!}$.

Example

How many different 5-letter arrangements can be made using the letters from the word CHAMPION?

Solution

There are 8 distinct letters in the word CHAMPION, and 5 are to be used to form different letter arrangements. The order of the letters matters, so the problem is a permutation problem. To arrange 5 letters out of 8, use the formula $_nP_r = \dfrac{n!}{(n-r)!}$.

Step 1

Substitute 8 for n and 5 for r in the formula $_nP_r = \dfrac{n!}{(n-r)!}$.

$$_nP_r = \frac{n!}{(n-r)!}$$
$$_8P_5 = \frac{8!}{(8-5)!}$$
$$_8P_5 = \frac{8!}{3!}$$

Copyright Protected

Step 2

Evaluate $\dfrac{8!}{3!}$.

Using a calculator, the value of $\dfrac{8!}{3!}$ is 6 720. Therefore, 6 720 different 5-letter arrangements can be made using the letters in the word CHAMPION.

The number of objects taken at a time cannot exceed the total number of objects. For example, it is impossible to arrange 4 marbles taken 5 at a time. Algebraically, this situation is represented as $_4P_5 = \dfrac{4!}{(-1)!}$,

which results in an undefined negative factorial. However, it is possible to find the arrangement of 4 marbles taken 4 at a time. Algebraically, this situation is defined as $_4P_4 = \dfrac{4!}{0!}$, which is 24. Therefore, in the

formula $_nP_r = \dfrac{n!}{(n-r)!}$, n must be greater than or equal to r.

$0! = 1$

Example

Solve for n in the equation $_nP_2 = 110$.

Solution

Step 1

Apply the formula $_nP_r = \dfrac{n!}{(n-r)!}$.

In the equation $_nP_2 = 110$, rewrite $_nP_2$ as $\dfrac{n!}{(n-2)!}$.

$$_nP_2 = 110$$
$$\frac{n!}{(n-2)!} = 110$$

Step 2

Rewrite $n!$ as $n(n-1)(n-2)!$.

$$\frac{n!}{(n-2)!} = 110$$
$$\frac{n(n-1)(n-2)!}{(n-2)!} = 110$$

Step 3

Divide out common factors, and expand.

$$\frac{n(n-1)(n-2)!}{(n-2)!} = 110$$
$$n(n-1) = 110$$
$$n^2 - n = 110$$

NOTES

Step 4

Bring all terms to one side, and factor.

$$n^2 - n = 110$$
$$n^2 - n - 110 = 0$$
$$(n+10)(n-11) = 0$$

Step 5

Solve for n.
$$(n+10)(n-11) = 0$$

$$n + 10 = 0 \qquad\qquad n - 11 = 0$$
$$n = -10 \qquad\qquad n = 11$$

Since $n \geq 2$, the value of n is 11.

Class Exercise 3

Evaluate $_{12}P_5$.

You can also use a graphing calculator to evaluate expressions such as $_9P_3$ or $_6P_1$. To evaluate $_9P_3$ using a TI-83 or similar calculator, press $\boxed{9}$ $\boxed{\text{MATH}}$ $\boxed{\triangleleft}$ to access the PRB menu. Select 2: $_nP_r$, and press $\boxed{3}$ $\boxed{\text{ENTER}}$. The result is 504.

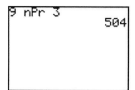

Class Exercise 4

If there are 6 children, how many different arrangements are possible for seating 4 of them in a row?

 Copyright Protected

You can also permute objects while keeping some objects grouped together. For example, when arranging a family in a photo in which the parents have to sit next to each other, you have to consider how many ways the parents can be arranged within the family group and how many ways the parents can be arranged within their own parent group.

Example

Dan, Rob, Carl, Pete, Elle, and Fran are seated in a row. How many different seating arrangements are possible if Dan, Rob, and Elle must sit next to each other?

Solution

This is a permutation problem in which some objects are grouped together.

Step 1

Determine the number of distinct groups. Since Dan, Rob, and Elle are all in one group, there are 4 distinct groups:

| Dan, Rob, and Elle | Carl | Pete | Fran |

Step 2

Determine the number of arrangements of the distinct groups. One possible arrangement of these groups is as follows:

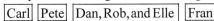

| Carl | Pete | Dan, Rob, and Elle | Fran |

The block | Dan, Rob, and Elle | can be placed in any location of the seating arrangement. Therefore, there are 4! different arrangements of these 4 distinct groups

Step 3

Determine the number of arrangements of the group of 3.

Dan, Rob, and Elle can be placed in any order. Therefore, there are 3! different arrangements of Dan, Rob, and Elle within their group.

Step 4

Determine the number of possible seating arrangements. Applying the fundamental counting principle, the number of possible seating arrangements is $4! \times 3! = 144$.

You can also calculate the number of permutations in which two specific objects must **not** be grouped together. The general procedure for finding the number of permutations in which two specific objects must not be grouped together is to subtract the number of permutations with the objects together from the total number of permutations.

Keep in mind that this rule is valid for only two objects that must be separate. It will not apply to two or more objects that must be separate.

NOTES

Example

How many different arrangements of all the letters in the word CALCULUS are possible so that the 2 C's are **not** together?

Solution

This is a permutation problem in which some objects are separated.

Step 1

Determine the total number of possible arrangements without the restriction.

In the word CALCULUS, there are 8 non-distinct letters that involve 2 C's, 1 A, 2 L's, 2 U's, and 1 S. Therefore, the number of arrangements without restriction is $\frac{8!}{2!2!2!} = 5040$.

The number of arrangements of the letters in the word CALCULUS is 5 040.

Step 2

Determine the number of arrangements with the 2 C's together. Consider the 2 C's as one group.

CC	A	L	L	U	U	S

There are 7 blocks altogether, but not all the blocks are distinct. There are 2 blocks with the letter L and 2 blocks with the letter U. Therefore, the number of permutations of the 7 groups in which the 2 C's are together is $\frac{7!}{2!2!} = 1260$.

Step 3

Determine the number of arrangements in which the 2 C's are not together.

Subtract the 1 260 arrangements from the 5 040 arrangements.
5 040 − 1 260 = 3 780

The number of arrangements in which the 2 C's are not together is 3 780.

Copyright Protected

Class Exercise 5

A father, a mother, and their 2 sons and 2 daughters have to stand in a row for a family picture. The father must be in the first spot, and the mother must be in the last spot. If the sons must be side by side and the daughters must be side by side, then what is the number of different possible arrangements for the family picture?

Class Exercise 6

There are 6 distinct sports cars lining up for a parade. How many arrangements are possible if 2 particular sports cars are **not** allowed to appear after each other?

PRACTICE EXERCISES

Evaluate the following expressions without using technology. Express your answer as a whole number.

1. $_{11}P_3$

2. $_{17}P_4$

Solve for n in the following equations.

3. $_{n+1}P_2 = 2$

4. $_nP_2 = 240$

5. Kyla intends to listen to her 4 new CDs one by one. How many different CD arrangements are possible for Kyla to listen to?

6. Six friends are running in a five-kilometre race. Sonya finished first, Chris was second, and Lewis was third. Maria, Heather, and Kell are still running. How many different outcomes are possible in the race?

Copyright Protected

7. Sarah is a piano teacher, and she has 9 gifts to give her 9 piano students. The gifts are 3 identical music books, 4 identical tuning forks, a Mozart CD, and a box of chocolates. How many different distributions of the gifts are possible?

8. For the boys' relay race at the local school's track meet, 8 runners take turns (called legs) to run the race. The coach, Mr. Smith, must decide the order for the 8 runners. Mr. Smith wants Curt and Adam to run the first 2 legs of the relay race, in either order, and Ben to run the last leg of the relay race. What is the number of different possible arrangements for the 8 runners in the relay race according to Mr. Smith's plan?

9. In a 100 m race with 8 competitors, what is the number of different outcomes for the top three positions in the race?

10. How many letter arrangements are possible using all the letters in the word KITCHENS if the letters H, E, and N must be together in any order?

Lesson 4 COMBINATIONS

NOTES

A permutation is an arrangement of objects in which order matters. A **combination** refers to a selection of objects in which the order does not matter.

For example, a coach needs to select three swimmers for the school swim team. He has five swimmers to choose from, and he wants to know the number of possible selections of swimmers. He selects the swimmers Ann, Bob, and Charlie.

If Ann, Bob, and Charlie were selected in a different order, would it result in a different selection? In other words, if the swimmers were selected as Bob, Charlie, and Ann, would that order result in a different selection than the previous order? It makes no difference how the swimmers are selected; they are all on the school team. Since the order of the selected swimmers does not matter, this problem is classified as a combination problem.

Example

There are five teams competing in a hockey tournament: the Invaders, the Knights, the Thunder, the Wildcats, and the Shredders. Gold, silver, and bronze medals are awarded to the top three hockey teams. A hockey coach wants to know how many different medal distributions are possible.

Is this problem classified as a combination problem or a permutation problem?

Solution

If the Invaders, the Fury, and the Shredders are each awarded a medal, then two of the possible outcomes are as follows:

Medal	Scenario 1	Scenario 2
Gold	Invaders	Knights
Silver	Knights	Shredders
Bronze	Shredders	Invaders

The final outcome of the hockey tournament is different if the Invaders win the gold medal or if the Knights win the gold medal. The order in which the medals are distributed matters for the purpose of assigning medals. Therefore, this problem is classified as a permutation problem.

Class Exercise 1

A charity raffle requires contestants to choose five numbers from 1 to 49 for their tickets. A contestant wants to know how many raffle tickets are possible. Classify this problem as a combination problem or permutation problem.

COMBINATIONS OF n DISTINCT OBJECTS TAKEN r AT A TIME

Consider 4 distinct shapes: a circle, a triangle, a square, and a pentagon. If 2 of the 4 shapes are arranged at a time, then the following permutations are possible:

If the order in which the shapes are chosen does not matter, then the following combinations are possible:

There are fewer combinations than permutations of shapes.
Each combination of shapes will result in 2, or 2!, permutations.
Therefore, to find the number of combinations, divide the number of permutations by the number of permutations for each combination.

$$\frac{_4P_2}{2!}$$
$$=\frac{12}{2}$$
$$=6$$

In general, the number of combinations of n objects taken r at a time is given by the formula $_nC_r = \dfrac{_nP_r}{r!}$. Since $_nP_r = \dfrac{n!}{(n-r)!}$, the formula can be expressed as follows:

$$_nC_r = \frac{_nP_r}{r!}$$

$$_nC_r = \frac{\dfrac{n!}{(n-r)!}}{r!}$$

$$_nC_r = \frac{n!}{(n-r)!r!}$$

The number of combinations of n objects taken r at a time is

$$_nC_r = \frac{n!}{(n-r)!r!}.$$

The notation $\begin{pmatrix} n \\ r \end{pmatrix}$ can also be used to represent the number of combinations of n objects taken r at a time.

Example

Jane wants to make a pizza with 3 toppings. There are 6 pizza toppings to choose from:

- Cheese
- Bacon
- Mushrooms
- Green peppers
- Pepperoni
- Olives

How many different pizzas can Jane make?

Solution

The order in which the toppings are chosen does not matter. For example, a pizza with pepperoni, cheese, and olives is the same as a pizza with olives, pepperoni, and cheese. Therefore, this is a combination problem.

Since there are 6 pizza toppings, and Jane can select only 3, the number of possible pizzas is given by $_6C_3$.

Step 1

In the formula $_nC_r = \dfrac{n!}{(n-r)!r!}$, substitute 6 for n and 3 for r.

$$_nC_r = \frac{n!}{(n-r)!r!}$$

$$_6C_3 = \frac{6!}{3!3!}$$

Step 2

Determine the value of $_6C_3$.

$$_6C_3 = \frac{6!}{3!3!}$$

$$_6C_3 = \frac{720}{36}$$

$$_6C_3 = 20$$

Therefore, Jane can make 20 different pizzas.

Copyright Protected

Class Exercise 2

Ms. Joseph is organizing groups of students for an activity in gym class. Her gym class has 22 students. If 4 students are randomly placed in a group, in how many different ways can she choose the group?

The number of objects taken r at a time cannot exceed the total number of objects. For example, it is impossible to find the number of combinations of 4 marbles taken 5 at a time. Algebraically, this scenario is defined as $_4C_5 = \dfrac{4!}{(-1)!5!}$, which results in an undefined negative factorial. However, it is possible to find the number of combinations of 4 marbles taken 4 at a time. Algebraically, this situation is defined as $_4C_4 = \dfrac{4!}{0!4!}$, which is 1.

Therefore, in the formula $_nC_r = \dfrac{n!}{(n-r)!r!}$, n must be greater than or equal to r.

$0! = 1$

Example

Determine the value of n in the equation $_nC_2 = 15$.

Solution
Step 1

Apply the formula $_nC_r = \dfrac{n!}{(n-r)!r!}$.

In the equation $_nC_2 = 15$, rewrite $_nC_2$ as $\dfrac{n!}{(n-2)!2!}$.

$$_nC_2 = 15$$
$$\frac{n!}{(n-2)!2!} = 15$$

NOTES

Step 2

Rewrite $n!$ as $n(n-1)(n-2)!$.

$$\frac{n!}{(n-2)!\,2!} = 15$$

$$\frac{n(n-1)(n-2)!}{(n-2)!\,2!} = 15$$

Step 3

Cancel out common factors.

$$\frac{n(n-1)(n-2)!}{(n-2)!\,2!} = 15$$

$$\frac{n(n-1)}{2!} = 15$$

Step 4

Solve for n.

$$\frac{n(n-1)}{2!} = 15$$

$$\frac{n^2 - n}{2 \times 1} = 15$$

$$n^2 - n = 30$$

$$n^2 - n - 30 = 0$$

$$(n+5)(n-6) = 0$$

$$n + 5 = 0 \qquad n - 6 = 0$$

$$n = -5 \qquad\quad n = 6$$

Since $n \geq 2$, the solution is $n = 6$.

Class Exercise 3

Determine the value of n in the equation $_nC_2 = 28$.

You can also use a graphing calculator to evaluate expressions such as $_6C_3$. To evaluate $_6C_3$ using a TI-83 or similar calculator, press $\boxed{6}$ $\boxed{\text{MATH}}$ $\boxed{\triangleleft}$ to access the PRB menu. Select $3: {}_nC_r$, and press $\boxed{3}$ $\boxed{\text{ENTER}}$. The result is 20.

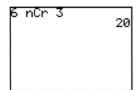

Class Exercise 4

A committee is required to organize a fundraiser. There are 10 people available to join the committee. How many different 6-member committees are possible?

The fundamental counting principle can be used to solve more complex combination problems.

Example

Amy is a first-year student registered in the faculty of science in a particular university, and she must take 5 courses. She must take an English course as well as 2 courses from column A and 2 courses from column B in the following chart:

Column A	Column B
Chemistry	Sociology
Physics	Psychology
Biology	Performing arts
Calculus	Commercial law
	Computer education
	Accounting

Determine number of different program choices available to Amy in order to meet the necessary faculty of science requirements.

Solution

The order in which the courses are chosen does not matter.

Step 1

Determine the number of possible selections from column A.
Amy must select 2 courses from column A. There are 4 courses in column A. Therefore, the number of possible selections from column A is $_4C_2 = 6$.

Step 2

Determine the number of possible selections from column B.
To meet the requirements, Amy must select 2 courses from column B. There are 6 courses in column B. Therefore, the number of possible selections from column B is $_6C_2 = 15$.

Step 3

Determine the number of different program choices available.
Amy must take an English course. Therefore, by applying the fundamental counting principle, the total number of different program choices available to Amy is
$1 \times {_4C_2} \times {_6C_2} = 1 \times 6 \times 15 = 90$.

Class Exercise 5

The staff in the emergency room of a particular hospital consists of 3 doctors and 12 nurses. How many different hospital teams consisting of 2 doctors and 5 nurses can be formed?

COMBINATIONS OF *n* OBJECTS TAKEN (*n* – *r*) AT A TIME

The number of combinations of *n* objects taken $n - r$ at a time is equal to the number of combinations of *n* objects taken *r* at a time. In other words, the value of $_nC_{n-r}$ is equal to the value of $_nC_r$.

For example, consider the five letters A, B, C, D, and E. If 3 letters are selected at time, then the following combinations of letters are possible:

(A,B,C)	(A,D,E)
(A,B,D)	(B,C,D)
(A,B,E)	(B,C,E)
(A,C,D)	(B,D,E)
(A,C,E)	(C,D,E)

Copyright Protected

There are 10 combinations of 5 letters selected 3 letters at a time.

If two letters are chosen at time, then the following combinations of letters are possible:

(A,B)   (B,D
(A,C)   (B,E)
(A,D)   (C,D)
(A,E)   (C,E)
(B,C)   (D,E)

There are 10 combinations of 5 letters selected 2 letters at a time.

The number of combinations of 5 letters selected 3 at a time is equal to the number of combinations of 5 letters selected 2 letters at time.
This relationship can be expressed as $_5C_3 = {_5}C_{5-3}$ or $_5C_3 = {_5}C_2$.

Example

Prove algebraically that $_nC_r = {_n}C_{n-r}$.

Solution
Step 1

Apply the formula $_nC_r = \dfrac{n!}{(n-r)!\,r!}$ to each side of the equation.

$$_nC_r = {_n}C_{n-r}$$

$$\frac{n!}{(n-r)!\,r!} = \frac{n!}{\left(n-(n-r)\right)!\,(n-r)!}$$

Step 2
Simplify the right side of the equation.

$$\frac{n!}{(n-r)!\,r!} = \frac{n!}{\left(n-(n-r)\right)!\,(n-r)!}$$

$$\frac{n!}{(n-r)!\,r!} = \frac{n!}{(n-n+r)!\,(n-r)!}$$

$$\frac{n!}{(n-r)!\,r!} = \frac{n!}{r!\,(n-r)!}$$

Both sides of the equation are equal. Therefore $_nC_r = {_n}C_{n-r}$.

PRACTICE EXERCISES

Evaluate the following expressions without using technology.

1. $_7C_5$

2. $_{15}C_4$

Solve for n in the following equations.

3. $_nC_2 = 66$

4. $_{n-1}C_2 = 6$

5. A tennis club has 40 members. The club is going to choose 3 members to serve on the board of directors. What is the number of different boards that can be formed?

6. A certain ice-cream parlour has 31 flavours of ice cream. If 2 different flavours are chosen, how many different 2-scoop ice-cream cones can be made?

7. Mr. Fraser has been asked to donate 6 of his sculptures to the local art gallery. If Mr. Fraser owns 25 sculptures, how many different donations of 6 sculptures are possible?

Copyright Protected

8. Terry and 19 of his friends are being considered for a trip. Only 5 people can go on this trip. What is the number of different groups that can go on the trip if Terry is included in each group?

9. A 6-member committee is to be chosen from a group of 5 men and 4 women. If the chosen committee must consist of 4 men and 2 women, how many different committees are possible?

Use the following information to answer the following question.

A chef in a restaurant wants to offer a stir-fry meal as the lunch special. To create a stir-fry meal, he needs 1 type of meat, 3 vegetables, and 1 type of noodle. He has the following items to create a stir-fry meal:

Meat	Vegetables	Noodles
Beef	Celery	Vermicelli
Chicken	Carrots	Rice noodles
Pork	Mushrooms	
	Cauliflower	
	Broccoli	

10. What is the number of different stir-fry meals the chef can create?

Lesson 5   *SOLVING PROBABILITY PROBLEMS INVOLVING PERMUTATIONS AND COMBINATIONS*

NOTES

The probability of an event $P(E)$ is determined by the ratio of the number of favourable outcomes (S) to the number of equally likely outcomes (N).

This relationship is given by the formula $P(E) = \dfrac{S}{N}$. In situations where the number of outcomes (either possible or successful) is large, using permutations or combinations may be necessary.

SOLVING PROBABILITY PROBLEMS INVOLVING PERMUTATIONS

When solving probability problems that involve permutations, the order of events is important.

While certain common techniques are followed to solve most probability problems, more than one method can usually be used to arrive at the correct solution.

Example

After a championship game, there are 10 hockey players that randomly line up for a picture. What is the probability that the captain and the goalie stand together in the picture?

Assume the captain and goalie are not the same person.

Solution

Step 1

Determine an expression for the number of successful outcomes.
Let the letter C represent the captain, and let G represent the goalie.
Let the remaining players be represented by P_1, P_2, P_3, P_4, P_5, P_6, P_7, and P_8.

One possible arrangement is $\boxed{C, G}$, $P_1, P_2, P_3, P_4, P_5, P_6, P_7, P_8$.

The block $\boxed{C, G}$ can be placed in any location of the arrangement.
As well, C and G can be placed in any order within the block.

Therefore, the number of possible arrangements with the captain and goalie standing together is $9! \times 2!$.

Step 2

Determine an expression for the number of equally likely outcomes.
Since there are no restrictions with respect to the location of the players in the line, there are $10! = 3\,628\,800$ possible arrangements, or outcomes.

Step 3

Determine the probability that captain and the goalie stand together.

Apply the formula $P(E) = \dfrac{S}{N}$.

Let $S = 9! \times 2!$ and $N = 10!$.

$$P(E) = \frac{S}{N}$$

$$P(C \text{ and } G \text{ stand together}) = \frac{9! \times 2!}{10!}$$

$$P(C \text{ and } G \text{ stand together}) = \frac{9! \times 2!}{10 \times 9!}$$

$$P(C \text{ and } G \text{ stand together}) = \frac{2}{10}$$

$$P(C \text{ and } G \text{ stand together}) = 0.2$$

The probability that the captain and the goalie stand together in the picture is 0.2.

Class Exercise 1

If the letters in word ABOUT are randomly arranged, what is the probability that the vowels are placed together? Express your solution as a fraction.

Sometimes, it is easier to determine the probability of an event's complement. The sum of the probability of an event $P(E)$ and its complementary event $P(\overline{E})$ is equal to 1. Therefore, $P(E) + P(\overline{E}) = 1$, or $P(E) = 1 - P(\overline{E})$.

Example

Lisa is organizing an executive committee consisting of a president, a vice-president, and a secretary. The executive committee is formed from a group of 5 women and 4 men.

What is the probability that the committee will consist of at least 1 man?

NOTES

Solution
The solution could be obtained directly by calculating the sum of the probabilities of 1 man, 2 men, and of 3 men. Another approach is to calculate the probability of no men (or all women) on the executive committee and subtract that result from 1.

Step 1
Determine an expression for the number of executive committees with no males or all women.
Since there are 5 women, the number of executive committees no males is $_5P_3$.

Step 2
Determine an expression for the number of executive committees.
Since there are 9 people that can form the executive committee, the number of possible committees is $_9P_3$.

Step 3
Determine the probability that the committee will have no men.
Apply the formula $P\left(\overline{E}\right) = \dfrac{S}{N}$.

Let $S = {_5P_3}$ and $N = {_9P_3}$.

$$P\left(\overline{E}\right) = \frac{S}{N}$$
$$P\left(\text{no men}\right) = \frac{_5P_3}{_9P_3}$$
$$P\left(\text{no men}\right) = \frac{60}{504}$$
$$P\left(\text{no men}\right) = \frac{5}{42}$$

Step 4
Determine the probability that the committee has at least one man.
$$P(E) = 1 - P\left(\overline{E}\right)$$
$$P\left(\text{at least one man}\right) = 1 - P\left(\text{no men}\right)$$
$$P\left(\text{at least one man}\right) = 1 - \frac{5}{42}$$
$$P\left(\text{at least one man}\right) = \frac{37}{42}$$

The probability that the executive committee will consist of at least one man is $\dfrac{37}{42}$.

Class Exercise 2

If a 3-letter arrangement is made using the letters in word PICKLE, what is the probability that the 3-letter arrangement will consist of at least one vowel?

SOLVING PROBABILITY PROBLEMS INVOLVING COMBINATIONS

Probability problems in which the order of selection does not matter involve the use of combinations. When solving probability problems that involve combinations, first determine the different combinations, and then apply the formula $P(E) = \dfrac{S}{N}$.

Example

A bag contains 8 red marbles and 6 yellow marbles. Two marbles are drawn at the same time from the bag at random.

a) Expressed as a fraction, what is the probability that both marbles drawn from the bag are yellow?

Solution

Step 1

Determine an expression for the number of successful outcomes. Since there are 6 yellow marbles, the number of selections of 2 yellow marbles from 6 yellow marbles can be represented by the expression ${_6}C_2$.

Step 2

Determine an expression for the number of equally likely outcomes. Since there are 14 marbles in the bag, the number of selections of 2 marbles from 14 marbles can be represented by the expression ${_{14}}C_2$.

NOTES

Step 3
Determine the probability that the marbles are yellow.

Apply the formula $P(E) = \dfrac{S}{N}$.

Let $S = {}_6C_2$ and $N = {}_{14}C_2$.

$$P(E) = \frac{S}{N}$$

$$P(\text{yellow and yellow}) = \frac{{}_6C_2}{{}_{14}C_2}$$

$$P(\text{yellow and yellow}) = \frac{15}{91}$$

b) Expressed as a fraction, what is the probability that 1 marble is red and 1 marble is yellow?

Solution
Step 1
Determine an expression for the number of successful outcomes. Since there are 8 red marbles in the bag, the number of selections of 1 red marble from 8 red marbles can be represented by the expression ${}_8C_1$.

Since there are 6 yellow marbles in the bag, the number of selections of 1 yellow marble from 6 yellow marbles can be represented by the expression ${}_6C_1$.

According to the fundamental counting principle, the number of selections of 1 marble and 1 yellow marble can be represented by the expression ${}_8C_1 \times {}_6C_1$.

Step 2
Determine an expression for the number of equally likely outcomes. Since there are 14 marbles in the bag, the number of selections of 2 marbles from 14 marbles can be represented by the expression ${}_{14}C_2$.

Step 3
Determine the probability that 1 red marble and 1 yellow marble are chosen.

Apply the formula $P(E) = \dfrac{S}{N}$.

$$P(E) = \frac{S}{N}$$

$$P(\text{red and yellow}) = \frac{{}_8C_1 \times {}_6C_1}{{}_{14}C_2}$$

$$P(\text{red and yellow}) = \frac{48}{91}$$

 Copyright Protected

Class Exercise 3

After trick-or-treating on Halloween, Gavin counted all of the candy he collected in a bag. He counted 40 chocolate bars, 23 lollipops, and 11 pieces of licorice. If he pulls out 2 pieces of candy from the bag, what is the probability that he chooses at least one piece of licorice?

PRACTICE EXERCISES

1. The letters T, T, O, O, and H are randomly pulled out of a bag without replacement. What is the probability, to the nearest hundredth, that the letters spell TOOTH?

2. Trina purchases 10 tickets from a charity raffle. Each ticket in the raffle has 6 different numbers between the numbers 1 and 20. If there is only one prize, what is the probability of Trina winning the prize? Express your solution as a fraction in reduced form.

3. For a spelling contest, 3 boys and 2 girls are arranged is a row. What is the probability that the seating arrangement has a girl at each end? Express your solution as a fraction in reduced form.

4. Ashley draws 3 cards at the same time from a standard deck of 52 cards. What is the probability that Ashley pulls out 3 aces? Express your solution as a fraction in reduced form.

5. A door lock requires a 5-digit code. If there are no repeated digits in the code, what is the probability that a person guesses the code correctly in exactly 2 attempts? Express your solution as a fraction in reduced form.

Use the following information to answer the next two questions.

In a box of 8 calculators, there are 3 that have dead batteries. A student selects 2 calculators at the same time without replacement.

6. What is the probability that both calculators have dead batteries?

7. What is the probability that at least one calculator has good batteries?

Use the following information to answer the next three questions.

Rick and Devon are two brothers that play for the same baseball team consisting of 9 players. The coach of the baseball team sets up a specific batting order for each game.

8. What is the probability that Devon will bat right after Rick?

9. What is the probability that Rick bats first, and Devon bats last?

10. What is the probability that at least one of the brothers is within first 3 players to bat?

REVIEW SUMMARY

- The fundamental counting principle states that if a task is made up of several stages in which there are m choices for stage 1, n choices for stage 2, p choices for stage 3, and so on, then the total ways that the entire task can be accomplished (stage 1, 2, 3, and so on) is $m \times n \times p \times \ldots$.

- The symbol $n!$ (read as n factorial) represents the product of all the natural (counting) numbers from n down to 1. The formal definition of $n!$ is $n \times (n-1) \times (n-2) \times \ldots \times 2 \times 1$.

- Factorials are defined only for positive integers, and by definition, $0! = 1$.

- The arrangement of a set of objects in a particular order is called a permutation.

- The number of permutations of n distinct objects in a row is given by $n!$.

- When some of the objects to be arranged are identical, the number of permutations of n objects can be calculated using the formula $\dfrac{n!}{a!b!c!\ldots}$, where a objects are one kind, b objects are a second kind, c objects are a third kind, and so on.

- The number of permutations of n objects taken r at a time, which is denoted $_nP_r$, is defined by the formula $_nP_r = \dfrac{n!}{(n-r)!}$.

- A combination refers to a selection of objects in which the order does not matter.

- The number of combinations of n objects taken r at a time is $_nC_r = \dfrac{n!}{(n-r)!r!}$.

- The notation $\dbinom{n}{r}$ can also be used to represent the number of combinations of n objects taken r at a time.

- When solving probability problems that involve permutations, the order of events is important.

- Probability problems in which the order of events does not matter involve the use of combinations.

PRACTICE TEST

1. How many different outfits can Sally put together from 5 different tops, 4 different skirts, and 3 different pairs of shoes?

2. Jen is having a party at her house and is expecting 7 friends to come. She wants to give each friend a gift. She has 8 gifts to give away, but she decides she really likes 1 particular gift and keeps it for herself. How many different distributions of gifts are possible?

3. A car dealership manager wants to line up 9 vehicles in a row along one side of the dealership. There are 2 identical sports cars, 3 identical sport utility vehicles, and 4 identical trucks. How many ways can the dealership arrange the 9 vehicles in a row?

4. There are 12 women auditioning for 4 different roles. How many different assignments are possible for the 4 roles?

5. A restaurant offers 3-topping ice cream sundaes. The costumer has 9 different toppings to choose from. How many different 3-topping sundaes can a customer order?

6. At Vinny's Pizzeria, customers can order the 2-topping special in which 2 different toppings from an assortment of toppings are added to a pizza. Vinny claims he can make 190 different 2-topping special pizzas. How many different toppings are used at Vinny's Pizzeria?

7. How many different divisions of 15 golfers into 3 groups are possible so that 3 golfers are in one group, 5 golfers are in a second group, and 7 golfers are in a third group?

Use the following information to answer the next two questions.

Karen and Patricia are trying out for a volleyball team consisting of 8 female players. Including Karen and Patricia, there are 12 females trying out for the team.

8. If the team is picked at random, how many different selections for the team are possible?

9. If the team is picked at random, what is the probability that Karen and Patricia will both make the team?

Use the following information to answer the two questions.

Max is creating letter arrangements using all the letters in the word NANAIMO.

10. How many different letter arrangements can Max create?

11. What is the probability that M and O are together in either order?

Copyright Protected

RATIONAL EXPRESSIONS AND EQUATIONS

When you are finished this unit, you will be able to…
- Determine equivalent forms of rational expressions (limited to numerators and denominators that are monomials and binomials)
- Find the product or quotient of rational expressions
- Find the sum or difference of rational expressions with the same denominator and different denominators, which may or may not contain common factors
- Determine non-permissible values when performing operations on rational expressions
- Algebraically solve a rational equation
- Solve problems by modelling a situation using a rational equation

PREREQUISITE SKILLS AND KNOWLEDGE

Prior to starting this unit, you should be able to…
- Add, subtract, multiply, and divide rational numbers (fractions)
- Simplify (reduce) rational numbers
- Add, subtract, multiply, and divide polynomials
- Factor polynomials (common factor, difference of squares, trinomial factoring, grouping)
- Solve single-variable linear and quadratic equations
- Translate word problems into algebraic expressions

Lesson 1 INTRODUCTION TO RATIONAL EXPRESSIONS AND NON-PERMISSIBLE VALUES

NOTES

A rational number is any number that can be written as a fraction, with the following restrictions placed on the fraction:
- The numerator and denominator must both be integers.
- The denominator cannot equal 0.

If these restrictions are not met, the number is not a rational number. For example, the numbers 4, $5\frac{1}{2}$, and -3.5 can all be expressed as

fractions: $\frac{4}{1}, \frac{11}{2}$, and $-\frac{7}{2}$. Each of the fractions is rational, since none of them conflicts with the stated restrictions.

Examples of non-rational numbers include $\sqrt{2}$, $4^{\frac{2}{3}}$, and π.

A **rational expression** is the quotient of two polynomials. Much like rational numbers, there are restrictions for the numerator and denominator of a rational expression:

- Variables cannot have a fractional degree (a variable in a radical, $x^{\frac{1}{2}}$ or $\sqrt{x}$), because then the expression would not be the quotient of two polynomials.
- Powers cannot have a variable degree (a variable in the exponent, 2^x), again because the expression would not be the quotient of two polynomials.
- The denominator cannot equal 0.

Constants are considered to be polynomials of degree 0. For example, the function $f(x) = 54$ can be written as $f(x) = 54x^0$, which is polynomial function.

Example

a) Is the expression $\dfrac{2x^2 - 1}{2x + 1}$ a rational expression?

Solution

The expression $\dfrac{2x^2 - 1}{2x + 1}$ is a quotient of polynomials, so it is a rational expression.

b) Is the expression $x^4 + x + 3$ a rational expression?

Solution

Although the expression $x^4 + x + 3$ may not appear to be a quotient, it can be expressed as a fraction with a denominator of 1: $\dfrac{x^4 + x + 3}{1}$.

Both the numerator and the denominator are polynomials. This is a rational expression.

 Copyright Protected

c) Is the expression $\dfrac{x^{\frac{1}{3}} + \sqrt{x}}{x + 3^x}$ a rational expression?

Solution

The expression $\dfrac{x^{\frac{1}{3}} + \sqrt{x}}{x + 3^x}$ is a quotient, but neither the numerator nor the denominator is a polynomial. There are terms in the numerator with fractional degrees, and the denominator contains a term with a variable degree. This is not a rational expression.

Class Exercise 1

a) Determine whether the expression $\dfrac{4x^3 + 1}{x}$ is rational.

b) Determine whether the expression $\dfrac{m - n}{\sqrt{6}p}$ is rational.

c) Determine whether the expression $\dfrac{x^2 + 2\sqrt{x}}{3x - 1}$ is rational.

d) Determine whether the expression $9c^5 + 8^d$ is rational.

NON-PERMISSIBLE VALUES

Since a rational expression is the quotient of two polynomials, the expression will be undefined if the denominator is equal to 0. The values of the variable that make the denominator equal to 0 are called **non-permissible values** (NPVs).

The plural expression *non-permissible values* is used even if there is only one non-permissible value.

here are a number of different methods that can be used to indicate the non-permissible values of a rational expression. One method is to write "The non-permissible values are $x = 2$ and $x = -1$." A second method is simply to write "$x \neq 2$ and $x \neq -1$."

In this case, there is no reference to non-permissible values. You can also use the abbreviation NPVs and write "The NPVs are $x = 2$ and $x = -1$."

Example

When is the rational expression $\dfrac{25a + 4}{2a}$ undefined?

Solution

A rational expression is undefined when its denominator equals 0. For $\dfrac{25a + 4}{2a}$, the denominator will equal 0 if $a = 0$. This rational expression is undefined when $a = 0$. The non-permissible value for a is 0.

In some cases (as in the previous example), the non-permissible values are easy to identify. In other cases, the polynomial in the denominator may have to be factored to identify the non-permissible values. The rational expression may also have no non-permissible values and be defined for all values of the variables.

Example

a) Identify the non-permissible values for the expression $\dfrac{x - 3}{23}$.

Solution

Non-permissible values are found when the denominator equals 0. Values for the variable that produce a 0 in the numerator are of no concern. Since the denominator in the expression $\dfrac{x - 3}{23}$ is a constant and can never equal 0, the expression has no NPVs.

b) Identify the non-permissible values for the expression $\dfrac{23}{x - 3}$.

Solution

The denominator of the expression $\dfrac{23}{x - 3}$ will equal 0 when $x = 3$. Therefore, the NPV for x is 3.

Class Exercise 2

a) Identify the non-permissible values for the rational expression $\dfrac{3x^2}{-4x}$.

b) Identify the non-permissible values for the rational expression $\dfrac{x^2 - 1}{2x - 6}$.

Example

a) State any non-permissible values for the expression $\dfrac{2x+1}{x^2-x}$.

Solution

Factor the denominator of the expression $\dfrac{2x+1}{x^2-x}$ to produce the

equivalent rational expression $\dfrac{2x+1}{x(x-1)}$. The denominator will be

equal to 0 if either of the two factors equals 0; that is, if $x=0$ or

if $(x-1)=0$. Solving these two equations gives the NPVs for the

rational expression $\dfrac{2x+1}{x^2-x}$ as $x=0$ and 1.

b) State any non-permissible values for the expression $\dfrac{2x+1}{x^2-4}$.

Solution

Set the denominator of the expression $\dfrac{2x+1}{x^2-4}$ equal to 0, and solve the

equation to find when the variable will equal 0.

$$x^2-4=0$$
$$x^2=4$$
$$x=\pm\sqrt{4}$$
$$x=\pm 2$$

The non-permissible values for the rational expression $\dfrac{2x+1}{x^2-4}$ are

$x=\pm 2$. Note the importance of retaining both the positive and
negative square roots to ensure all restrictions are accounted for.
This may be easier to see if the denominator is factored.

$$x^2-4=0$$
$$(x-2)(x+2)=0$$
$$x-2=0 \quad \text{or} \quad x+2=0$$
$$x=2 \qquad\qquad x=-2$$

When you are asked to
evaluate a radical, such as
$\sqrt{9}$, it is the principal
square root, 3, that you
must give. However,
when you have to take the
square root of both sides of
an equation, such as
$x^2=4$, you must include
the positive and negative
square roots in the
solution, $x=\pm\sqrt{4}$, which
gives $x=\pm 2$. This is
reasonable because
squaring both +2 and –2
gives 4, so both values are
solutions to $x^2=4$.

c) State any non-permissible values for the expression $\dfrac{2x+1}{x^2+1}$.

Solution

For the expression $\dfrac{2x+1}{x^2+1}$, there are no non-permissible values,

because there are no real values of *x* that would make the denominator
equal to 0. (Setting the denominator equal to 0 gives $x^2+1=0$ or
$x^2=-1$).

NOTES

Class Exercise 3

a) Identify the non-permissible values for the rational expression $\dfrac{4x}{x^2-16}$.

b) Identify the non-permissible values for the rational expression $\dfrac{a^2-9}{a-6}$.

c) Identify the non-permissible values for the rational expression $\dfrac{2m+1}{m+3m}$.

PRACTICE EXERCISES

1. Which of the following expressions is a rational expression?

   A. $\dfrac{\sqrt{x}}{y}$

   B. $\sqrt{2x}$

   C. $\dfrac{24}{x^{\frac{3}{2}}}$

   D. $\sqrt[3]{x} + \sqrt[3]{8}$

2. Which of the following expressions is **not** a rational expression?

   A. $\dfrac{x-1}{x^2}$

   B. $x^{(2+2)}$

   C. $\dfrac{1}{x^{3x}}$

   D. $2x + 7$

Determine the non-permissible values for the following rational expressions.

3. $\dfrac{(x+2)(2x)}{3(x-2)(x)}$

4. $\dfrac{5(x^2-1)}{x^2-9}$

5. $\dfrac{x+6}{6x^2-15x}$

6. $\dfrac{2+3x}{2x^2+6x}$

Lesson 2 *SIMPLIFYING RATIONAL EXPRESSIONS*

Rational expressions are not always found in their most simplified or reduced form. There may be factors common to both the numerator and the denominator that can be eliminated. To see if there are any common factors, it is often necessary to factor the numerator, the denominator, or both.

The simplest reduction of a rational expression involves factoring a constant out of the numerator and denominator separately and then reducing the expression.

Example

Factor and reduce the expression $\dfrac{2x+2}{2x-2}$.

Solution
Factor the numerator and denominator, and then reduce.
$$\frac{2x+2}{2x-2} = \frac{\cancel{2}(x+1)}{\cancel{2}(x-1)}$$
$$= \frac{x+1}{x-1}$$

You cannot cancel terms such as $\dfrac{2x}{2x}$ or $\dfrac{2}{-2}$.
You can eliminate only common factors, not common terms.

The NPVs for the rational expression $\dfrac{2x+2}{2x-2}$ can be found when the denominator is set equal to 0.

Always use the denominator in its original form:
$$2x - 2 = 0$$
$$2x = 2$$
$$x = 1$$

The non-permissible value is $x = 1$.

Always use the original expression to determine NPVs. In the previous example, the NPV was the same for both the original and simplified forms of the expression. However, if the simplification process involves eliminating common factors containing variables, the simplified form of the expression will be missing factors that could yield additional NPVs.

Rational expressions will be equivalent only if their domains are the same. The original non-simplified rational expression is used to identify all the restrictions.

Both the initial and final rational expressions are said to be equivalent forms. The difference in the two forms is that the final form has had a common factor removed from both the numerator and the denominator. It is in simplified (reduced) form. If all common factors (constants and variables) are factored out and reduced, the final equivalent form is called the simplest form.

Copyright Protected

Example

Simplify the rational expression $\dfrac{4x^2}{2x}$, and identify the non-permissible values.

Solution
Step 1

Factor the rational expression $\dfrac{4x^2}{2x}$ fully.

The $4x^2$ in the numerator can be expressed as $(2)(2)(x)(x)$, but this factorization is not necessary.

Step 2
State any non-permissible values.
The expression is undefined when $2x = 0$. Therefore, the NPV is $x = 0$.

Step 3
Simplify.
Dividing both the numerator and the denominator by 2 and x produces the following simplified (reduced) rational expression.

$$\dfrac{\overset{2}{\cancel{4}}\,x\cancel{x}}{\cancel{2}\,\cancel{x}} = \dfrac{2x}{1} \text{ or } 2x$$

This reduced form has no non-permissible values, but the initial rational expression did have the stated non-permissible value of $x = 0$. This example shows why the original rational expression must be used to find all non-permissible values.

The simplified form and NPVs can be stated together as

$$\dfrac{4x^2}{2x} = 2x, x \neq 0 \,.$$

In this example, $2x$ was divided out of both the numerator and the denominator, reducing the expression to a more simplified form. This is sometimes referred to as "cancelling a factor" of $2x$ from the numerator and denominator. However, it is important to note that the factor being eliminated does not entirely disappear; it leaves a value of 1 in its place.

Class Exercise 1

a) Simplify $\dfrac{12x}{3x - 9}$, and state any non-permissible values.

b) Simplify $\dfrac{8x^3}{48x}$, and state any non-permissible values.

c) Simplify $\dfrac{10x^2 + 2x}{6x^2 + 4x}$, and state any non-permissible values.

In more complex rational expressions, it may be necessary to eliminate a binomial common factor.

Example

Express the rational expression $\dfrac{3x + 6}{2x + 4}$ in its simplest form, and state any non-permissible values.

Solution

Step 1

Factor completely.

$\dfrac{3x + 6}{2x + 4}$

$= \dfrac{3(x+2)}{2(x+2)}$

Step 2

State any non-permissible values.

The expression is undefined when the original denominator equals 0.

$2x + 4 = 0$

$\qquad x = -2$

Therefore, the non-permissible value is $x = -2$.

Step 3

Simplify.

$\dfrac{3\cancel{(x+2)}}{2\cancel{(x+2)}}$

$= \dfrac{3}{2}$

The simplest form of the given rational expression is $\dfrac{3}{2}$, where

$x \neq -2$.

Eliminating common terms instead of common factors is a frequent mistake.

$\dfrac{4x+1}{4x} \neq \dfrac{\cancel{4x}+1}{\cancel{4x}}$

$\qquad \neq 1$

In this expression $4x$ cannot be eliminated because it is not a common factor of all terms in the numerator. The expression $\dfrac{4x+1}{4x}$ is already in simplified form.

Copyright Protected

Class Exercise 2

a) Simplify and state any non-permissible values for $\dfrac{18-4m}{-2m+9}$.

b) Simplify and state any non-permissible values for $\dfrac{x^2-25}{2x^2+10x}$.

c) Simplify and state any non-permissible values for $\dfrac{b^2+b}{b+1}$.

PRACTICE EXERCISES

1. What are the restrictions on the values of x in the expression $\dfrac{(x+1)(x+2)}{(x+1)(x+3)}$?

    A. $x \neq 1$ and $x \neq 3$

    B. $x \neq -1$ and $x \neq -3$

    C. $x \neq 1$, $x \neq 2$, and $x \neq 3$

    D. $x \neq -1$, $x \neq -2$, and $x \neq -3$

2. Reduce the expression $\dfrac{3x^2 - 1}{x}$ if possible, stating any restrictions on the variable.

3. Write the expression $\dfrac{x-2}{x^3 - 4x}$ in its simplest form, and state any non-permissible values of the variable.

4. Reduce the expression $\dfrac{x-1}{\left(x^2 - 1\right)}$, and compare the non-permissible values of the original and simplified forms.

5. Compare strategies for writing equivalent forms of rational expressions to the strategies for writing equivalent forms of rational numbers.

6. Reduce the expression $\dfrac{18 - 50y^2}{20y + 12}$ to its simplest form, stating restrictions on the variable.

Use the following information to answer the next question.

Marsha showed her work as she simplified the rational expression $\dfrac{a^2 + 12a}{2a}$.

$$\dfrac{a^2 + 12a}{2a}$$
$$= \dfrac{a(a + 12)}{2a}$$
$$= \dfrac{a + 12}{2}$$
$$= a + 6$$

7. Identify and correct any errors that Marsha made in simplifying the rational expression.

Lesson 3 *MULTIPLYING RATIONAL EXPRESSIONS*

NOTES

Multiplying rational expressions is very similar to multiplying rational numbers. The numerators are multiplied together, and the denominators are multiplied together. The final expression should always be expressed in lowest terms with non-permissible values (NPVs) stated.

Example

Multiply $\left(\dfrac{1}{2}\right)\left(\dfrac{4}{7}\right)$.

Solution
Multiply the terms in each numerator as well as the terms in each denominator.

Reduce the expression by removing a common factor of 2 from the numerator and the denominator.

$$\dfrac{1}{2}\cdot\dfrac{4}{7}$$
$$=\dfrac{1\times4}{2\times7}$$
$$=\dfrac{4}{14}$$
$$=\dfrac{2}{7}$$

There are several ways to indicate the operation of multiplication: a dot, multiplication sign, or brackets.

The expression $\dfrac{1}{2}\cdot\dfrac{4}{7}$ is equivalent to $\dfrac{1}{2}\times\dfrac{4}{7}$ or $\left(\dfrac{1}{2}\right)\left(\dfrac{4}{7}\right)$.

When two or more rational expressions are to be multiplied, eliminating common factors can be done first, regardless of which numerator or denominator they are found in (you may know this as cross-cancelling). Simplifying before multiplying avoids having to work with large or complicated products.

From the previous example, 4 and 2 can be reduced by dividing by a common factor of 2.

$$\dfrac{1}{2}\cdot\dfrac{4}{7}$$
$$=\dfrac{1\times\overset{2}{\cancel{4}}}{\underset{1}{\cancel{2}}\times7}$$
$$=\dfrac{1\times2}{1\times7}$$
$$=\dfrac{2}{7}$$

 Copyright Protected

Example

Multiply the rational expression $\left(\dfrac{3x^2}{4}\right)$ by $\left(\dfrac{12x}{x}\right)$, and state any NPVs.

Solution

Reduce the expression.

Divide 12 and 4 by a common factor of 4 (cross-cancel), and divide x in the numerator and denominator by a common factor of x. The NPVs can be identified using the original denominators.

$$\frac{3x^2}{4} \cdot \frac{12x}{x}$$

$$= \frac{3x^2}{\overset{}{\underset{1}{\cancel{4}}}} \cdot \frac{\overset{3}{\cancel{12}}\,\overset{1}{\cancel{x}}}{\underset{1}{\cancel{x}}}$$

$$= \frac{3x^2}{1} \cdot \frac{3}{1}$$

$$= 9x^2,\ x \neq 0$$

The non-permissible values can be stated beside the solution.

Class Exercise 1

a) Multiply the rational expression $\dfrac{x^3 y}{10}$ by $\dfrac{2xy}{x^2}$, and state any non-permissible values.

It is often more efficient to simplify the multiplication process by first eliminating common factors and then multiplying. More simplifying can then occur if necessary.

b) Multiply the rational expression $\left(\dfrac{(8)(a)(b)}{(2)(2)}\right)$ by $\left(\dfrac{(4)(c)}{(c)(c)(c)}\right)$, and state any non-permissible values.

NOTES

Example

Factor $\left(\dfrac{x^2 + 2x}{3x}\right)\left(\dfrac{9x}{x+2}\right)$ where possible, and eliminate common factors.

Then, multiply the rational expressions, stating all non-permissible values.

Solution

$$\left(\dfrac{x^2 + 2x}{3x}\right)\left(\dfrac{9x}{x+2}\right)$$

$$= \left(\dfrac{(x)(x+2)}{3x}\right)\left(\dfrac{9x}{x+2}\right)$$

$$= \left(\dfrac{\cancel{x}\,(x+2)}{3\cancel{x}}\right)\left(\dfrac{\overset{3}{\cancel{9}}\,x}{(x+2)}\right)$$

$$= \dfrac{3x}{1}$$

$$= 3x, \ x \neq 0, -2$$

Even though the question may tell you to multiply, your first step should be to simplify where possible to make any required multiplying easier.

Class Exercise 2

Multiply the rational expressions $\left(\dfrac{x+3}{x^2 - 1}\right)$ and $\left(\dfrac{x+1}{x+3}\right)$, and state any NPVs.

The solution should be left in factored form; it does not need to be expanded.

Example

Multiply the rational expressions $\left(\dfrac{2x}{x}\right)$, $\left(\dfrac{3}{x}\right)$, and $\left(\dfrac{x+1}{2}\right)$, and note any restrictions on the variable.

Solution

$$\left(\dfrac{2x}{x}\right)\left(\dfrac{3}{x}\right)\left(\dfrac{x+1}{2}\right)$$

$$= \left(\dfrac{\cancel{2}\,\cancel{x}}{\cancel{x}}\right)\left(\dfrac{3}{x}\right)\left(\dfrac{x+1}{\cancel{2}}\right)$$

$$= \dfrac{3(x+1)}{x}, \ x \neq 0$$

This example illustrates that the multiplication process can be applied to more than two rational expressions.

Class Exercise 3

Simplify the rational expression $(2)\left(\dfrac{x-5}{2x}\right)\left(\dfrac{x^2-3x}{x-5}\right)$, and state any NPVs.

PRACTICE EXERCISES

1. Write the expression $\left(\dfrac{(x+1)^3}{24x}\right)\left(\dfrac{6(2x)}{2x^2-2}\right)$ in simplest form, and state any restrictions on the variable.

2. Simplify the expression $\left(\dfrac{3(x+1)^2}{4(x-1)^2}\right)\left(\dfrac{4(x+1)^2}{3(x-1)^2}\right)$, and state any NPVs.

3. Which of the following expressions is equivalent to $\dfrac{3}{x}$?

    A. $(-x)\left(\dfrac{x}{3}\right)$

    B. $\left(\dfrac{2}{3}\right)\left(\dfrac{6}{x}\right)$

    C. $\left(\dfrac{3}{3x}\right)(2)$

    D. $\left(\dfrac{-x}{4x^2}\right)\left(\dfrac{-12x}{x}\right)$

4. Write the rational expression $\left(\dfrac{x^2-4}{x+7}\right)\left(\dfrac{2x^2+14x}{2x-4}\right)$ in simplest form, and list all the NPVs.

Copyright Protected

Use the following information to answer the next two questions.

The rational expression $\dfrac{2}{x}$ is found as the result of multiplying two or more rational expressions (and reducing).

5. State two rational expressions that could give this result, and state any NPVs for these rational expressions.

6. State two rational expressions that could give this result, where $x \neq 4$ is a restriction on the variable.

7. Which of the following statements about the expression
$$\left(\frac{(x+1)(x+2)(x+3)...(x+n)}{1} \right)\left(\frac{1}{(x+1)(x+2)...(x+n-1)} \right), \text{ where } n \text{ is a positive integer greater}$$
than 1, is **true**?

A. After reducing, the numerator becomes $(x + n)$.

B. After reducing, the denominator becomes 0.

C. The expression cannot be simplified.

D. There are n non-permissible values.

8. Simplify the rational expression $\dfrac{3x^3 + 2x^2}{x+1} \times \dfrac{15x}{9x^2 + 6x}$, and state any NPVs.

Lesson 4   DIVIDING RATIONAL EXPRESSIONS

One rational expression divided by another can be rewritten as the first expression multiplied by the reciprocal of the second expression.

This is the same approach to multiplying rational numbers (fractions).

Example

Divide the rational expression $\dfrac{x^2}{2}$ by $\dfrac{x^2}{2}$.

Solution

Multiply the first expression by the reciprocal of the second expression.

$$\frac{x^2}{2} \div \frac{x^2}{2}$$
$$= \frac{x^2}{2} \times \frac{2}{x^2}$$
$$= \frac{2x^2}{2x^2}$$
$$= 1, x \neq 0$$

Conceptually, this makes sense since the first expression is being divided by itself (an identical expression). Any number divided by itself is 1 (with the exception of 0). Any variable divided by itself is 1 (with the restriction that the variable cannot equal 0).

Class Exercise 1

Divide the rational expression $\dfrac{3x}{10}$ by $\dfrac{12}{30}$.

DIVISION AND NON-PERMISSIBLE VALUES

Once a quotient of rational expressions is expressed as a product, the steps to simplify are the same as any multiplication problem. The answer is complete when all the non-permissible values (NPVs) are listed.

When dividing, identify the NPVs of the original denominators as well as any NPVs of the denominator that is generated when the reciprocal of the second expression is written.

Copyright Protected

Example

Simplify the expression $\dfrac{2(x^2-9)}{3x} \div \dfrac{(x+3)}{2x}$, and identify the restrictions on the variable.

Solution

$$\dfrac{2(x^2-9)}{3x} \div \dfrac{(x+3)}{2x}$$

$$= \left(\dfrac{2(x+3)(x-3)}{3x}\right)\left(\dfrac{2x}{(x+3)}\right)$$

$$= \dfrac{4(x-3)}{3}, \; x \neq 0, -3$$

From the initial division statement, the restriction is $x \neq 0$ for both denominators. The restrictions are $x \neq 0$ and $x \neq -3$. Both of these restrictions must be listed for the complete set of NPVs.

Class Exercise 2

a) Simplify the rational expression $\dfrac{3(x-8)}{x^2} \div \dfrac{12(x-8)}{x(x+4)}$, and state the NPVs.

Answers should be left in factored form where possible. It is an unnecessary step to expand the final answer.

b) Simplify the rational expression $\dfrac{x-5}{2x} \div \dfrac{x-5}{x^2-3x}$, and state the NPVs.

c) Simplify the rational expression $\dfrac{x^2-16}{x+4} \div \dfrac{x^2+2x}{2x+4}$, and state the NPVs.

Example

Divide and state all restrictions on the variable for the expression

$$\frac{\left(x^2-49\right)}{\left(x^4-1\right)} \div \frac{(x-7)}{(x-1)^2}.$$

Solution

$$\frac{\left(x^2-49\right)}{\left(x^4-1\right)} \div \frac{(x-7)}{(x-1)^2}$$

$$=\frac{\left(x^2-49\right)}{\left(x^4-1\right)} \times \frac{(x-1)^2}{(x-7)}$$

$$=\frac{(x+7)(x-7)}{\left(x^2+1\right)\left(x^2-1\right)} \times \frac{(x-1)(x-1)}{(x-7)}$$

$$=\frac{(x+7)\,\cancel{(x-7)}}{\left(x^2+1\right)\cancel{(x-1)}(x+1)} \times \frac{\cancel{(x-1)}(x-1)}{\cancel{(x-7)}}$$

$$=\frac{(x+7)(x-1)}{\left(x^2+1\right)(x+1)}$$

There is another difference of squares here that can be factored to make simplifying possible.

This is fully simplified. To find the restrictions on the variable, examine the original denominators and the new denominator when the reciprocal is taken.

$$x^4-1=0 \qquad (x-1)^2=0 \qquad x-7=0$$
$$x^4=1 \qquad \sqrt{(x-1)^2}=\sqrt{0} \qquad x=7$$
$$x=\pm\sqrt[4]{1} \qquad x-1=0$$
$$x=\pm1 \qquad x=1$$

Therefore, the restrictions are 1, –1, and 7.

 Copyright Protected

PRACTICE EXERCISES

1. Simplify the expression $\dfrac{5}{\left(\dfrac{20}{x^2}\right)}$.

Use the following information to answer the next question.

A triangle has an area defined by the formula of base times altitude divided by 2. The base is represented by the expression $(x-1)^2$, and the height is represented by the expression $\left(\dfrac{2x}{x-1}\right)^2$.

2. Determine the area of the triangle in simplified form, and state any restrictions on the variable.

3. Which of the following expressions for y makes the equation $\dfrac{x}{3} \div y = \dfrac{2}{x}$ **true**?

A. $y = \dfrac{x^2}{6}$

B. $y = \dfrac{6}{x}$

C. $y = \dfrac{x}{2}$

D. $y = \dfrac{2x}{3x}$

4. Simplify and state the non-permissible values for the expression $\dfrac{x-4}{x+1} \div \dfrac{x^2-16}{x^2-1}$.

5. Reduce the expression $\dfrac{4(1-x)}{x} \div \dfrac{x-1}{2x}$, stating all NPVs.

Lesson 5 *ADDING AND SUBTRACTING RATIONAL EXPRESSIONS*

The process of adding and subtracting rational expressions involves finding a common denominator for all expressions, writing equivalent expressions with that new denominator, and then adding or subtracting the numerators of the new expressions.

SIMPLIFYING EXPRESSIONS

To add or subtract rational expressions, it is necessary to find a common denominator. If the common denominator found is the lowest common denominator (LCD), there will be less reducing to perform in later steps.

To find the lowest common denominator, the first step is to ensure that each rational expression involved is in its most simplified form to begin with.

Example

What is the lowest common denominator of the expressions $\dfrac{\left(x^2-1\right)}{\left(x+1\right)}$

and $\dfrac{2x}{1}$?

Solution

The first rational expression can be simplified by factoring the numerator and eliminating common factors.

$$\frac{\left(x^2-1\right)}{\left(x+1\right)}$$

$$=\frac{(x-1)\,\cancel{(x+1)}}{\cancel{(x+1)}}$$

$$=\frac{x-1}{1}$$

After the first expression is simplified, the expressions have a common denominator of 1, and no more work is required on the denominators.

NOTES

Adding and subtracting rational expressions is similar to adding and subtracting rational numbers.

$$\frac{1}{4}+\frac{2}{3}$$
$$=\frac{?}{12}+\frac{?}{12}$$
$$=\frac{1(3)}{12}+\frac{2(4)}{12}$$
$$=\frac{3}{12}+\frac{8}{12}$$
$$=\frac{11}{12}$$

NOTES

COMMON DENOMINATORS

The process of finding common denominators for rational expressions is basically the same as finding common denominators for rational numbers.

Example

What is the lowest common denominator for the rational expressions $\dfrac{1}{2x}$, $\dfrac{1}{3}$, and $\dfrac{1}{(x+1)}$, $x \neq 0, -1$?

Solution

The lowest common denominator (LCD) is $(2x)(3)(x+1)$. This is the LCD because the three denominators have no factors in common. It is preferable to leave the LCD in factored form like this rather than expanding.

Class Exercise 1

Find the lowest common denominator for the rational expressions $\dfrac{2}{5x}$, $\dfrac{3x+1}{2}$, and $\dfrac{x^2-4}{(x-2)^2}$.

The lowest common denominator (LCD) of rational numbers is often the larger denominator.

$$\frac{1}{6} + \frac{1}{3} = \frac{}{6}$$

The LCD may also be a common multiple of the two denominators that is larger than either denominator but smaller than the product of the two.

$$\frac{1}{6} + \frac{1}{4} = \frac{}{12}$$

Sometimes, the LCD can be found by multiplying the two denominators together.

$$\frac{1}{6} + \frac{1}{5} = \frac{}{30}$$

EQUIVALENT RATIONAL EXPRESSIONS

Finding an expression that is equivalent to a given rational expression can involve simplifying by removing common factors from the numerator and denominator or multiplying the numerator and denominator by the same factor, making the rational expression more complicated.

Example

Write an equivalent rational expression to $\dfrac{2x}{3}$ in the form $\dfrac{?}{6}$.

Solution

The denominator on the right side of the equation is twice that of the left side. This means the numerator on the right will be twice the left numerator.

$$\frac{2x}{3} = \frac{?}{6}$$
$$\frac{2x}{3} = \frac{4x}{6}$$

Up to this point, the process of factoring and cancelling common factors has been used to simplify the expression. In order to find common denominators, it is often necessary to make an expression more complex.

Example

Write an equivalent rational expression to $\dfrac{2x}{3}$ in the form $\dfrac{?}{3(x+1)}, x \neq -1$.

Solution

The denominator on the right side has been multiplied by a factor of $(x+1)$. The numerator $2x$ must also be multiplied by this factor to produce an equivalent rational expression.

$$\frac{2x}{3} = \frac{?}{3(x+1)}$$

$$\frac{2x}{3} = \frac{2x(x+1)}{3(x+1)}, x \neq -1$$

There are two things to note at this point:

1. Do not cancel the common factors of $x + 1$ in the numerator and denominator. This would just return the expression to its original form.

2. The expression $2x(x+1)$ would have to be expanded before adding or subtracting so that like terms could be combined.

Once a common denominator has been identified, each rational expression involved must be rewritten as an equivalent expression with that new common denominator.

Example

Find the lowest common denominator for the expression

$\dfrac{2x+6}{4x} + \dfrac{x-1}{2(x+1)}$, and write equivalent expressions with the new common

denominator.

Solution

Step 1

Simplify each expression where possible.

A common factor of 2 can be eliminated from the first expression.

$$\frac{2x+6}{4x} + \frac{x-1}{2(x+1)}$$

$$= \frac{\cancel{2}(x+3)}{\cancel{4}x} + \frac{x-1}{2(x+1)}$$

$$= \frac{x+3}{2x} + \frac{x-1}{2(x+1)}, x \neq 0, -1$$

Step 2

Identify the lowest common denominator (LCD).

The denominators $2x$ and $2(x+1)$ have a common factor of 2. When there are repeated common factors like this, include it only once in the LCD. Therefore, the LCD is $(2)(x)(x+1)$.

Step 3

Write an equivalent expression with this new denominator, $(2)(x)(x+1)$.

$$\frac{x+3}{2x}+\frac{x-1}{2(x+1)}$$

$$=\frac{(x+3)(x+1)}{2x(x+1)}+\frac{(x-1)(x)}{2(x+1)(x)}$$

$$=\frac{x^2+4x+3}{(2)(x)(x+1)}+\frac{x^2-x}{(2)(x)(x+1)}, x\neq 0,-1$$

For the first expression, the original denominator $2x$ is multiplied by $(x+1)$ to make the new denominator. Therefore, the numerator $(x+3)$ will also be multiplied by $(x+1)$.

For the second expression, the original denominator $(2)(x+1)$ is multiplied by (x) to make the new denominator. Therefore, the numerator $(x-1)$ will also be multiplied by (x).

Class Exercise 2

a) Write an equivalent expression, with the lowest common denominator, for the rational expression $\dfrac{6}{10y}-\dfrac{1}{15y^2}$.

b) Write an equivalent expression, with the lowest common denominator, for the rational expression $\dfrac{x-4}{2x}+\dfrac{x-2x^2}{2x-4x^2}$.

Example

Add the expressions $\dfrac{3x^2}{2x}$ and $\dfrac{x+2}{x-5}$, and then state the NPVs.

Solution

Step 1

Simplify where possible, and identify the LCD.

$$\frac{3x^2}{2x}+\frac{x+2}{x-5}$$

$$=\frac{3x\cancel{(x)}}{(2)\cancel{(x)}}+\frac{x+2}{x-5}$$

$$=\frac{3x}{2}+\frac{x+2}{x-5}$$

The expressions are now simplified, and there are no common factors in the denominators, so the LCD will be $2(x-5)$.

Brackets can be used to indicate separate factors that show either common factors to be eliminated, possible NPVs in the denominator, or both.

Step 2

Write equivalent expressions with the new denominator, $2(x-5)$.

$$\frac{3x}{2}+\frac{x+2}{x-5}$$

$$=\frac{3x(x-5)}{2(x-5)}+\frac{2(x+2)}{2(x-5)}$$

$$=\frac{3x^2-15x+2x+4}{2(x-5)}$$

Step 3

Combine like terms in the numerators, keeping the common denominator unchanged.

$$\frac{3x^2-15x+2x+4}{2(x-5)}$$

$$=\frac{3x^2-13x+4}{2(x-5)}$$

Step 4

Check if the expression can be reduced further, and state the NPVs.

The expression is in simplest form, since it cannot be factored further. The NPVs are $x=0$ and $x=5$, which can be written beside the expression.

Remember to look back at the original denominators to list all the NPVs.

NOTES

Example

Subtract the expression $\dfrac{x-5}{x^2-4}$ from the expression $\dfrac{x}{x-2}$, and state the NPVs.

Solution

Step 1
Simplify where possible, and identify the LCD.

$$\frac{x}{x-2} - \frac{x-5}{x^2-4}$$

$$= \frac{x}{x-2} - \frac{x-5}{(x+2)(x-2)}$$

The expressions can be factored but not simplified. However, it is easier to identify the LCD and make equivalent expressions when the denominators are in factored form.

The LCD will be $(x-2)(x+2)$.

Step 2
Write equivalent expressions with the new denominator.

$$\frac{x}{x-2} - \frac{x-5}{(x+2)(x-2)}$$

$$= \frac{x(x+2)}{(x-2)(x+2)} - \frac{x-5}{(x+2)(x-2)}$$

$$= \frac{x^2+2x}{(x-2)(x+2)} - \frac{x-5}{(x+2)(x-2)}$$

Step 3
Combine like terms in the numerators, keeping the common denominator unchanged.

$$\frac{x^2+2x}{(x-2)(x+2)} - \frac{x-5}{(x+2)(x-2)}$$

$$= \frac{x^2+2x-(x-5)}{(x-2)(x+2)}$$

$$= \frac{x^2+2x-x+5}{(x-2)(x+2)}$$

$$= \frac{x^2+x+5}{(x-2)(x+2)}$$

Step 4

Check if the expression can be reduced further, and state the NPVs.
The expression is in simplest form, since it cannot be factored further.
The NPVs are $x = -7$, $x = -2$, and $x = 2$, which can be written beside
the expression.

$$\frac{x^2 + x + 5}{(x-2)(x+2)}, x \neq -7, \pm 2$$

Class Exercise 3

a) Add the expression $\frac{5x^2 + 1}{x+2}$ to the expression $\frac{1 - 4x^2}{x+2}$, and state

any NPVs.

b) Subtract the expression $\frac{(5a - a^2)}{3a}$ from the expression $\frac{2a}{3a}$, and state

any NPVs.

If the denominators of the given expressions are the same, combine numerators, and then simplify the resulting expression as needed. Alternatively, in the case

of $\frac{2a}{3a} - \frac{(5a - a^2)}{3a}$,

a could first be eliminated from the numerator and denominator of both expressions. Either way, some simplification will be required.

c) Subtract the expression $\frac{m-1}{m+3}$ from the expression $\frac{m}{m-1}$, and state

any NPVs.

d) Subtract the expression $\frac{x}{1-x}$ from the expression $\frac{x}{x-1}$, and state

any NPVs.

The denominator $1 - x$ can be written as $x - 1$ if -1 is factored out as $-1(-1 + x)$. This can now be rewritten as $-1(x - 1)$. Once you factor the -1 out, you are now subtracting a negative, which makes the problem a sum.

PRACTICE EXERCISES

1. Simplify the expression $\dfrac{2}{3x} + \dfrac{3x}{4} - 1$.

2. When the rational expression $\dfrac{x^2 - 1}{12x^2}$ has a new denominator of $12x^2(2x)$, it will have a new numerator of

   A. $2(x^2 - 1)$

   B. $2x(x+1)(x-1)$

   C. $6x(x^2 - 1)$

   D. $6(x+1)(x-1)$

3. Subtract the expression $\dfrac{6}{a}$ from the expression $\dfrac{a-1}{2a+2}$, and state the non-permissible values for the expression.

4. Add the expressions $\dfrac{2x-12}{2x-2}$ and $\dfrac{x+1}{x^2-1}$, and state the non-permissible values for the expression.

Use the following information to answer the next question.

Marc was asked by his teacher to simplify the expression $\dfrac{9x+27}{x^2-9}+\dfrac{4x^2+x}{x^2-3x}$ and state any non-permissible values. His solution is shown in the following steps:

1. $\quad = \dfrac{9(x+3)}{(x-3)(x+3)}+\dfrac{x(4x+1)}{x(x-3)}$

2. $\quad = \dfrac{9}{x-3}+\dfrac{4x+1}{x-3}$

3. $\quad = \dfrac{4x+10}{x-3}$

4. The non-permissible value is $x \neq 3$.

Marc determined he had made an error in his solution.

5. Marc made his error in step

    A. 1

    B. 2

    C. 3

    D. 4

Lesson 6 RATIONAL EQUATIONS AND PROBLEM SOLVING

NOTES

Rational expressions can appear within equations. In these cases, the methods for simplifying rational expressions are instrumental in determining the value for the variable.

Example

a) Add the expressions $\dfrac{1}{x}$ and $\dfrac{2}{x}$.

Solution
Since the denominators are the same, adding the numerators produces the simplified form $\dfrac{3}{x}$, where $x \neq 0$.

b) Solve the rational equation $\dfrac{1}{x} + \dfrac{2}{x} = \dfrac{3}{4}$ by inspection.

Solution
By simplifying the left side of the equation, the equation becomes $\dfrac{3}{x} = \dfrac{3}{4}$.

The word *solve* means to find a value for the variable in an equation.

By observation, the only value for x that makes this statement true is $x = 4$. The NPV for the variable is $x = 0$.

In this case, the variable had one value, which was apparent with little simplification required. In more complex cases, a series of steps will assist in the process of solving rational equations. The goal is to rewrite the equation without fractions by multiplying each expression in the equation by the lowest common multiple (LCM) of the denominators and then solving for the variable.

Example

Solve the rational equation $\dfrac{2}{x} + \dfrac{3}{2x} = \dfrac{4}{x+1}$.

Solution
Step 1
Find the lowest common multiple (LCM) of the denominators, and multiply each term by that LCM.

The LCM of the denominators is $(2x)(x+1)$. Multiply this by every term.

$$(2x)(x+1)\left[\frac{2}{x} + \frac{3}{2x} = \frac{4}{x+1}\right]$$

$$(2x)(x+1)\frac{2}{x} + (2x)(x+1)\frac{3}{2x} = (2x)(x+1)\frac{4}{x+1}$$

 Copyright Protected

Step 2

Remove all denominators from the equation by eliminating common factors.

$$(2x)(x+1)\frac{2}{x}+(2x)(x+1)\frac{3}{2x}=(2x)(x+1)\frac{4}{x+1}$$

$$(2\cancel{x})(x+1)\frac{2}{\cancel{x}}+(2\cancel{x})(x+1)\frac{3}{2\cancel{x}}=(2x)(\cancel{x+1})\frac{4}{\cancel{x+1}}$$

$$4(x+1)+3(x+1)=8x$$

Step 3

Remove all brackets by multiplying (distributing) where possible.

$$4(x+1)+3(x+1)=8x$$
$$4x+4+3x+3=8x$$

Step 4

Combine like terms, and solve for the variable.

$$4x+4+3x+3=8x$$
$$7x+7=8x$$
$$7=x$$

Step 5

State any NPVs for the variable by using the original denominators, and compare these to the solution.

From the initial rational equation $\frac{2}{x}+\frac{3}{2x}=\frac{4}{x+1}$, the NPVs are $x=0$ and $x=-1$. There is no conflict between the NPVs and the solution, so $x=7$.

NOTES

Any value found as a solution to the rational equation that is also an NPV is not an accepted solution. A solution that is also a NPV is called an extraneous solution. If this is the only solution obtained, then you can write "no solutions exist."

It is recommended that you verify all possible solution values to check for any extraneous roots.

Step 6

Verify the solution by substituting it into the original equation and simplifying. If equality is preserved (the left and right sides of the equation are equal), then the solution is verified.

$x=7$	
$\dfrac{2}{(7)}+\dfrac{3}{2(7)}$	$\dfrac{4}{(7)+1}$
$=\dfrac{2}{7}+\dfrac{3}{14}$	$=\dfrac{4}{8}$
$=\dfrac{2(2)+3}{14}$	$=\dfrac{1}{2}$
$=\dfrac{7}{14}$	
$=\dfrac{1}{2}$	

The solution $x=7$ has been verified.

Example

Solve the rational equation $\dfrac{2x^2}{x-3} = 1 - \dfrac{4x+6}{3-x}$, and verify.

Solution

Step 1

Find the lowest common multiple (LCM) of the denominators, and multiply each term by that LCM.

If -1 is factored out of the denominator $(3-x)$, then the LCM of the denominators will be $(x-3)$, and the right side of the equation can be written as a sum.

$$\frac{2x^2}{x-3} = 1 - \frac{4x+6}{3-x}$$

$$\frac{2x^2}{x-3} = 1 - \frac{4x+6}{-1(-3+x)}$$

$$\frac{2x^2}{x-3} = 1 + \frac{4x+6}{x-3}$$

Multiply each term by the LCM.

$$(x-3)\left[\frac{2x^2}{x-3} = 1 + \frac{4x+6}{x-3}\right]$$

$$(x-3)\left(\frac{2x^2}{x-3}\right) = (x-3)(1) + (x-3)\left(\frac{4x+6}{x-3}\right)$$

The negative sign can appear in several places:
$$-\frac{1}{2} = \frac{-1}{2} = \frac{1}{-2}$$
These are equivalent expressions, since each fraction is equal to –0.5 in decimal form.

Step 2

Remove all denominators by eliminating common factors.

$$(x-3)\left(\frac{2x^2}{x-3}\right) = (x-3)(1) + (x-3)\left(\frac{4x+6}{x-3}\right)$$

$$(\cancel{x-3})\left(\frac{2x^2}{\cancel{x-3}}\right) = (x-3)(1) + (\cancel{x-3})\left(\frac{4x+6}{\cancel{x-3}}\right)$$

$$2x^2 = x - 3 + 4x + 6$$

Step 3

Gather like terms, and solve the resulting quadratic equation.

$$2x^2 = x - 3 + 4x + 6$$
$$2x^2 - 5x - 3 = 0$$
$$(2x+1)(x-3) = 0$$
$$2x+1 = 0 \quad \text{or} \quad x-3 = 0$$
$$x = -\frac{1}{2} \qquad\qquad x = 3$$

Recall how to factor a trinomial when $a > 1$. You may know this method as decomposition.
For the trinomial $2x^2 - 5x - 3 = 0$, identify two factors that have a product of –6 and a sum of –5. The factors are 1 and –6. Write the middle term as the sum of these factors, and then factor by grouping.

$$2x^2 - 5x - 3 = 0$$
$$2x^2 + x - 6x - 3 = 0$$
$$x(2x+1) - 3(2x+1) = 0$$
$$(2x+1)(x-3) = 0$$

Copyright Protected

Step 4

State any NPVs for the variable, and compare these to the solution.

The NPV from the original equation $\dfrac{2x^2}{x-3} = 1 - \dfrac{4x+6}{3-x}$ is $x = 3$.

Therefore, since $x \neq 3$, the solution is $-\dfrac{1}{2}$.

Step 5

Verify the solution using the original equation.

$x = -\dfrac{1}{2}$	
$\dfrac{2\left(-\dfrac{1}{2}\right)^2}{\left(-\dfrac{1}{2}\right) - 3}$	$1 - \dfrac{4\left(-\dfrac{1}{2}\right) + 6}{3 - \left(-\dfrac{1}{2}\right)}$
$= \left(\dfrac{2}{4}\right) \div \left(-\dfrac{7}{2}\right)$	$= 1 - \left(4 \div \dfrac{7}{2}\right)$
$= \left(\dfrac{2}{4}\right) \times \left(-\dfrac{7}{2}\right)$	$= 1 - \dfrac{8}{7}$
$= -\dfrac{1}{7}$	$= -\dfrac{1}{7}$

The solution $x = -\dfrac{1}{2}$ has been verified.

Class Exercise 1

a) Solve the rational equation $\dfrac{5}{x-1} - \dfrac{12}{x^2-1} = 1$, and verify.

b) Solve the rational equation $3 + \dfrac{2}{3+x} = 5$, and verify.

c) Solve the rational equation $\dfrac{2}{x+4} = \dfrac{5}{3x+12}$, and verify.

Like rational numbers, if there is a single expression on each side of a rational equation, you can cross-multiply and then solve for the variable.

$$\frac{3}{8} = \frac{9}{x}$$
$$3x = 72$$
$$x = \frac{72}{3}$$
$$x = 24$$

NOTES

PROBLEM SOLVING

Rational expressions and equations are frequently used to solve mathematical problems encountered in physics, engineering, mathematics, and everyday life.

To set up an appropriate equation, it is necessary to identify the variables involved and translate a word problem into its mathematical equivalent. Once the rational equation is written, use the steps outlined in this chapter to solve the equation. Depending on the context, some solution values will need to be rejected.

A variable, such as x, represents an unknown quantity. Read questions carefully to see what quantity needs to be found. Often, the required quantity is stated at the end of the word problem.

Example

Stephen received a mark of 10 out of 25 on the first unit exam. The second unit exam is equally weighted and has the same number of questions. What mark does Stephen need to achieve on the second exam to have an overall average of 50%?

Solution

Step 1

Assign a variable to represent the unknown, and set up an equation using the given information.

Let x represent the mark on the second exam. The overall average mark of 50% can be found by adding the two marks and dividing by 2.

$$\frac{\text{exam 1 mark} + \text{exam 2 mark}}{2} = 50\%$$

$$\frac{\left(\dfrac{10}{25}\right) + \left(\dfrac{x}{25}\right)}{2} = 0.50$$

To set up the rational equation, it can be helpful to first identify the value that the equation will equal and then work backward to figure out how that total can be calculated.

Step 2

Solve the rational equation.

Simplify the left side of the equation, and then cross-multiply to solve for x.

$$\frac{\left(\dfrac{10}{25}\right) + \left(\dfrac{x}{25}\right)}{2} = 0.50$$

$$\left(\frac{10 + x}{25}\right) \div 2 = 0.50$$

$$\left(\frac{10 + x}{25}\right) \times \frac{1}{2} = 0.50$$

$$\frac{10 + x}{50} = 0.50$$

$$10 + x = 25$$

$$x = 15$$

Step 3

Verify your answer by substituting the solution into the original equation and simplifying.

$x = 15$	
$\begin{aligned}&\dfrac{\left(\dfrac{10}{25}\right)+\left(\dfrac{x}{25}\right)}{2}\\[2ex]=\ &\dfrac{\left(\dfrac{10}{25}\right)+\left(\dfrac{15}{25}\right)}{2}\\[2ex]=\ &\dfrac{\left(\dfrac{25}{25}\right)}{2}\\[2ex]=\ &\dfrac{1}{2}\\[1ex]=\ &0.50\end{aligned}$	0.50

Therefore, if Stephen achieves a mark of 15 out of 25 on the second exam, he will have an overall average of 50%.

Example

Two cyclists are racing through the Rocky Mountains. Cyclist 2 is twice as fast as cyclist 1. The route they take is 100 km long, and cyclist 2 arrives at the finish line 2 h earlier than cyclist 1. What is the speed of cyclist 1?

Solution

Step 1

Assign a variable to represent the unknown, and set up an equation using the given information.

Let x represent the speed of cyclist 1. If cyclist 2 finishes the race a total of 2 h earlier, set up a rational equation that compares the cyclists' times to finish the race. Specifically, the slower cyclist's time (cyclist 1 has the longer time) minus the faster cyclist's time (cyclist 2 has the shorter time) will equal the difference in their arrival time (2 h).

$$\text{longer time} - \text{shorter time} = 2\text{ h}$$
$$\text{cyclist 1 time} - \text{cyclist 2 time} = 2\text{ h}$$
$$\frac{100}{x} - \frac{100}{2x} = 2,\ x \neq 0$$

NOTES

Many word problems involve the relationship between distance (d), speed (s), and time (t). For these problems, the formulas required are

$$d = st,\ s = \frac{d}{t},\ \text{and } t = \frac{d}{s}.$$

The units in a word problem should simplify to the required unit if the equation is set up correctly.

$$\frac{(100)\ \text{km}}{(x)\dfrac{\text{km}}{\text{h}}} - \frac{(100)\ \text{km}}{(2x)\dfrac{\text{km}}{\text{h}}} = 2\text{ h}$$

$$\frac{(100)}{\dfrac{(x)}{\text{h}}} - \frac{(100)}{\dfrac{(2x)}{\text{h}}} = 2\text{ h}$$

$$\frac{(100)\text{h}}{(x)} - \frac{(100)\text{h}}{(2x)} = 2\text{ h}$$

Step 2
Solve the rational equation.

Multiply the equation by the lowest common multiple to eliminate the denominators, and then solve for x.

The LCM is $2x$.

$$\frac{100}{x} - \frac{100}{2x} = 2$$

$$(2\cancel{x})\frac{100}{\cancel{x}} - (2\cancel{x})\frac{100}{2\cancel{x}} = (2x)2$$

$$200 - 100 = 4x$$

$$100 = 4x$$

$$25 = x$$

Therefore, the speed of cyclist 1 is 25 km/h.

Class Exercise 2

A sailboat has an average speed of 20 km/h in still water. It takes the same time for the sailboat to travel 70 km against the wind as it does to travel 130 km with the same wind. What is the speed of the wind?

The quadratic formula is

$$x = \frac{-b \pm \sqrt{b^2 - 4ac}}{2a}.$$

Sometimes, a rational equation that models a given context will simplify to a quadratic equation. In this case, factor the quadratic or use the quadratic formula to determine the solution values.

Check for any extraneous solutions, and reject solutions that do not fit the problem.

 Copyright Protected

Example

Simon, a cross-country runner, trains year-round on a 36 km course. He finds that in winter, because of slippery road conditions, his average running speed is 3 km/h slower than his average summer running speed. As a result, it takes him 1 h longer in the winter to run the 36 km course.

If x represents Simon's average summer running speed, determine the value of x.

Solution

Step 1

Determine the time taken to complete the course in summer.

Recall that $\text{time} = \dfrac{\text{distance}}{\text{speed}}$.

The time taken to complete the course in summer is $\dfrac{36}{x}$ h .

Step 2

Determine the time taken to complete the course in winter.
Simon's speed in the winter is 3 km/h slower than his average summer running speed.
From the given information, the time taken to complete the course in

winter is $\dfrac{36}{x-3}$ h .

Step 3

Determine the equation that represents the difference between the time it takes Simon to complete the course in summer and the time it takes him to complete the course in winter.
The difference between the times is 1 h. Therefore, the equation that

represents the situation is $\dfrac{36}{x-3} - \dfrac{36}{x} = 1$.

Step 4

Solve the rational equation.

Multiply the equation by the lowest common multiple to eliminate the denominators, and then solve for x.

The LCM is $x(x-3)$.

$$\frac{36}{x-3} - \frac{36}{x} = 1$$

$$x(x-3)\left(\frac{36}{x-3}\right) - x(x-3)\left(\frac{36}{x}\right) = x(x-3)$$

$$36x - 36(x-3) = x^2 - 3x$$

$$36x - 36x + 108 = x^2 - 3x$$

$$0 = x^2 - 3x - 108$$

NOTES

Solve this equation using the quadratic formula.

$$x = \frac{-b \pm \sqrt{b^2 - 4ac}}{2a}$$

$$x = \frac{-(-3) \pm \sqrt{(-3)^2 - 4(1)(-108)}}{2(1)}$$

$$x = \frac{3 \pm \sqrt{9 + 432}}{2}$$

$$x = \frac{3 \pm \sqrt{441}}{2}$$

$$x = \frac{3 \pm 21}{2}$$

$$x = \frac{3 + 21}{2} \qquad x = \frac{3 - 21}{2}$$

$$x = 12 \qquad\qquad x = -9$$

Simon's speed cannot be a negative number. Therefore, –9 is rejected, and Simon's average summer running speed is 12 km/h.

Step 5
Verify the solution.

$x = 12$	
$\dfrac{36}{12-3} - \dfrac{36}{12}$ $= 4 - 3$ $= 1$	$= 1$

The solution $x = 12$ is verified.

PRACTICE EXERCISES

1. Solve the rational equation $\dfrac{2}{x-1} = \dfrac{3}{x}$. State any restrictions on the variable.

2. Solve the equation $\dfrac{3x+1}{6x} = \dfrac{x+1}{2x+1}$, and state any NPVs.

3. Solve the equation $\dfrac{x}{x+1} = \dfrac{-2}{2x+2}$.

4. For the rational equation $\dfrac{2}{x} - \dfrac{5}{3x} = 4$, state the LCM and NPVs, and then solve.

5. The solution to $\dfrac{13}{y+1} = 4$ is

    A. $y = \dfrac{3}{2}$ **B.** $y = \dfrac{9}{4}$

    C. $y = \dfrac{4}{9}$ **D.** $y = \dfrac{2}{3}$

6. Isolate x in the equation $\dfrac{9y}{4} - \dfrac{x}{2} = \dfrac{4}{y}$.

Use the following information to answer the next two questions.

Two people have to travel 528 km for business purposes. One person travelled by bus, and the other person travelled by airplane. The airplane travelled at a speed 6 times faster than the bus. The bus required 4 h more than the airplane to make the trip.

7. If x represents the average speed of the bus, determine the equation that represents the difference between the time it takes the bus to travel 528 km and the time it takes the airplane to travel 528 km.

8. What is the average speed of the bus?

REVIEW SUMMARY

- A rational expression is the quotient of two polynomials.

- The values for the variable that make the denominator of a rational expression equal to 0 are called non-permissible values (NPVs).

- To find the NPVs, set the denominator equal to 0 (factoring as required), and solve for the variable. There may be no NPVs, one, or several.

- When simplifying a rational expression, factor, and then eliminate common factors. State all NPVs using the denominator of the original expression. The expression is in simplified form when no common factors remain in the numerator and denominator.

- To multiply rational expressions, simplify first (using cross-cancelling as required), and then multiply the numerators and denominators separately. State the NPVs using the original expression.

- To divide rational expressions, rewrite the problem as a product. Then, follow the steps for multiplying rational expressions. When stating the NPVs, remember to look at the denominators in the original quotient as well as the new denominator in the product.

- To add or subtract rational expressions, simplify each expression first, and then identify the lowest common denominator (LCD). Write equivalent expressions with the new common denominator, and then combine the numerators only. Check if the resulting expression can be simplified further, and then identify the NPVs using the original denominators.

- When solving a rational equation, rewrite the equation without denominators by multiplying all terms on both sides of the equation by the lowest common multiple (LCM) of the denominators and then eliminating the denominators. Gather like terms, and solve for the variable. Verify the solution by substituting it into the original equation to see if the left side equals the right side. Identify the NPVs, and compare them to the solution values obtained. If any of the solution values are NPVs, these values must be removed from the solution set.

- When solving a word problem, assign a variable to the unknown, and use it to write the required rational expressions. Once the relationship between the rational expressions is determined and the equation is written, follow the steps for solving rational equations. It is important to identify the NPVs and consider any restrictions that may be placed on the variable as a result of the context.

PRACTICE TEST

1. Which of the following expressions is an equivalent form of $\dfrac{2}{(x-1)}$?

   A. $\dfrac{2x^2}{x^2-1}$

   B. $\dfrac{3}{6(x-1)}$

   C. $\dfrac{2(x^2-1)}{(x+1)}$

   D. $\dfrac{4}{2x-2}$

2. Simplify the expression $\dfrac{8x+4}{6x+3}$ by eliminating any common factors. State any non-permissible values for the variable.

Use the following information to answer the next question.

A student would like to create a rational expression with two non-permissible values. The NPVs are $a=0$ and $a=1$.

3. Which of the following statements is **true**?

   A. The expression can have any number of factors involving the variable a in the numerator and denominator as long as after simplifying, the denominator contains only the factors of $(a)(a-1)$.

   B. The expression must have the variable x in the numerator and the factors $(a)(a-1)$ in the denominator.

   C. One possible expression that the student could use is $\dfrac{1}{(x)(x-1)}$.

   D. One possible expression that the student could use is $\dfrac{2}{2a^2-2a}$.

Use the following information to answer the next two questions.

Rectangle A has an area that is represented by the expression $18x - x^2$ and a width of x. Rectangle B has an area represented by the expression $x^2 + 2x$ and a width of $x + 2$. The area of a rectangle is given by $A = lw$, where l is the length and w is the width.

4. Write an expression in simplified form for the length of rectangle A divided by the length of rectangle B. State any non-permissible values.

5. If the length of rectangle A is 5 times larger than the length of rectangle B, what is the width of rectangle B?

6. When the rational expression $\dfrac{x^2 - 7x}{x^2 - a^2} \div \dfrac{x^2 - 49}{x + 7}$ is simplified, the numerator is 1. Given this fact, solve for the unknown constant a^2. State all non-permissible values.

7. Simplify the expression $\dfrac{5y}{12y^2 + 6y} + \dfrac{3y}{10y - 7y}$, and state all NPVs.

8. The reciprocal of the expression $4 - x$ is added to $\dfrac{5}{3}$, and the result is equal to $\dfrac{7}{6}$. What is the unknown number?

Use the following information to answer the next question.

Michelle is constructing a poster for history class. Her history teacher gave each student a rectangular piece of poster board with an area of $12\,\mathrm{m}^2$. She decides to modify the dimensions of the board while keeping the same area. Michelle determines that if she increases width of the board by 1 m, she will have to decrease the length of the board by 2 m to keep the same area.

9. If the area of a rectangle is $\text{area} = \text{length} \times \text{width}$, what is the width of the original poster board Michelle's teacher gave each student?

Use the following information to answer the next question.

In electronics, the relationship between two resistances, R_1 and R_2, of two resistors wired in a parallel circuit and their combined resistance, R, is given by the formula $\dfrac{1}{R} = \dfrac{1}{R_1} + \dfrac{1}{R_2}$, where R, R_1, and R_2 are positive numbers.

10. If the combined resistance is 4, and the difference between R_1 and R_2 is 6, what is the value of larger resistance?

 Copyright Protected

LOGARITHMIC AND EXPONENTIAL FUNCTIONS

When you are finished this unit, you will be able to…

- Convert expressions from exponential form to logarithmic form and vice versa
- Evaluate a logarithmic expression with and without a calculator
- Understand the relationship between a logarithmic function and an exponential function algebraically and graphically
- Understand and apply laws of logarithms
- Apply the change of base formula to simplify and evaluate logarithmic expressions
- Determine the solution of an exponential equation in which the bases are powers of one another
- Determine the solution of an exponential equation in which the bases are not powers of one another
- Define characteristics of the graph of $y = ab^x$, where and $b > 0$.
- Solve application problems involving exponential growth or decay
- Define characteristics of the graph of $y = \log_a x$.
- Solve application problems that involve logarithmic scales

PREREQUISITE SKILLS AND KNOWLEDGE

Prior to starting this unit, you should be able to…

- Convert expressions from exponential form to logarithmic form and vice versa
- Evaluate a logarithmic expression with and without a calculator
- Understand the relationship between a logarithmic function and an exponential function algebraically and graphically
- Understand and apply laws of logarithms
- Apply the change of base formula to simplify and evaluate logarithmic expressions
- Determine the solution of an exponential equation in which the bases are powers of one another
- Determine the solution of an exponential equation in which the bases are not powers of one another
- Define characteristics of the graph of r $y = ab^x$, where and $b > 0$.
- Solve application problems involving exponential growth or decay
- Define characteristics of the graph of $y = \log_a x$.
- Solve application problems that involve logarithmic scales

225

Lesson 1 DEFINING LOGARITHMS

NOTES

A logarithmic expression is of the form $\log_a y$, where a is called the base, $a > 0$, and $a \neq 1$. The value of is defined as the number, x, that makes the statement true.

For example, $\log_2 32$ is defined as the number, x, that makes the statement $2^x = 32$ true. Thus, $\log_2 32 = 5$ because $2^5 = 32$.

Example

Evaluate the expression $\log_4 16$.

Solution

The value of $\log_4 16$ is equal to the value of x, which makes the statement $4^x = 16$ true. Thus, $\log_4 16 = 2$ because $4^2 = 16$.

Example

Evaluate the expression $\log_3 27$.

Solution

The expression $\log_3 27$ is equal to the value of x, which makes the statement $3^x = 27$ true. Thus, $\log_3 27 = 3$ because $3^3 = 27$.

Class Exercise 1

Evaluate the expression $2\log_9 81$.

From the definition of a logarithm, it follows that an exponential equation can be converted to a logarithmic equation by applying the property that if $y = a^x$, then $x = \log_a y$, where $a > 0$ and $a \neq 1$. This is consistent with avoiding negative bases in exponential functions.

Example

Write the equation $3^2 = 9$ in logarithmic form.

Solution

Apply the property that if $y = a^x$, then $x = \log_a y$. Therefore, the logarithmic form of $3^2 = 9$ is $2 = \log_3 9$.

Example

Write the equation $2^{-x} = \dfrac{1}{64}$ in logarithmic form.

Solution

The logarithmic form of $2^{-x} = \dfrac{1}{64}$ is $-x = \log_2 \dfrac{1}{64}$.

Example

Write the equation $4 = \log_5 625$ in exponential form.

Solution

Apply the property that if $x = \log_a y$, then $y = a^x$. The exponential form of $4 = \log_5 625$ is $625 = 5^4$.

Class Exercise 2

Express the equation $\log_6 216 = 3$ in exponential form.

Example

Write the equation $12 = 4 \log_4 64$ in exponential form.

Solution

Step 1
Divide both sides by 4.
$12 = 4 \log_4 64$
$\ \ 3 = \log_4 64$

Step 2
Convert the logarithmic equation into an exponential equation.
Apply the property that if $c = \log_b a$, then $a = b^c$.

Therefore, the exponential form of $12 = 4 \log_4 64$ is $64 = 4^3$.

NOTES

Class Exercise 3

a) Write the equation $30\,000 = 150\left(2\right)^{\frac{m}{40}}$ in logarithmic form.

b) Write the equation $4a = \log_2\left(b - 10\right)$ in exponential form.

Once you are comfortable with the structure of logarithmic expressions, it may no longer be necessary to convert to an exponential equation before evaluating.

You can evaluate logarithms by first converting the logarithmic expression into an exponential equation, then solving the exponential equation.

Example

Evaluate the expression $\log_2 8$.

Solution

Step 1

Let $\log_2 8 = x$. Rewrite $\log_2 8 = x$ in exponential form.

The exponential form of $\log_2 8 = x$ is $2^x = 8$.

The expression $\log_2 8$ is equal to the exponent that gives a result of 8 when 2 is the base.

Step 2

Solve the exponential equation $2^x = 8$.

$2^x = 8$

$2^x = 2^3$

The value of x is 3. Therefore, $\log_2 8 = 3$.

Example

Evaluate the expression $\log_2 16$.

Solution

Step 1

Let $\log_2 16 = x$. Rewrite $\log_2 16 = x$ in exponential form.

The exponential form of $\log_2 16 = x$ is $2^x = 16$.

Step 2

Solve the exponential equation $2^x = 16$.

$2^x = 16$

$2^x = 2^4$

The value of x is 4. Therefore, $\log_2 16 = 4$.

Class Exercise 4

a) Evaluate the expression $\log_2 \left(\dfrac{1}{64} \right)$.

b) Evaluate the expression $\log_3 81 + \log_3 \left(\dfrac{1}{27} \right)$.

EVALUATING COMMON LOGARITHMS

Logarithms with base 10 are called **common logarithms**. Examples of common logarithms include $\log_{10} 100$, $\log_{10} 81$, and $\log_{10} \dfrac{8}{17}$. Logarithms with a base of 10 are written without a base indicated. When no base is indicated, it is assumed to be base 10. For example, $\log_{10} 100 = \log 100$ and $\log_{10} M = \log M$.

NOTES

If $a > 0$, then $\log_a a = 1$

The change of base formula, explained later in this chapter, allows you to change any logarithm to a common logarithm that can be evaluated using a calculator.

Example

Evaluate $\log_{10} 10$.

Solution

Let $\log_{10} 10 = x$. The exponential form of $\log_{10} 10 = x$ is $10^x = 10$.
Since $10^x = 10$, the value of x is 1.

Therefore, $\log_{10} 10 = 1$.

Class Exercise 5

Evaluate $\log\left(\dfrac{1}{1000}\right)$.

You can evaluate common logarithms with a calculator using the log button. On a TI-83 or similar calculator, it appears as $\boxed{\text{LOG}}$. On other calculators, the logarithm button can appear as $\boxed{\log}$.

On most scientific calculators, enter the number, then press $\boxed{\log}$. On most graphing calculators, press $\boxed{\text{LOG}}$, enter the number, then press $\boxed{)}$ $\boxed{\text{ENTER}}$.

Example

Using technology, evaluate $\log 819$ to the nearest thousandth.

Solution

Use a TI-83 or similar calculator to evaluate $\log 819$.

Press $\boxed{\text{LOG}}$ $\boxed{8}$ $\boxed{1}$ $\boxed{9}$ $\boxed{)}$ $\boxed{\text{ENTER}}$.

```
log(819)
        2.913283902
```

Rounded to the nearest thousandth, $\log 819$ is 2.913.

Class Exercise 6

Evaluate $\log 1782$ to the nearest thousandth.

PRACTICE EXERCISES

Write each of the following equations in logarithmic form.

1. $6^2 = 36$

2. $9^0 = 1$

3. $5^x = y - 11$

4. $\left(\dfrac{1}{3}\right)^{x+1} = 9$

5. $10^{\log(0.001)} = x$

Write each of the following equations in exponential form.

6. $\log 0.0001 = -4$

7. $-5 = \log_{\left(\frac{1}{4}\right)} 1024$

8. $4x = 8\log_2 256$

9. $\log(x+9) = 108$

10. $\dfrac{\log_3 \sqrt{27}}{2} = -a$

Evaluate each of the following expressions.

11. $\log_5 25$

12. $\log_2 1$

13. $4\log_6\left(\dfrac{1}{6}\right)$

14. $\log 10\,000 - \log 0.00001$

15. $\log_5 1 + \log_5\left(\dfrac{1}{125}\right)$

Evaluate each of the following expressions using technology. Round the solution to the nearest thousandth.

16. $\log 957$

17. $\log 5887$

Lesson 2 THE LAWS OF LOGARITHMS

The laws of logarithms provide a useful way to work with logarithmic expressions.

PRODUCT LAW OF LOGARITHMS

The **product law of logarithms** is $\log_a\left(M \bullet N\right) = \log_a M + \log_a N$, where M and N are positive real numbers. This law states that the sum of two logarithms with the same base, a, is equal to the logarithm of the product of those two numbers, where $a > 0$.

The product law of logarithms provides a method for evaluating and simplifying the logarithm of a product.

Example

Evaluate $\log_2\left(128 \times 64\right)$.

> *Solution*
> **Step 1**
> Write the logarithm of the product $\left(128 \times 64\right)$ as the logarithm of 128 plus the logarithm of 64.
> $\log_2\left(128 \times 64\right) = \log_2 128 + \log_2 64$
>
> **Step 2**
> Evaluate each logarithm, and add the results.
> $\log_2 128 + \log_2 64$
> $= 7 + 6$
> $= 13$
>
> Therefore, the value of $\log_2\left(128 \times 64\right)$ is 13.

Class Exercise 1

Simplify $\log_5 25a$.

The product law of logarithms can also be used in reverse. The sum of the logarithm of M and the logarithm of N can be converted to the logarithm of the product $\left(M \times N\right)$ such that $\log_a M + \log_a N = \log_a\left(M \bullet N\right)$.

Example

Evaluate $\log_6 4 + \log_6 9$.

Solution

Step 1

Write the sum of the logarithm of 4 and the logarithm of 9 as the logarithm of the product (4×9).

$$\log_6 4 + \log_6 9 = \log_6 (4 \times 9)$$

Step 2

Evaluate the single logarithm.

$$\log_6 (4 \times 9)$$
$$= \log_6 36$$
$$= 2$$

Therefore, $\log_6 4 + \log_6 9 = 2$.

Class Exercise 2

Express $\log(x+1) + \log(x-3)$ as a single simplified logarithm.

The product law of logarithms is still applicable when there are more than two multiplicands.

Example

Express $\log_n 7 + \log_n 9 + \log_n 3n$ as a single simplified logarithm.

Solution

Since there is a sum of logarithms and all the logarithms have the same base (n), apply the product law of logarithms to simplify the expression.

$$\log_n 7 + \log_n 9 + \log_n 3n$$
$$= \log_n (7 \times 9 \times 3n)$$
$$= \log_n (189n)$$

Therefore, $\log_n 7 + \log_n 9 + \log_n 3n = \log_n (189n)$.

 Copyright Protected

Class Exercise 3

If $\log_3 m = x$, determine an expression in terms of x that is equivalent to $\log_3 (27 \times 9 \times m)$.

QUOTIENT LAW OF LOGARITHMS

The quotient law of logarithms is $\log_a \left(\dfrac{M}{N} \right) = \log_a M - \log_a N$, where M and N are positive real numbers. This law states that the difference of two logarithms with the same base, a, is equal to the logarithm of the quotient of those two numbers, where $a > 1$.

The quotient law of logarithms provides a method for evaluating and simplifying the logarithm of a quotient.

Example

Evaluate $\log_2 \left(\dfrac{4}{8} \right)$.

Solution

Step 1

Write the logarithm of the quotient $\left(\dfrac{4}{8} \right)$ as the logarithm of 4 minus the logarithm of 8.

$$\log_2 \left(\frac{4}{8} \right) = \log_2 4 - \log_2 8$$

Step 2

Evaluate each logarithm, and subtract the results.

$\log_2 4 - \log_2 8$
$= 2 - 3$
$= -1$

Therefore, the value of $\log_2 \left(\dfrac{4}{8} \right)$ is -1.

Class Exercise 4

If $\log_6 m = x$, determine an expression in terms of x that is equivalent to $\log_6\left(\dfrac{36}{m}\right)$.

The **quotient law of logarithms** can also be used in reverse.
The difference between the logarithm of M and the logarithm of N can be converted to the logarithm of the quotient $\dfrac{M}{N}$, such that

$$\log_a M - \log_a N = \log_a\left(\frac{M}{N}\right).$$

Example
Evaluate $\log_7 245 - \log_7 5$.

Solution

Step 1
Write the difference between the logarithm of (245) and the logarithm of (5) as the logarithm of the quotient $\left(\dfrac{245}{5}\right)$.

$$\log_7 245 - \log_7 5 = \log_7\left(\frac{245}{5}\right)$$

Step 2
Evaluate the single logarithm.
$$\log_7\left(\frac{245}{5}\right)$$
$$= \log_7 49$$
$$= 2$$

Class Exercise 5

Express $\log_2\left(72x^2\right) - \log_2\left(9x\right)$ as a simplified, single logarithm.

A common mistake is expressing $\log_a M - \log_a N$ as $\dfrac{\log_a M}{\log_a N}$. It is important to remember that $\log_a M - \log_a N \neq \dfrac{\log_a M}{\log_a N}$.

POWER LAW OF LOGARITHMS

The **power law of logarithms** is $\log_a\left(M^n\right) = n\log_a M$, where M is a real number. This law states that the logarithm of a power, M^n, is equal to the product of the exponent of that power, n, and the logarithm of the base of that power, M, for any base, a, where $a > 1$. This means the exponent becomes the multiplier.

The power law of logarithms can be used to evaluate and simplify the logarithm of a power.

Example

Evaluate $\log_8\left(64^7\right)$.

Solution
Step 1
Simplify the given expression using the power law of logarithms.
$\log_8\left(64^7\right) = 7\log_8 64$

Step 2
Evaluate $7\log_8 64$.
$7\log_8 64$
$= 7(2)$
$= 14$

Therefore, $\log_8\left(64^7\right) = 14$.

Class Exercise 6

Determine an expression written in terms of k that is equivalent to $\log_3\left(81^{5-k}\right)$.

NOTES

COMBINING LOGARITHMIC LAWS

The laws of logarithms can be combined to simplify and evaluate expressions where the individual logarithms all have the same base.

Example

Evaluate $\log_2 6 - 2\log_2 3 + \log_2 12$.

Solution

Apply the laws of logarithms to simplify the expression before evaluating it.

Step 1

Apply the power law of logarithms to the middle term in the expression, and simplify.

$\log_2 6 - 2\log_2 3 + \log_2 12$
$= \log_2 6 - \log_2 \left(3^2\right) + \log_2 12$
$= \log_2 6 - \log_2 9 + \log_2 12$

Step 2

Apply the quotient law of logarithms to the first two terms in the expression, and simplify.

$\log_2 6 - \log_2 9 + \log_2 12$
$= \log_2 \left(\dfrac{6}{9}\right) + \log_2 12$
$= \log_2 \left(\dfrac{2}{3}\right) + \log_2 12$

Step 3

Apply the product law of logarithms, and simplify.

$\log_2 \left(\dfrac{2}{3}\right) + \log_2 12$
$= \log_2 \left(\dfrac{2}{3} \times 12\right)$
$= \log_2 \left(\dfrac{24}{3}\right)$
$= \log_2 8$

Step 4

Evaluate $\log_2 8$.

$\log_2 8 = 3$

Therefore, $\log_2 6 - 2\log_2 3 + \log_2 12 = 3$.

Copyright Protected

Class Exercise 7

Evaluate $\log 100 + 3\log 10 - \log 10\,000$.

Example

Express $6\log_5 k - 5\log_5 m^2$ as a single simplified logarithm.

Solution

Step 1

Apply the power law of logarithms to both terms.

$6\log_5 k - 5\log_5 m^2$

$= \log_5\left(k^6\right) - \log_5\left(m^2\right)^5$

Step 2

Apply the power law of exponents to the last term.

$\log_5\left(k^6\right) - \log_5\left(m^2\right)^5$

$= \log_5\left(k^6\right) - \log_5\left(m^{10}\right)$

Step 3

Apply the quotient law of logarithms.

$\log_5\left(k^6\right) - \log_5\left(m^{10}\right)$

$= \log_5\left(\dfrac{k^6}{m^{10}}\right)$

The expression $\log_5\left(\dfrac{k^6}{m^{10}}\right)$ cannot be simplified any further.

Therefore, $6\log_5 k - 5\log_5 m^2 = \log_5\left(\dfrac{k^6}{m^{10}}\right)$.

Class Exercise 8

Express $3\log_8 y - \log_8\left(y^4\right) + \log_8 x$ as a single simplified logarithm.

NOTES

CHANGE OF BASE FORMULA

A useful relationship connecting logarithmic expressions with different bases is the **change of base formula**, $\log_b c = \dfrac{\log_a c}{\log_a b}$, where $a > 0$ and $a \neq 1$. Once applied, it allows work to be done in base a instead of base b.

The change of base formula allows for a calculator to be used to evaluate a logarithmic expression that is not written in base 10.

Example

Evaluate the expression $\log_7 20$ to the nearest tenth.

Solution

Step 1

Apply the change of base formula using base 10 so that a calculator can be used.

$$\log_7 20 = \frac{\log_{10} 20}{\log_{10} 7}$$

Step 2

Use a TI-83 or similar calculator to evaluate $\dfrac{\log 20}{\log 7}$.

$$\frac{\log 20}{\log 7} \approx 1.5$$

Example

Evaluate the expression $\log_6 4 + \log_6 13$ to the nearest tenth.

Solution

Step 1

Apply the product law of logarithms, and simplify.

$\log_6 4 + \log_6 13$
$= \log_6 (4 \times 13)$
$= \log_6 52$

Step 2

Apply the change of base formula using base 10 so that a calculator can be used.

$$\log_6 52 = \frac{\log 52}{\log 6}$$

Step 3

Use a TI-83 or similar calculator to evaluate $\dfrac{\log 52}{\log 6}$.

$$\frac{\log 52}{\log 6} \approx 2.2$$

When logarithms have different bases, the laws of logarithms cannot be used to combine the expressions into a single logarithm. In this case, apply the change of base formula to express each term in the same base. Once all the terms are expressed in the same base, you can apply the laws of logarithms to combine the terms into a single logarithm.

Example

Express $4\log_4(3x) - \log_2(x^3)$ as a single simplified logarithm in the form of $\log_2 a$.

Solution

To rewrite the expression as a single logarithm with base 2, both terms need to be in base 2.

Step 1

Express $\log_4(3x)$ with a base of 2.

Apply the change of base formula, $\log_b c = \dfrac{\log_a c}{\log_a b}$.

$$4\log_4(3x) - \log_2(x^3)$$
$$= 4\left[\dfrac{\log_2(3x)}{\log_2 4}\right] - \log_2(x^3)$$

Step 2

Evaluate .

$$4\left[\dfrac{\log_2(3x)}{\log_2 4}\right] - \log_2(x^3)$$
$$= 4\left[\dfrac{\log_2(3x)}{2}\right] - \log_2(x^3)$$
$$= 2\log_2(3x) - \log_2(x^3)$$

Step 3

Apply the power law of logarithms to the first term.

$$2\log_2(3x) - \log_2(x^3)$$
$$= \log_2(3x)^2 - \log_2(x^3)$$
$$= \log_2(9x^2) - \log_2(x^3)$$

NOTES

Step 4

Apply the quotient law of logarithms to express $\log_2\left(9x^2\right)-\log_2\left(x^3\right)$ in the form $\log_2 a$.

$$\log_2\left(9x^2\right)-\log_2\left(x^3\right)$$
$$=\log_2\left(\frac{9x^2}{x^3}\right)$$
$$=\log_2\left(\frac{9}{x}\right)$$

Class Exercise 9

Evaluate $3\log_5 4-\log_5 17$ to the nearest tenth.

Class Exercise 10

Express $3\log_2 x+9\log_8\left(5x\right)$ as a single simplified logarithm in the form of $\log_2 a$.

PRACTICE EXERCISES

Simplify and evaluate the following expressions.

1. $\log_3\left(9 \times 27\right)$

2. $\log_2 384 - \log_2 3$

3. $\log_9\left(\dfrac{\sqrt[3]{729}}{81}\right)$

4. $\log_5 2 + \log_5\left(\dfrac{25}{2}\right)$

5. $\log_3 6 - \log_3 54$

6. $\log_7 14 + \log_7\left(\dfrac{1}{2}\right) + \log_7\left(\dfrac{1}{7}\right)$

7. $\log_4\left(64^{10}\right)$

8. $\log_{\frac{1}{2}}\left(64^{17}\right)$

Evaluate the following expressions.

9. $\log 5 + \log 4 - \log 200$

10. $\log_3 162 - \log_3 4 + \log_3 6$

11. $2\log_{\sqrt{3}} 6 - 2\log_{\sqrt{3}} 2 - 5\log_{\sqrt{3}} 1$

12. $3\log_6 12 + 2\log_6\left(\dfrac{1}{2}\right) - \log_6 2$

Express the following expressions as a single simplified logarithm.

13. $3\log_2 x + 2\log_2 (5x)$

14. $2\log_b (3m) - \log_b (18m)$

15. $\log_x a + 3\log_x b - 2\log_x a$

16. $3\log_3 x + \log_3 y + 4\log_3 y - \log_3 (xy)$

17. If $\log_b 9 = m$, what is the expression $\log_b \left(\dfrac{1}{81}\right)$ in terms of m?

Lesson 3 SOLVING EXPONENTIAL EQUATIONS

An **exponential equation** is one in which the variable appears in the exponent. Some examples of exponential equations include $7^x = 7$, $12^{x-1} = 6$, and $2^{3x-1} + 3 = 8$.

It is possible to solve exponential equations in which the powers have the same base (e.g., $7^x = 7$), as well as equations in which the powers do not have the same base (e.g., $12^{x-1} = 6$).

NOTES

In the equation $7^x = 7$, the expression 7^x has a base of 7 and an exponent of x. Similarly, the number 7 has a base of 7 and an exponent of 1.

SOLVING EXPONENTIAL EQUATIONS IN WHICH THE BASES ARE EQUAL

A method of solving an exponential equation is based on the property that if both sides of an equation have the same base (where the base is not equal to 0 or 1), then the exponents on each side of the equation must also be equal. In other words, if $b^x = b^y$ and b is not equal to 0 or 1, then $x = y$.

Example

Solve for x in the equation $3^{x+5} = 3$.
Since the bases on each side of the equation $3^{x+5} = 3$ are equal, the exponents on each side of the equation must also be equal.

Solution
Equate the exponents, and solve for x.
The exponent of 3^{x+5} is $x + 5$, and the exponent of 3 is 1.
$x + 5 = 1$
$x = 1 - 5$
$x = -4$

The value of x is –4.

Note: $3 = 3^1$

Example

Solve for m in the equation $\left(\dfrac{1}{2}\right)^{2m+5} = \dfrac{1}{2}$.

Solution
Since the bases on each side of the equation are equal, the exponents on each side of the equation must be equal.

Equate the exponents, and solve for m.
$2m + 5 = 1$
$2m = -4$
$m = \dfrac{-4}{2}$
$m = -2$

The value of m is –2.

Class Exercise 1

Determine the value of p in the equation $9^{-8-9p} = 9$.

SOLVING EXPONENTIAL EQUATIONS IN WHICH THE BASES ARE NOT EQUAL

Often, exponential equations will have bases that are not equal but can be written as powers of the same number. When the bases are not equal, try changing the base of a power by rewriting the expression in terms of a different base. For example, 8^k can be written as a power of 2 by first recognizing that the base 8 can be written as 2^3. Then, 2^3 can be substituted for 8 so that $8^k = \left(2^3\right)^k = 2^{3k}$.

Example

Solve for x in the equation $9 = 27^{2x+1}$.

Solution

Step 1

Write the equation so that the powers have the same base.
Since both sides can be written as powers with base 3, replace 9 with 3^2 and 27 with 3^3.

$$9 = 27^{2x+1}$$
$$3^2 = \left(3^3\right)^{2x+1}$$

Step 2

Simplify the equation using the laws of exponents.
Apply the power law of exponents to the right side of the equation.

$$3^2 = \left(3^3\right)^{2x+1}$$
$$3^2 = 3^{6x+3}$$

The power law of exponents is $\left(a^m\right)^n = a^{mn}$.

Step 3

Apply the property that if $b^x = b^y$, where $b \neq 0$ and $b \neq 1$, then $x = y$.
If both sides of the equation have the same base, the exponents on both sides are also equal. Therefore, equate the exponents.
$2 = 6x + 3$

Step 4

Solve for x.
$$2 = 6x + 3$$
$$-1 = 6x$$
$$x = -\frac{1}{6}$$

Therefore, the value of x is $-\frac{1}{6}$.

Copyright Protected

Example

Solve for x in the equation $\dfrac{1}{2} = 16^{x+2}$.

Solution

Step 1

Write the equation so that the powers have the same base.
Since both sides can be written as powers with base 2, replace 16 with 2^{-4}.

Apply the negative exponent rule, and replace $\dfrac{1}{2}$ with 2^{-1}.

$\dfrac{1}{2} = 16^{x+2}$

$2^{-1} = \left(2^4\right)^{x+2}$

Step 2

Apply the power law of exponents to both sides of the equation.

$2^{-1} = \left(2^4\right)^{x+2}$

$2^{-1} = 2^{4x+8}$

Step 3

Both sides of the equation have the same base, so equate the exponents.

$-1 = 4x + 8$

Step 4

Solve for x.

$-1 = 4x + 8$

$-9 = 4x$

$-\dfrac{9}{4} = x$

Therefore, the value of x is $-\dfrac{9}{4}$.

Class Exercise 2

Solve the following exponential equations.

a) $125 = \left(\dfrac{1}{25}\right)^{x+9}$

NOTES

The negative exponent rule
is $a^{-n} = \dfrac{1}{a^n}$, where $a \neq 0$.

b) $2^{3x+27} = 8$

SOLVING EXPONENTIAL EQUATIONS USING LOGARITHMS

Sometimes bases cannot be easily rewritten so that they are equal. For example, consider the equation $4^x = 7^5$. There is no convenient way to rewrite 4 and 7 so that they have the same base.

You can solve an exponential equation by converting it into a logarithmic equation, then applying the change of base formula. This method of solving is ideal for equations of the form $a = b^c$, where c represents a monomial or a binomial.

Example

Solve $1.10^x = 4$ algebraically to the nearest thousandth.

Note: If $y = a^x$, then $x = \log_a y$, where $a > 0$ and $a \neq 1$.

Solution
Step 1
Isolate x by rewriting the equation in logarithmic form.
$$1.10^x = 4$$
$$\log_{1.10} 4 = x$$

Step 2
Apply the change of base formula to the expression $\log_{1.10} 4$ using base 10.
$$\log_{1.10} 4 = x$$
$$\frac{\log 4}{\log 1.10} = x$$

Step 3
Find an approximate solution using a calculator.
$$x = \frac{\log 4}{\log 1.10}$$
$$x \approx 14.545$$

Therefore, the value of x is approximately 14.545.

Copyright Protected

Class Exercise 3

Solve $80^{2x} - 4 = 5$ algebraically to the nearest thousandth.

An approximate solution can also be obtained by taking the logarithm of each side of the equation in a common base. Base 10 logarithms are commonly used for this purpose. From there, the goal is to isolate and solve for the variable. This method of solving is ideal for exponential equations with a variable in the exponent on both sides of the equation where the powers cannot be rewritten with the same base.

Example

Solve $5^{x-7} = 6^{-3x}$ algebraically to the nearest thousandth.

Solution

Step 1
Take the common logarithm of each side of the equation.
$$5^{x-7} = 6^{-3x}$$
$$\log\left(5^{x-7}\right) = \log\left(6^{-3x}\right)$$

It is important to take the common logarithm of both sides of the equation in order to preserve equality.

Step 2
Apply the power law of logarithms to both sides of the equation.
$$\log\left(5^{x-7}\right) = \log\left(6^{-3x}\right)$$
$$(x-7)\log 5 = -3x\log 6$$

If the exponent is a binomial, make sure to multiply the entire binomial by the logarithm.
$$\log\left(5^{x-7}\right) \neq x - 7\log 5$$

Step 3
Expand the left side of the equation.
$$(x-7)\log 5 = -3x\log 6$$
$$x\log 5 - 7\log 5 = -3x\log 6$$
$$x\log 5 + 3x\log 6 = 7\log 5$$

Step 4
Isolate x.
$$x\log 5 + 3x\log 6 = 7\log 5$$
$$x\left(\log 5 + 3\log 6\right) = 7\log 5$$
$$x = \frac{7\log 5}{\log 5 + 3\log 6}$$

Step 5

Using a calculator, determine the solution, correct to the nearest thousandth.

$$x = \frac{7\log 5}{\log 5 + 3\log 6}$$
$$x \approx 1.613$$

Therefore, the value of x is approximately 1.613.

Example

Solve $9^{x+6} = 4^{2x}$ algebraically to the nearest thousandth.

Solution

Step 1

Take the common logarithm of each side of the equation.

$$9^{x+6} = 4^{2x}$$
$$\log\left(9^{x+6}\right) = \log\left(4^{2x}\right)$$

Step 2

Apply the power law of logarithms to both sides of the equation.

$$\log\left(9^{x+6}\right) = \log\left(4^{2x}\right)$$
$$(x+6)\log 9 = 2x\log 4$$

Step 3

Expand the left side of the equation.

$$(x+6)\log 9 = 2x\log 4$$
$$x\log 9 + 6\log 9 = 2x\log 4$$

Step 4

Isolate x.

$$x\log 9 + 6\log 9 = 2x\log 4$$
$$x\log 9 - 2x\log 4 = 6\log 9$$
$$x\left(\log 9 - 2\log 4\right) = 6\log 9$$
$$x = \frac{6\log 9}{\log 9 - 2\log 4}$$

Step 5

Using a calculator, determine the solution to the nearest thousandth.

$$x = \frac{6\log 9}{\log 9 - 2\log 4}$$
$$x = -22.913$$

Therefore, the value of x is approximately –22.913.

Class Exercise 4

Solve $2^x = 5^{x-3}$ algebraically. Round the answer to the nearest thousandth.

SOLVING EXPONENTIAL EQUATIONS USING A GRAPHING CALCULATOR

The solution to an exponential equation can be found using a TI-83 or similar graphing calculator. One method used to solve an exponential equation graphically is to bring all terms to one side of the equation, then find the x-intercepts of the related function.

Example

Solve $\left(\dfrac{3}{2}\right)^{x-1} = 7^{8x+1}$ graphically. Round the answer to the nearest hundredth.

Solution

Step 1
Bring all terms to one side of the equation.

$$\left(\frac{3}{2}\right)^{x-1} = 7^{8x+1}$$

$$\left(\frac{3}{2}\right)^{x-1} - 7^{8x+1} = 0$$

Step 2
Graph the related function using a TI-83 or similar calculator.

Press $\boxed{Y=}$, enter the equation as $Y_1 = 1.5 \wedge (X-1) - 7 \wedge (8X+1)$, and press $\boxed{\text{GRAPH}}$. An appropriate window setting is $x:[-2.5, 2.5, 1]$ and $y:[-2.5, 2.5, 1]$. The resulting graph is shown.

NOTES

Step 3
Determine the *x*-intercept of the graph.

Press $\boxed{\text{2nd}}$ $\boxed{\text{TRACE}}$, and select 2:zero. When asked for a left bound, position the cursor just left of the first zero, and press $\boxed{\text{ENTER}}$.

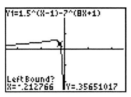

When asked for a right bound, position the cursor just right of the same zero, and press $\boxed{\text{ENTER}}$.

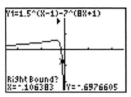

At the "Guess?" prompt, press $\boxed{\text{ENTER}}$. The results are the coordinates of the zero of the function.

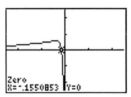

The *x*-intercept is approximately (–0.16, 0). Therefore, the value of *x* in the equation $2^{x-1} = 7^{8x+1}$ is approximately –0.16.

Another method used to solve an exponential equation is to graph each side of the equation as two separate functions, then identify their points of intersection.

Example

Solve $5^{1-x} = 6^{x+3}$ graphically to the nearest hundredth.

Solution
Step 1
Graph each side of the equation $5^{1-x} = 6^{x+3}$.

Press $\boxed{\text{Y=}}$, enter the equation as two separate functions, $Y_1 = 5 \wedge (1 - X)$ and $Y_1 = 6 \wedge (X + 3)$, and press $\boxed{\text{GRAPH}}$.
An appropriate window setting is $x:[-5, 5, 1]$ and $y:[-5, 50, 5]$.

It can be tricky to determine the appropriate window setting; therefore, some trial and error may be needed.

The resulting graph is shown.

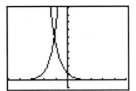

Step 2
Find the point of intersection.

Press ⟨2nd⟩ ⟨TRACE⟩, and select 5:intersect. When asked for a first curve, position the cursor just left or right of the first intersection point, and press ⟨ENTER⟩.

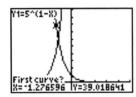

When asked for a second curve, position the cursor just left or right of the first intersection point, and press ⟨ENTER⟩.

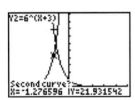

At the "Guess?" prompt, press ⟨ENTER⟩.

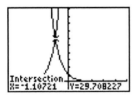

The point of intersection is approximately $(-1.11, 29.71)$. The solution is equal to the x-coordinate of the point of intersection. Therefore, the value of x in the equation $5^{1-x} = 6^{x+3}$ is approximately -1.11.

PRACTICE EXERCISES

Solve for x in the following equations by rewriting each power in terms of the same base.

1. $4^{2x+1} = 64^{x-5}$

2. $12^{x+3} = \left(\dfrac{1}{12}\right)^{8x}$

3. $6^{12x-7} - 2 = 4$

4. $7\left(2^{3x-14}\right) = 28$

Solve for x in the following equations using logarithms, and round to the nearest hundredth.

5. $8^{6x-5} = 9^{11x}$

6. $4\left(5\right)^{x-2} = 232$

7. $13 = 125^{4x-1} - 7$

8. $42^{4x+3} = 3^{-5x}$

Solve for x in the following equations by graphing, and round to the nearest hundredth.

9. $7^{x-4} = 6^{6-x}$

10. $3^{2x-1} - 8 = 0$

Copyright Protected

Lesson 4   SOLVING PROBLEMS INVOLVING EXPONENTIAL FUNCTIONS

An **exponential function** is of the form $y = ab^x$, where $b > 0$ and $b \neq 1$.
Since $y = ab^0 = a$, the value of a gives the y-intercept of the graph.
The value of b changes the shape of the graph. To understand the effect of variable b on the graph of $y = ab^x$, consider the following cases.

NOTE: b is called the base, and x is called the exponent.

Case 1: b > 1

Let $a = 1$ and $b = 2$. Sketch the function $y = 2^x$ using a table of values.

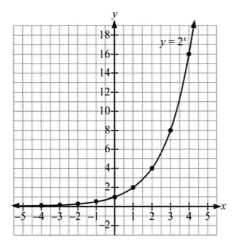

$y = 2^x$	
x	y
−4	0.0625
−3	0.125
−2	0.25
−1	0.5
0	1
1	2
2	4
3	8
4	16

Negative values of b are excluded because exponential expressions with negative bases and rational exponents do not always give real numbers.
For example, $(-4)^{\frac{1}{2}}$ is equivalent to $\sqrt{-4}$, which has no real number value.

The function $y = 2^x$ is equivalent to $y = 1(2)^x$.

When $b > 1$, the graph of $y = ab^x$ will have the general shape shown by the graph of $y = 2^x$. This general shape models **exponential growth**. As the x-values increase, the y-values get larger and larger toward positive infinity. As the x-values decrease, the y-values decrease and approach the x-axis, but never touch or cross it. Therefore, the domain is $x \in R$, and the range is $y > 0$. Since the value of a is 1, the y-intercept is located at $(0, 1)$.

Case 2: 0 < b < 1

Let $a = 1$ and $b = \dfrac{1}{2}$. Sketch the function $y = \left(\dfrac{1}{2}\right)^x$ using a table of values.

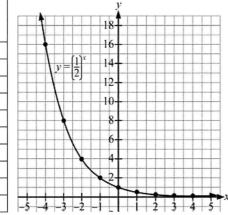

$y = \left(\dfrac{1}{2}\right)^x$	
x	y
−4	16
−3	8
−2	4
−1	2
0	1
1	0.5
2	0.25
3	0.125
4	0.0625

NOTES

When $0 < b < 1$, the graph of $y = ab^x$ will have the general shape shown by the graph of $y = \left(\dfrac{1}{2}\right)^x$. This general shape models **exponential decay**.

As the x-values increase, the y-values decrease and approach the x-axis, but never touch or cross it. As the x-values decrease, the y-values get larger and larger toward positive infinity. The domain is $x \in R$, and the range is $y > 0$. Since the value of a is 1, the y-intercept is located at (0, 1).

The following list summarizes the characteristics of the graph of an exponential function $y = ab^x$, where $b > 0$.
- If $b > 1$, the graph of the function models exponential growth.
- If $0 < b < 1$, the graph of the function models exponential decay.
- The domain is $x \in R$, since all x-values are permissible.
- The range is $y > 0$, since the y-values approach the x-axis, but never touch or cross it.
- The y-intercept is (0, a), since $y = ab^0 = a$ for all exponential functions.
- There are no x-intercepts, since the graph never touches or crosses the x-axis.

An exponential function can be used to model a situation in which a quantity is increasing or decreasing at an exponential rate.

SOLVING PROBLEMS THAT INVOLVE EXPONENTIAL GROWTH

A common example in which an exponential function is used to model exponential growth is population growth.

Example

A bacterial culture has an initial population of 100, and the population doubles every 4 h.

a) Create a table of values showing the population growth of the bacterial culture over a 20 h period.

Solution

Let $P(t)$ represent the population of bacteria at time, t, in hours.

The population when $t = 0$ corresponds to the initial bacteria population, which is 100.

The amount of time it takes for the population to double is called the **doubling period**.

t	$P(t)$
0	100
4	$100(2) = 200$
8	$100(2)(2) = 100(2^2) = 400$
12	$100(2)(2)(2) = 100(2^3) = 800$
16	$100(2)(2)(2)(2) = 100(2^4) = 1\ 600$
20	$100(2)(2)(2)(2)(2) = 100(2^5) = 3\ 200$

The population grows exponentially with time.

b) Determine the exponential function representing the population growth of the bacterial culture.

Solution
At any given time, the bacterial culture's population, $P(t)$, is given by $P(t) = 100(2)^n$, where n is the number of doubling periods. Since the population doubles every 4 h, the number of doubling periods is equal to $\dfrac{t}{4}$, where t is the elapsed time in hours.

The general population equation for the bacterial culture can be written as $P(t) = 100(2)^{\frac{t}{4}}$.

c) What is the bacteria population after 36 h?

Solution
In the function $P(t) = 100(2)^{\frac{t}{4}}$, let $t = 36$.

$$P(t) = 100(2)^{\frac{t}{4}}$$
$$P(36) = 100(2)^{\frac{36}{4}}$$
$$P(36) = 100(2)^{9}$$
$$P(36) = 51\ 200$$

Therefore, the population of bacteria after 36 h is 51 200.

A general formula that defines a quantity growing exponentially is given by $N_t = N_0 \times R^{\frac{t}{p}}$, where the following apply:

- N_t—the quantity at time, t.
- N_0—the initial size or value (when $t = 0$).
- R—the growth rate. For example, when a quantity doubles in size, $R = 2$; when it triples, $R = 3$; when it increases by 25%, $R = 1.25$, and so on.
- t—the elapsed time.
- p—the period of time that it takes the quantity to grow by rate R. For example, if it takes 3 h for a population to double, then $p = 3$.

NOTES

The general formula $N_t = N_0 \times R^{\frac{t}{p}}$ can be used to determine the exponential equation that defines a particular problem.

Example

Jana invests \$5 800 and earns interest at a rate of 6.7% per year compounded annually.

a) Determine the function that represents the amount of Jana's investment, $A(t)$, in dollars, after t years.

Solution

Step 1

Define the variables whose values are given in the problem with respect to the function $A(t) = A_0 \times R^{\frac{t}{p}}$.

The initial amount of the investment is \$5 800, so $A_0 = 5\ 800$.
The investment earns interest at 6.7% per year, so the rate of growth is $R = 1 + 0.067 = 1.067$. Since it takes 1 year for the investment to increase 6.7%, the period is $p = 1$.

Step 2

Substitute the values $A_0 = 5\ 800$, $R = 1.067$, and $p = 1$ into the function.

$$A(t) = A_0 \times R^{\frac{t}{p}}$$
$$A(t) = 5\ 800(1.067)^{\frac{t}{1}}$$
$$A(t) = 5\ 800(1.067)^{t}$$

The function that represents the amount of Jana's investment after t years is $A(t) = 5\ 800(1.067)^{t}$.

b) How much will Jana's investment be worth after 12 years?

Solution

The elapsed time is 12 years. Evaluate $A(12)$.
$$A(t) = 5\ 800(1.067)^{t}$$
$$A(12) = 5\ 800(1.067)^{12}$$
$$A(12) = 12\ 629.93242$$

After 12 years, Jana's investment will be worth \$12 629.93.

c) How long will it take the investment to quadruple?

Solution

Step 1

In the function $A(t) = 5\,800(1.067)^t$, let $A(t) = 4 \times 5\,800 = 23\,200$.

$$A(t) = 5\,800(1.067)^t$$
$$23\,200 = 5\,800(1.067)^t$$

Step 2

Divide both sides by 5 800.

$$23\,200 = 5\,800(1.067)^t$$
$$4 = 1.067^t$$

Step 3

Solve for t.

$$4 = 1.067^t$$
$$\log 4 = \log 1.067^t$$
$$\log 4 = t \log 1.067$$
$$\frac{\log 4}{\log 1.067} = t$$
$$t \approx 21.3766$$

Therefore, it will take approximately 21.4 years for the investment to quadruple.

Class Exercise 1

The population of a certain species of spiders starts at 32 and grows exponentially. The population of spiders after 5 weeks is 32 768. What is the doubling period of this certain species of spiders?

SOLVING PROBLEMS THAT INVOLVE EXPONENTIAL DECAY

The general formula $N_t = N_0 \times R^{\frac{t}{p}}$ can be used to solve exponential decay problems. Exponential decay problems occur when $0 < R < 1$ in the general formula $N_t = N_0 \times R^{\frac{t}{p}}$.

An example of exponential decay is radioactive half-life. The **half-life** of a radioactive substance is the amount of time it takes for half of a radioactive substance to undergo nuclear decay.

NOTES

You can also solve for t by converting the equation $4 = 1.067^t$ to logarithmic form.

$$4 = 1.067^t$$
$$\log_{1.067} 4 = t$$
$$\frac{\log 4}{\log 1.067} = t$$
$$21.3766 \approx t$$

NOTES

Half of a sample of
iodine-126 decays in
13 days.

Example

The half-life of iodine-126 is 13 days. The initial mass of iodine-126
is 10 g.

a) Determine the function, $A(t)$, that represents the amount of iodine-126
after t days.

Solution
Step 1
Identify the variables whose values are given in the problem with

respect to the function $A(t) = A_0 \times R^{\frac{t}{p}}$.

When $t = 0$, the mass is 10 g; therefore, $A_0 = 10$. The growth rate is
$R = \dfrac{1}{2}$.

It takes 13 days for the mass of iodine-126 to decrease to half its initial
mass. Therefore, the period is $p = 13$.

Step 2
Substitute the values $A_0 = 10$, $R = \dfrac{1}{2}$, and $p = 13$ into the function

$A(t) = A_0 \times R^{\frac{t}{p}}$.

$A(t) = A_0 \times R^{\frac{t}{p}}$

$A(t) = 10\left(\dfrac{1}{2}\right)^{\frac{t}{13}}$

The function that represents the amount of iodine-126 after t days is

$A(t) = 10\left(\dfrac{1}{2}\right)^{\frac{t}{13}}$.

b) To the nearest tenth of a gram, how much iodine-126 will remain
after 2 weeks?

Solution
The elapsed time is 2 weeks, which is equivalent to 14 days.
Evaluate $A(14)$.

$A(t) = 10\left(\dfrac{1}{2}\right)^{\frac{t}{13}}$

$A(14) = 10\left(\dfrac{1}{2}\right)^{\frac{14}{13}}$

$A(14) = 4.740387572$

The mass of iodine-126 left after 2 weeks will be approximately 4.7 g.

c) How long will the mass of iodine-126 take to decay to 1.25 g?

Solution
Step 1

In the function $A(t) = 10\left(\dfrac{1}{2}\right)^{\frac{t}{13}}$, let $A(t) = 1.25$.

$$A(t) = 10\left(\frac{1}{2}\right)^{\frac{t}{13}}$$

$$1.25 = 10\left(\frac{1}{2}\right)^{\frac{t}{13}}$$

Step 2
Divide both sides by 10.

$$1.25 = 10\left(\frac{1}{2}\right)^{\frac{t}{13}}$$

$$0.125 = \left(\frac{1}{2}\right)^{\frac{t}{13}}$$

Step 3
Solve for t.

$$\log(0.125) = \log\left(\frac{1}{2}\right)^{\frac{t}{13}}$$

$$\log(0.125) = \frac{t}{13}\log\left(\frac{1}{2}\right)$$

$$\frac{13\log(0.125)}{\log\left(\frac{1}{2}\right)} = t$$

$$t = 39$$

Therefore, it will take 39 days for the mass of iodine-126 to decay to 1.25 g.

Class Exercise 2

The value of a car decreases at a rate of 8.5% every year. If the car was originally worth $45 000, what will its value be after 18 years, to the nearest dollar?

NOTES

SOLVING PROBLEMS USING AN EXPONENTIAL GRAPH

A graph that relates to real-world investigations of exponential growth and decay can be used to solve problems. A graph can be interpreted and analyzed to make accurate predictions and conclusions. Characteristics, such as the intercepts, domain, and range, may be significant, depending on the context modelled using the function.

Example

A patient is injected with 10 mg of a radioactive isotope called technetium-99m, which is commonly used in various medical diagnoses.

The following graph shows the amount of the isotope, m, in milligrams, remaining in the patient's body over the next 24 h.

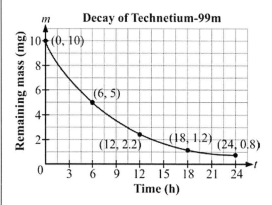

a) Approximately how long does it take until only 2 mg of the isotope remains in the patient?

Solution

Using the given graph of the exponential function, determine the value of t when $m = 2$.

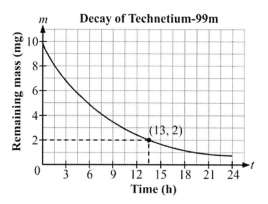

The graph of the exponential function shows that when $m = 2$, t is equal to about 13.

Therefore, it takes approximately 13 h until only 2 mg of the isotope remains in the patient.

b) How much of the isotope remains after 18 h?

Solution

Using the given graph of the exponential function, determine the value of m when $t = 18$.

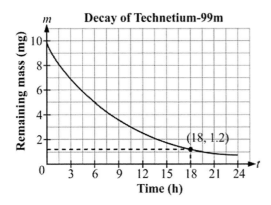

The graph of the exponential function shows that after 18 h, there is 1.2 mg of isotope left in the patient's body.

c) To the nearest 0.1 h, what is the half-life of the radioactive isotope?

Solution

If the original mass of the isotope is 10 mg at $t = 0$, then the half-life is the time taken for this mass to decay to half its original amount.

$$\frac{10}{2} = 5 \text{ mg}$$

According to the graph, the mass of 5 mg occurs at 6.0 h.
Therefore, the half-life of technetium-99m is 6.0 h.

The half-life of technetium-99m is exactly 6.0058 h.

Class Exercise 3

In 1990, a population of ducks was introduced to a certain pond. The population of ducks increased each year. The given graph shows the population, P, over 5 years since 1990.

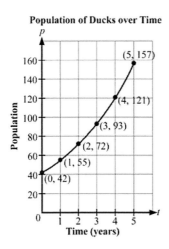

a) How many ducks were introduced to the pond in 1990?

b) What was the population of ducks in 1995?

c) The duck population first doubled in what year?

SOLVING PROBLEMS USING AN EXPONENTIAL REGRESSION

Exponential regression is a technique for finding the best-fitting exponential graph that passes through a set of ordered pairs. When ordered pairs or a table of values are used to model real-life examples of exponential data, an exponential regression is often performed. Exponential regressions are often performed on a TI-83 or similar calculator.

Example

The sales staff at a magazine looked at the growth rate in the number of subscribers during the previous decade. They found the number of subscriptions had grown exponentially, as shown in the given chart.

Year Recorded	Subscriptions (millions)
1	0.430
2	0.456
3	0.474
4	0.512
5	0.601
6	0.685
7	0.765
8	0.812
9	0.906
10	1.012

Copyright Protected

NOTES

What is the exponential regression function that best approximates the number of subscriptions, y, in millions, as a function of x, the year number of the decade? Round values for a and b to the nearest hundredth.

Solution

Step 1
Enter the x-values and y-values in lists L_1 and L_2, respectively.

Start by clearing any lists already present. Press 2nd + , select 4:ClrAllLists, and press ENTER . Press STAT , and select 1:Edit....
Enter the year number into list L_1 and the number of subscriptions into list L_2.

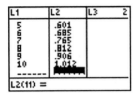

Step 2
Perform the exponential regression.

Press STAT ▷ to highlight CALC. Select 0:ExpReg, and press ENTER to obtain the following window.

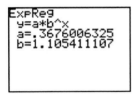

Step 3
Determine the exponential regression function.
Substitute the values of a and b into the exponential function $y = ab^x$.

$$y = ab^x$$
$$y = (0.37)(1.11)^x$$

The exponential regression function that best approximates the number of subscriptions in millions is $y = (0.37)(1.11)^x$.

You can graph an exponential regression function on a TI-83 or similar graphing calculator, then use the graph to solve problems.

NOTES

Example

Iodine-131 is a radioactive isotope used in thyroid uptake tests. Results of measurements taken of the mass of a sample of iodine-131 each day over a period of seven days are recorded in a table.

Day	0	1	2	3	4	5	6	7
Mass (mg)	54	49	43	39	33	29	24	22

a) Using a TI-83 or similar graphing calculator, graph the exponential regression function that best approximates the mass, $M(t)$, of iodine-131 after t days.

Solution

Step 1
Enter the data values into a TI-83 or similar calculator.

Start by clearing any lists already present. Press 2nd +, select 4:ClrAllLists, and press ENTER. Press STAT, and select 1:Edit.... Enter the day number into list L_1 and the mass of the isotope into list L_2.

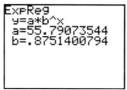

Step 2
Perform the exponential regression.

Press STAT ▷ to highlight CALC. Select 0:ExpReg, and press ENTER to obtain the following window.

```
ExpReg
 y=a*b^x
 a=55.79073544
 b=.8751400794
```

Step 3
Determine the exponential regression function.

Substitute the values of a and b into the exponential function $y = ab^x$.

$$y = ab^x$$
$$y = (55.79073544)(0.8751400794)^x$$

The exponential regression function that best approximates the decay of iodine-131 is $M(t) = (55.79073544)(0.8751400794)^t$.

When graphing the regression function, do not round the values for a and b unless stated otherwise.

Copyright Protected

Step 4
Graph the exponential function on a TI-83 or similar calculator.

Press $\boxed{Y =}$, and input the unrounded exponential regression function by pressing $\boxed{\text{VARS}}$, $\boxed{5}$, $\boxed{\triangleright}$, $\boxed{\triangleright}$, and selecting 1:RegEQ.

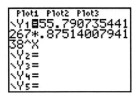

Use the window settings x: [–2, 30, 5] and y: [–2, 70, 5]. Press $\boxed{\text{GRAPH}}$ to obtain the following window.

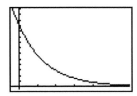

b) Use the graph to predict which day the mass of iodine-131 will decay to 5 mg. Round solution to the nearest day.

Solution

In the function $M(t) = (55.79073544)(0.8751400794)^t$, let $M(t) = 5$, and solve for t.

Step 1
Press $\boxed{Y=}$, and input a second function as $Y_2 = 5$. Press $\boxed{\text{GRAPH}}$ to obtain to following window.

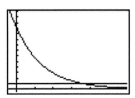

Step 2
Determine the point of intersection.

Press $\boxed{\text{2nd}}$ $\boxed{\text{TRACE}}$, and choose 5:intersect.

For "First curve?", position the cursor just left or right of the intersection point, and press $\boxed{\text{ENTER}}$. For "Second curve?", position the cursor just left or right of the intersection point, and press $\boxed{\text{ENTER}}$.

NOTES

For "Guess?", press ENTER.

The point of intersection is $(18.086122, 5)$. Therefore, it will take approximately 18 days for a mass of iodine-131 to decay to 5 mg.

Class Exercise 4

Troy did an experiment in which he studied the growth rate of bacteria. He examined a bacterial culture through a microscope every ten minutes. He counted the number of bacteria in a small area and used that number to estimate the total number of bacteria. He recorded his observations in a table.

Time (minutes)	10	20	30	40	50	60
Bacteria count	542	599	633	702	752	818

a) Using a TI-83 or similar graphing calculator, graph the exponential regression function that best approximates the bacteria count, $B(t)$, after t minutes.

b) Use the graph to determine the initial number of bacteria, to the nearest whole.

c) Use the graph to determine the bacteria count after 2 hours. Round the bacteria count to the nearest whole.

PRACTICE EXERCISES

Use the following information to answer the next three questions.

A farmer's field has 1 800 mice. The population of mice increases 15% each year.

1. Determine an exponential function that models the population of mice after *t* years.

2. **To** the nearest whole number, determine the number of mice in the field after 4 years.

3. Rounded to the nearest month, how long will it take for the population of mice to double?

Use the following information to answer the next three questions.

A newly married couple invests $25 000 into a variety of stocks on January 1, 1989. The couple's annual average rate of return as a percentage is 6.5%.

4. Determine the exponential function describing the stock value, $V(t)$, in dollars, over time, *t*, in years, since 1989.

5. To the nearest hundredth of a dollar, what is the value of the stock on January 1, 2002?

6. In what year will the stock be worth double the initial investment?

Use the following information to answer the next three questions.

The given graph shows the mass, $M(t)$, in grams, of a radioactive compound over time, t, in days.

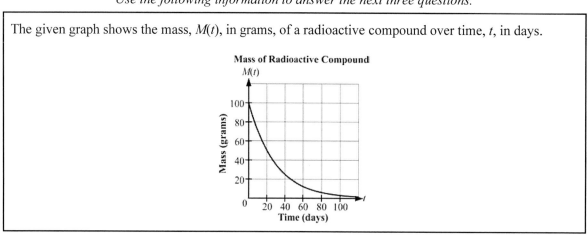

7. What was the initial mass of the radioactive compound?

 Copyright Protected

8. What is the half-life of the radioactive compound?

9. What is the function, $M(t)$, that represents the mass of the compound in grams after t days?

Use the following information to answer the next question.

A small publishing company initially recorded the number of titles it published every year since it opened in 1999, but it stopped collecting data after six years. The data collected by the company is shown in the given table.

Year	Number of Years after 1999	Number of Titles Published
1999	0	221
2000	1	238
2001	2	323
2002	3	369
2003	4	397
2004	5	426

Exponential regression can be performed on this data to get a function that gives the number of titles published as a function of the number of years after 1999.

10. What is the rate of growth of published titles per year between 1999 and 2004? Express your answer as a percentage to the nearest tenth.

Lesson 5 SOLVING PROBLEMS INVOLVING LOGARITHMIC FUNCTIONS

NOTES

Negative values of b are excluded because a logarithmic function with a negative b-value yields an exponential function with a negative base.

The exponential form of $y = \log_2 x$ is $2^y = x$.

A **logarithmic function** is of the form $y = \log_b x$, where $b > 0$, $b \neq 1$, and $x > 0$. The value of b changes the shape of the graph of the function. To understand the effect of variable b, consider the following cases.

Case 1: b > 1

Let $b = 2$ in the function $y = \log_b x$. Sketch the graph of $y = \log_2 x$ using a table of values.

$y = \log_2 x$	
x	y
$2^{-2} = 0.25$	-2
$2^{-1} = 0.5$	-1
$2^0 = 1$	0
$2^1 = 2$	1
$2^2 = 4$	2
$2^3 = 8$	3
$2^4 = 16$	4

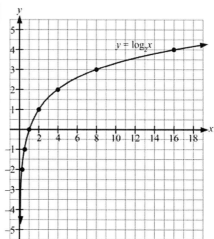

When $b > 1$, the graph of $y = \log_b x$ will have the general shape as shown by the graph of $y = \log_2 x$. As the x-values increase, the y-values increase to positive infinity. As the x-values decrease, they approach the y-axis, but never touch or cross it. The domain is $x > 0$, and the range is $y \in R$.

The x-intercept is (1, 0), which is true for all logarithmic functions of the form $y = \log_b x$, since $y = \log_b 1 = 0$.

The exponential form of $\log_b 1 = 0$ is $b^0 = 1$.

The equation $\log_b 1 = 0$ is true for any non-zero value of b.

The graph of $y = \log_2 x$ has the same shape as the graph of $y = 2^x$ but in a different orientation. This is because $y = \log_2 x$ and $y = 2^x$ are inverse functions.

The graph of an inverse function is a reflection of the original graph in the line $y = x$.

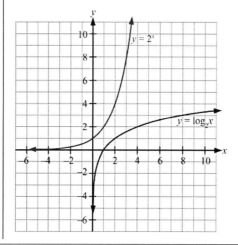

Case 2: $0 < b < 1$

Let $b = \dfrac{1}{2}$ in the function $y = \log_b x$. Sketch the graph of $y = \log_{\frac{1}{2}} x$ using a table of values.

The exponential form of $y = \log_{\frac{1}{2}} x$ is $\left(\dfrac{1}{2}\right)^y = x$.

$y = \log_{\frac{1}{2}} x$	
x	y
$\left(\dfrac{1}{2}\right)^{-4} = 16$	-4
$\left(\dfrac{1}{2}\right)^{-3} = 8$	-3
$\left(\dfrac{1}{2}\right)^{-2} = 4$	-2
$\left(\dfrac{1}{2}\right)^{-1} = 2$	-1
$\left(\dfrac{1}{2}\right)^{0} = 1$	0
$\left(\dfrac{1}{2}\right)^{1} = 0.5$	1
$\left(\dfrac{1}{2}\right)^{2} = 0.25$	2

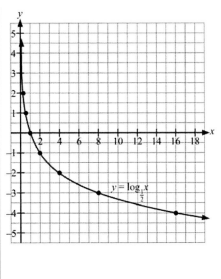

When $0 < b < 1$, the graph of $y = \log_b x$ will have the general shape shown by the graph of $y = \log_{\frac{1}{2}} x$. As the x-values increase, the y-values decrease toward negative infinity. As the x-values decrease, they approach the y-axis, but never touch or cross it. The domain is $x > 0$, and the range is $y \in R$. The x-intercept is $(1, 0)$.

NOTES

The graph of $y = \log_{\frac{1}{2}} x$ has the same shape as the graph of $y = \left(\dfrac{1}{2}\right)^x$ but in a different orientation.

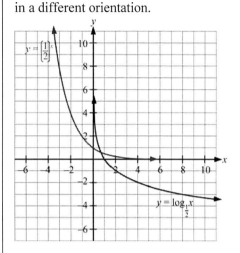

The characteristics of the graph of a logarithmic function $y = \log_b x$, where $b > 0$, $b \neq 1$, and $x > 0$, can be summarized in the following points:

• If $b > 1$, the graph of the function is increasing.
• If $0 < b < 1$, the graph of the function is decreasing.
• The domain is $x > 0$ because logarithmic functions are undefined for negative values.
• The range is $y \in R$.
• The x-intercept is $(1,\ 0)$, since $f(1) = \log_b 1 = 0$ for all logarithmic functions.
• There are no y-intercepts, since the graph never touches or crosses the y-axis.

APPLICATIONS OF LOGARITHMIC SCALES

Logarithms are often used to allow large differences to be represented by relatively small numbers. For example, 1 000 is 100 times greater than 10, but their logarithms (using base 10) are 3 and 1, respectively ($\log 1000 = 3$ and $\log 10 = 1$).

Three examples where logarithmic scales are used are the decibel scale for measuring the loudness of sounds, the Richter scale for measuring the intensity of earthquakes, and the pH scale for measuring acidity or alkalinity.

Loudness of Sound

The loudness of sound is measured in decibels so that the decibel measurement (dB) is dB = $10 \log L$, where L is the relative loudness of the sound compared with the threshold of hearing.

Example

The loudness of ordinary traffic is 10 000 000 times louder than the threshold of hearing. Determine the decibel measurement of ordinary traffic.

Solution

In the formula dB = 10log L, substitute 10 000 000for L, and solve for dB.

$$\text{dB} = 10\log L$$
$$\text{dB} = 10\log 10\,000\,000$$
$$\text{dB} = 10(7)$$
$$\text{dB} = 70$$

Therefore, the decibel measure of ordinary traffic is 70 dB.

The formula dB = 10log L can also be used to compare the loudness of two types of sounds. For example, to determine how many times louder a sound that has a relative loudness of L_1 is compared with a sound that has a relative loudness of L_2, calculate the value of the ratio $\dfrac{L_1}{L_2}$. In general, the formula $\dfrac{L_1}{L_2} = 10^{\left(\frac{\text{dB}_1 - \text{dB}_2}{10}\right)}$ can be used to compare a sound that has a relative loudness of L_1 with a sound that has a relative loudness of L_2.

Example

The measure of a telephone dial tone is 80 dB, and the measure of an ordinary conversation is 50 dB. How many times louder is a telephone dial tone than an ordinary conversation?

Solution

In the formula $\dfrac{L_1}{L_2} = 10^{\left(\frac{\text{dB}_1 - \text{dB}_2}{10}\right)}$, let $\text{dB}_1 = 80$ and $\text{dB}_2 = 50$, then solve.

$$\frac{L_1}{L_2} = 10^{\left(\frac{\text{dB}_1 - \text{dB}_2}{10}\right)}$$

$$\frac{L_1}{L_2} = 10^{\left(\frac{80 - 50}{10}\right)}$$

$$\frac{L_1}{L_2} = 10^{\left(\frac{30}{10}\right)}$$

$$\frac{L_1}{L_2} = 10^3$$

$$\frac{L_1}{L_2} = 1\ 000$$

Therefore, a telephone dial tone is 1 000 times louder than an ordinary conversation.

NOTES

Class Exercise 1

To the nearest whole number, how many times louder is an orchestra that has a decibel level of 98 than a whisper that has a decibel level of 20?

Earthquake Intensity

The magnitude of an earthquake is measured using the **Richter scale** with the formula $m = \log\left(\dfrac{I}{I_r}\right)$, where m is the magnitude on the Richter scale, I is the intensity of the earthquake, and I_r is the reference intensity of a very small and barely measurable earthquake. The formula used to compare an earthquake that has an intensity of I_1 with an earthquake that has an intensity of I_2 is $\dfrac{I_1}{I_2} = 10^{m_1 - m_2}$.

Example

Seismologists measure the intensities of earthquakes at several different locations to find the epicentre. Following a recent earthquake, seismologists determined that the magnitude at point A was 6.2, and the magnitude at point B was 3.4. To the nearest tenth, how many times more intense is the earthquake at point A compared with the earthquake at point B?

Solution

In the formula $\dfrac{I_1}{I_2} = 10^{m_1 - m_2}$, let $m_1 = 6.2$ and $m_2 = 3.4$, then solve.

$$\frac{I_1}{I_2} = 10^{m_1 - m_2}$$

$$\frac{I_1}{I_2} = 10^{6.2 - 3.4}$$

$$\frac{I_1}{I_2} = 10^{2.8}$$

$$\frac{I_1}{I_2} \approx 630.957$$

Therefore, the earthquake at point A is approximately 631.0 times more intense than the earthquake at point B.

Class Exercise 2

An earthquake in City M was measured to be 102 times more intense than an earthquake in City N. If the magnitude of the earthquake in City M was 5.8, what was the magnitude of the earthquake in City N, to the nearest tenth?

Acidity and Alkalinity

The acidity or alkalinity of a liquid is measured using the **pH scale**. A liquid that is very acidic has a relatively small pH value, and one that is very alkaline has a relatively large pH value. The range of pH values is from 0 to 14. Pure water, which is neutral (neither acidic nor alkaline), has a pH value of 7.

The formula to determine the pH of a liquid is $pH = -\log\left[H^+\right]$,

where $\left[H^+\right]$ represents the concentration of the hydrogen ion.

A comparison of the acidities of two liquids is obtained from the ratio of their $\left[H^+\right]$ concentrations. In general, the formula

$\dfrac{\left[H^+\right]_{\text{Liquid A}}}{\left[H^+\right]_{\text{Liquid B}}} = 10^{pH_{\text{Liquid B}} - pH_{\text{Liquid A}}}$ can be used to compare the acidities of two liquids.

NOTES

Example

Vinegar has a pH of 2.8, while lemonade has a pH of 3.0. How many times more acidic is vinegar than lemonade, to the nearest tenth?

Solution

In the formula, $\dfrac{\left[H^+\right]_{vinegar}}{\left[H^+\right]_{lemonade}} = 10^{pH_{lemonade} - pH_{vinegar}}$, let $pH_{vinegar} = 2.8$ and

$pH_{lemonade} = 3.0$, and solve.

$$\dfrac{\left[H^+\right]_{vinegar}}{\left[H^+\right]_{lemonade}} = 10^{pH_{lemonade} - pH_{vinegar}}$$

$$\dfrac{\left[H^+\right]_{vinegar}}{\left[H^+\right]_{lemonade}} = 10^{3.0-2.8}$$

$$\dfrac{\left[H^+\right]_{vinegar}}{\left[H^+\right]_{lemonade}} = 10^{0.2}$$

$$\dfrac{\left[H^+\right]_{vinegar}}{\left[H^+\right]_{lemonade}} \approx 1.58$$

Therefore, vinegar is approximately 1.6 times more acidic than lemonade.

Class Exercise 3

The pH of pure water is 7. To the nearest tenth, what is the pH of a solution that is 50 times more acidic than pure water?

SOLVING PROBLEMS USING A LOGARITHMIC REGRESSION

A **natural logarithm** is any logarithm that has a base of e, where e is an irrational number approximately equal to 2.71828. The notation ln is used to represent the natural logarithm $\log_e$. Therefore, the expression $\log_e y$ can be written as $\ln y$.

On a TI-83 or similar calculator, a natural **logarithmic regression** is used to find the best-fitting graph that models logarithmic data. Natural logarithmic regressions produce curves that are described by the function $y = a + b \ln x$, where $x > 0$.

Example

Sandra planted a tree in her backyard. When she planted the tree, it was 3 years old and measured 0.38 m in height. Sandra measured the height of the tree every year until it was 13 years old. The data she collected is as follows:

Age of Tree (years)	Height (m)
3	0.38
4	0.89
5	1.33
6	2.45
7	2.89
8	3.08
9	3.56
10	3.89
11	4.12
12	4.36
13	4.89

a) Determine the natural logarithmic function that models the height of tree, $H(t)$, in metres, after time, t, in years. Round the a- and b-values in the function to the nearest thousandth.

Solution

Step 1
Enter the x-values and y-values in lists L_1 and L_2, respectively.

Start by clearing any lists already present. Press $\boxed{\text{2nd}}$ $\boxed{+}$, select 4:ClrAllLists, and press $\boxed{\text{ENTER}}$. Press $\boxed{\text{STAT}}$, and select 1:Edit…. Enter the year numbers into list L_1 and the height values into list L_2.

Step 2
Perform the logarithmic regression.

Press $\boxed{\text{STAT}}$ $\triangleright$ to highlight CALC. Select 9:LnReg, and press $\boxed{\text{ENTER}}$ to obtain the following window.

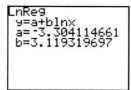

Step 3
Determine the natural logarithmic regression function.
Substitute the values of a and b into the function $y = a + b \ln x$.
Round the a- and b-values to the nearest thousandth.
$y = a + b \ln x$
$y = -3.304 + (3.119) \ln x$

The natural logarithmic regression function that best approximates the height of the tree, $H(t)$, after t years is $H(t) = -3.304 + (3.119) \ln t$.

b) Using the regression function, determine the height of the tree when it is 18 years old. Round your answer to the nearest tenth of a centimetre.

Solution
Step 1
Let $t = 18$ in the function $H(t) = -3.304 + (3.119) \ln t$.
$H(t) = -3.304 + (3.119) \ln t$
$H(18) = -3.304 + (3.119) \ln 18$

Step 2
Determine the value of $H(18)$.
$H(18) = -3.304 + (3.119) \ln 18$
$H(18) \approx 5.7110$

Therefore, the height of the tree when it is 18 years old could be approximately 5.7 m.

You can evaluate natural logarithmic expressions using the $\boxed{\text{LN}}$ key on a TI-83 or similar graphing calculator.

Copyright Protected

Class Exercise 4

Miranda gave birth to a baby boy. At birth, he measured 19.6 inches in length. Miranda measured his length every 3 months. The following table shows the length of Miranda's son:

Months after Birth	Length of Baby Boy (in)
3	23.9
6	25.4
9	28.3
12	29.9
15	31.2
18	32.3
21	33.4
24	34.6
27	35.3
30	36.1
33	36.9
36	37.7

a) Determine the natural logarithmic regression that gives the length of the baby boy as a function of the number of months after birth. Round the a- and b-values in the function to the nearest hundredth.

b) Use the regression function to find the length of Miranda's baby after 10 months. Round your solution to the nearest tenth of an inch.

PRACTICE EXERCISES

1. Following an earthquake, Katherine determined that the magnitude at point M was 7.8, and the magnitude at point N was 5.2. To the nearest whole number, how many times more intense is the earthquake at point M than the earthquake at point N?

Use the following information to answer the next two questions.

The loudness of a rock concert is 10^{12} times louder than the threshold of hearing.

2. Determine the decibel measurement for a rock concert.

3. The measure of an ordinary conversation is 50 dB. How many times louder is a rock concert than an ordinary conversation?

Use the following information to answer the next two questions.

The pH level of battery acid is 0.8. Battery acid is 50.3 times more acidic than soda pop.

4. Determine the pH level of soda pop, to the nearest tenth.

5. The pH level of milk is 6.7. To the nearest tenth, how many times more acidic is battery acid than milk?

Use the following information to answer the next two questions.

Earthquake X is 17 times more intense than earthquake Y and 10 times more intense than earthquake Z. The magnitude of earthquake X is 8.8 on the Richter scale.

6. What is the magnitude of earthquake Y, to the nearest tenth?

7. What is the magnitude of earthquake Z, to the nearest tenth?

Use the following information to answer the next three questions.

Zac injects himself with a particular brand of rapid-acting insulin to treat his diabetes. The concentration of insulin in his body after the injection is shown in following table:

Time (min)	50	150	250	350	450	550	650	750	850
Concentration (mu/L)	29.9	22.3	19.4	17.2	16.4	15.3	14.6	14.1	13.4

8. Using a TI-83 or similar graphing calculator, graph the natural logarithmic regression function that best approximates the concentration of insulin as a function of time, in minutes.

9. What is the concentration of insulin 3 hours after injection? Round your solution to the nearest tenth of a mu/L.

10. How long after the injection did the concentration of insulin fall below 15 mu/L? Round your solution to the nearest minute.

Copyright Protected

REVIEW SUMMARY

- The value of $\log_a y$ is defined as the number, x, that makes the statement $y = a^x$ true.

- An exponential equation can be converted to a logarithmic equation by applying the property that if $y = a^x$, then $x = \log_a y$, where $a > 0$ and $a \neq 1$.

- Evaluate logarithms by first converting the logarithmic expression into an exponential equation, then solving the exponential equation.

- Logarithms with base 10 are called common logarithms. You can evaluate common logarithms with a calculator using the $\boxed{\text{LOG}}$ or $\boxed{\text{log}}$ button.

- The logarithmic laws are as follows:

  - The product law of logarithms is $\log_a (M \cdot N) = \log_a M + \log_a N$.

  - The quotient law of logarithms is $\log_a \left(\dfrac{M}{N} \right) = \log_a M - \log_a N$.

  - The power law of logarithms is $\log_a (M^n) = n \log_a M$.

- When combining logarithmic expressions with different bases, you can apply the change of base formula $\log_b c = \dfrac{\log_a c}{\log_a b}$, where $a > 0$ and $a \neq 1$. The change of base formula allows for a calculator to be used to evaluate a logarithmic expression that is not written in base 10.

  - One method used to solve an exponential equation is based on the property that if both sides of an equation have the same base (where the base is not equal to 0), then the exponents on each side of the equation must also be equal.

- When exponential equations have bases that cannot be written as powers of the same base, an approximate solution can be obtained using logarithms. Base 10 logarithms are commonly used for this purpose.

- The value of a in the exponential function $y = ab^x$ is the y-intercept, and the value of b changes the shape of the graph of the function. If $b > 0$, the graph of the function models exponential growth. If $0 < b < 0$, the graph of the function models exponential decay. The domain is $x \in R$, and the range is $y > 0$.

- The general formula $N_t = N_0 \times R^{\frac{t}{p}}$ can be used to determine the exponential equation that defines a particular problem.

- Exponential regressions are often performed on a TI-83 or similar calculator to model exponential data. An exponential regression function is of the form $y = ab^x$.

- The value of b in the logarithmic function $y = \log_b x$ changes the shape of the graph of the function. If $b > 1$, the graph of the function is increasing. If $0 < b < 1$, the graph of the function is decreasing. The domain is $x > 0$, and the range is $y \in R$.

- Applications of logarithmic scales include the decibel scale for measuring the loudness of sounds, the Richter scale for measuring the intensity of earthquakes, and the pH scale for measuring acidity or alkalinity.

- Natural logarithmic regressions are often performed on a TI-83 or similar calculator to model logarithmic data. A natural logarithmic regression function is of the form $y = a + b \ln x$.

PRACTICE TEST

Evaluate each of the following expressions. If necessary, round the solution to the nearest tenth.

1. $\log_3 81$

2. $2\log_5 25$

3. $\dfrac{\log_2 81}{\log_2 9}$

4. $\log_8 121$

5. $3\log_7 11$

6. $\log_4 2 + \log_4 32$

7. $\log_8 4608 - 2\log_8 3$

8. $3\log_9 3 + \log_9 12 - 2\log_9 2$

Express each of the following expressions as a single simplified logarithm.

9. $3\log_7 (5m) - 9\log_7 m$

10. $\log_{\sqrt{2}} (n+1) + 4\log_{\sqrt{2}} 3$

11. $4\log_5 m - \log_5 n + \dfrac{1}{2}\log_5 p$

12. $\log_3 18a + \log_3 6 + 2\log_3 \left(\dfrac{1}{2a}\right)$

Copyright Protected

13. $\log_6 2A + 3\log_6 B - \log_6 A$

14. $2\log_c F + \dfrac{1}{6}\log_c G - 2\log_c H$

15. $4\log_5 K - \left(2\log_5 K + \log_5 M\right)$

Solve for x in the following equations by rewriting each power with the same base.

16. $6^{x-2} = 216^5$

17. $7^{13x+4} - 2 = 47$

18. $\left(4^{4x+1}\right)^3 = \left(16^{5x}\right)^4$

19. $\left(\dfrac{125}{8}\right)^{2x} = \left(\dfrac{4}{25}\right)^{x+5}$

Solve for x in the following equations using logarithms. Round the solutions to the nearest tenth.

20. $7^{2x+3} = 99$

21. $5^{x+5} - 76 = -12$

22. $5\left(2^x\right) = 5^{x-3}$

23. $7^{x-2} = 11^{13-x}$

Use the following information to answer the next three questions.

> The number of cellphone customers with a particular phone company increased by 25% every 6 months from 1996 to 2000. On January 1, 1996, there were 30 000 customers.

24. Determine the exponential function that represents the number of cellphones after t months.

25. How many cellphone customers were there on January 1, 1999?

26. In which month and year will there be 70 000 customers?

Copyright Protected

Use the following information to answer the next two questions.

Beginning on January 1, 2000, the populations of wolves and rabbits in a certain forest both grew at an exponential rate. The initial population of wolves was 56, and it increased by 25% every 2 months. The initial population of rabbits was 42, and it increased by 30% every month.

27. To the nearest tenth of a month, how long did it take for the wolf population and the rabbit population to become equal?

28. Determine the approximate difference between the wolf and rabbit populations at the end of September 2000. Round the population difference to the nearest whole.

Use the following information to answer the next three questions.

A soccer ball is dropped off a ledge. The height to which it rebounds from the ground can be modelled as an exponential function. The rebound height (h) in metres for the first 8 bounces (n) was plotted on a graph, and the curve of best fit was drawn.

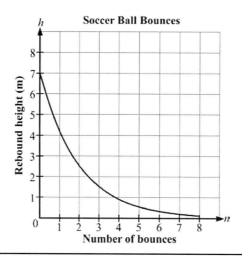

29. How tall is the ledge?

30. To the nearest half of a metre, what is the height of the ball after 5 bounces?

31. On which bounce is the rebound height 1.5 m?

Use the following information to answer the next three questions.

The population of salmon in a certain river is 20 000. The following table shows the population of salmon over 24 years.

Number of Years	Population of Salmon
0	20 000
4	15 727
8	12 323
12	9 987
16	8 436
20	6 584
24	5 813

32. Determine the exponential regression function that best represents the population of salmon, $P(t)$, after t years.

33. To the nearest whole number, how many salmon are left in 40 years?

34. What is the rate at which the salmon decrease per year? Express your answer as a percentage to the nearest hundredth.

35. The power gain, G, of an amplifier, measured in decibels, is given by the equation $G = 10 \log \left(\dfrac{P_o}{P_i} \right)$,

where P_o is the output power, measured in watts, and P_i is the input power, measured in watts. If the output power is 20 W and the power gain is 16 dB, what is the input power to the nearest tenth of a watt?

Use the following information to answer the next two questions.

The magnitude of an earthquake is determined using the formula $m = \log \left(\dfrac{I}{I_r} \right)$, where m is the

magnitude on the Richter scale, I is the intensity of the earthquake, and I_r is the reference intensity of a very small earthquake. An earthquake located in City P was determined to have an intensity of $9\ 653\ 55 I_r$.

36. What was the magnitude of the earthquake in City P, to the nearest tenth?

 Copyright Protected

37. An earthquake in City Q had a magnitude of 3.4. How much more intense was the earthquake in City P compared with the earthquake in City Q, to the nearest whole number?

Use the following information to answer the next two questions.

Heather bought a pet lizard. When she purchased her lizard, it was 4 weeks old and measured 10.4 cm in length. Every 2 weeks, she measured her lizard's length and collected the following data:

Age of Lizard (weeks)	Length (cm)
4	10.1
6	13.2
8	14.8
10	15.3
12	16.6
14	17.4
16	18.6
18	19.4
20	19.7
22	20.4

38. Determine the natural logarithmic regression function that gives the length of her lizard, $L(t)$, as a function of its age, t, in weeks. Round the values of a and b in the function to the nearest hundredth.

39. What should the length of the lizard be after 35 weeks? Round your answer to the nearest tenth of a centimetre.

40. How many weeks did it take the lizard to grow more than 16.0 cm in length? Round your answer to the nearest tenth of a week.

Copyright Protected

POLYNOMIAL FUNCTIONS

When you are finished this unit, you will be able to...

- Identify polynomial functions
- Identify the leading coefficient, degree, and constant term of a polynomial function
- Recognize the connection between the key values of a polynomial function of degree ≤ 3 and the characteristics of the corresponding graphs
- Sketch the graph of a constant, linear, quadratic, or cubic function given the equation
- Use regression functions to draw polynomial graphs and solve problems
- Use polynomial functions and their characteristics to solve problems

PREREQUISITE SKILLS AND KNOWLEDGE

Prior to starting this unit, you should be able to...

- Add, subtract, multiply, and divide polynomials
- Factor polynomials (common factor, difference of squares, trinomial factoring, grouping)
- Identify the roots of a polynomial equation
- Understand the relationship between the roots of an equation and the zeros of a graph of the related function
- Use the features of a graphing calculator to view and determine the characteristics of a graph

Lesson 1 POLYNOMIAL FUNCTIONS

NOTES

The form of the polynomial function shown here is called *standard* or *general form.*

POLYNOMIAL FUNCTIONS

A **polynomial function** is a function that can be written in the form $f(x) = a_n x^n + a_{n-1} x^{n-1} + a_{n-2} x^{n-2} + ... + a_2 x^2 + a_1 x + a_0$, where $a_0, a_1, a_2, ... a_n$ are real numbers and are called coefficients, and n is a whole number (that is, 0, 1, 2, 3, …).

The value of n, the largest exponent of the variable x, is called the degree of the polynomial function. The variable a_n, the coefficient of the highest degree term, is called the leading coefficient. The variable a_0 is the constant term, which is the y-intercept for the graph of the function.

Class Exercise 1

Determine if each of the following functions is a polynomial function. If the function is not a polynomial function, explain why.

a) $y = 3x^2 - \sqrt{2}x + 6$

b) $f(x) = 32$

c) $y = x^4 - 7x^{\frac{1}{2}} - 4$

d) $f(x) = 7x^2 - 6x^5 + \pi$

e) $y = 2x^6 - 1.4x^3 - 4x^{-2}$

f) $y = -x^7 - 5x^4 + \dfrac{2}{x}$

g) $f(x) = (3x - 1)(x + 2)$

h) $g(x) = \dfrac{1}{2}x^3 - 4.\dot{7}x^2 + \dfrac{x}{2}$

i) $y = 23x^4 - 3\sqrt{x} - 2x^3$

j) $y = 4x^5 - 3x^m + 6$

k) $h = 65t^4 - 3t^5 - 7t$

l) $y = 4^x$

Example

Determine the leading coefficient, degree, and constant term of the
function $f(x) = 5x^3 - 2x^2 + 3x - 1$.

Solution

The leading coefficient is 5.
The degree is 3.
The constant term is -1; therefore, the graph of this function has
a y-intercept of -1.

The terms in polynomial
functions are usually
written in order
from highest degree to
lowest degree.

Class Exercise 2

Determine the leading coefficient, degree, and y-intercept for the graph of
the function $f(x) = (5x+1)(x^2-1)$.

Class Exercise 3

Determine the leading coefficient, degree, and constant term for the graph
of the function $f(x) = (3x-2)(x^2-1) - 2(5x-6) + 1$.

NOTES

USING FUNCTION NOTATION

One of the advantages of function notation ($f(x) =$) is that it can be used as a directive to solve for the y-value for any particular value of x. The x- and y-values form an ordered pair of numbers that represent a point on the graph of the function.

Example

If $f(x) = x^3 - 3x - 1$, determine the value of $f(2)$ and a point on the graph of $y = f(x)$.

Solution

Determining the value of $f(2)$ means to find the value of y when $x = 2$.
Substitute 2 for x.
$$f(2) = 2^3 - 3(2) + 1$$
$$f(2) = 8 - 6 + 1$$
$$f(2) = 3$$
A point on the graph of $y = f(x)$ is represented by (2, 3).

Example

Given the function $g(x) = 6x - 4$, determine the value of x when $g(x) = 8$.

Solution

Determine the input, x, if the output is 8.

Substitute 8 for $g(x)$, and solve for x.
$$g(x) = 6x - 4$$
$$8 = 6x - 4$$
$$12 = 6x$$
$$x = 2$$

Class Exercise 4

Given the function $f(x) = 3x + 2$, determine the value of $f(-1)$, and state the corresponding coordinate point on the graph of $f(x) = 3x + 2$.

Copyright Protected

Class Exercise 5

Given the function $g(x) = x^2 + 7x + 6$, determine the values of x when $g(x) = -6$.

Class Exercise 6

If $f(x) = 2x^3 + kx^2 + 2x - 4$ and $f(-1) = 8$, determine the value of k.

PRACTICE EXERCISES

Determine if each of the following functions is a polynomial function. If a function is not a polynomial function, explain why it does not qualify. If the function is a polynomial function, give the following information:

a) The degree of the polynomial

b) The value of the leading coefficient when written in standard form

c) The value of the y-intercept of the graph of the function

1. $f(x) = \sqrt{3}x^3 - 2x^2 + 4x - 1$

2. $f(x) = 5x^3 - 2x^2 + \sqrt{3x} - 4$

3. $f(x) = \dfrac{3x^2 - 3x + 12}{6}$

4. $f(x) = 4$

5. $g(x) = (3x-2)(x-1) + (x-2)^2 - 3$

6. Given $f(x) = 2x^3 - 4x^2 - 6x + 8,$ determine the value of $f(-1)$ and a point on the graph of $y = f(x)$.

7. A linear function is given by $f(x) = -2(x+3) + 5$. What is the value of $f(-6)$?

8. For the linear function $f(x) = -\dfrac{3}{2}x + 7$, what is the value of $f\left(-\dfrac{3}{2}\right)$? Round your answer to the nearest hundredth.

9. For the linear function $f(x) = -20x + 5$, what is the sum of $f(-2)$ and $f(-5)$?

10. For the function $g(x) = -2x^2 - 3x + 15$, what is the value of $g(-2)$?

11. If $f(x) = x^2 - 2x + 5$, what is the value of $f(-2)$?

12. If $f(x) = x^2 - 13x - 20$, what is the largest value of x that satisfies the equation $f(x) = 10$?

Copyright Protected

13. Given that $g(x) = 13$ for the function $g(x) = 10 + \dfrac{3}{5}x$, what is the value of x?

14. For the function $f(x) = 3x^2 + kx^3 + 5x + m,$ determine the values of k and m if the leading coefficient is 4 when the function is written with decreasing powers and the y-intercept of the graph is -7.

Lesson 2 SKETCHING THE GRAPHS OF POLYNOMIAL FUNCTIONS FROM FACTORED FORM

NOTES

In this lesson, you will consider sketching the graphs of polynomial functions when they are written in factored form or can easily be changed to factored form.

FACTORED FORM OF A POLYNOMIAL FUNCTION

A polynomial function can be written in the form
$$f(x) = a(x - r_1)(x - r_2)(x - r_3)...(x - r_n),$$
where $r_1, r_2, r_3,...r_n$ are complex numbers.

REAL ZEROS, X-INTERCEPTS, AND ROOTS

When a polynomial function is written in the form
$$f(x) = a(x - r)_1(x - r_2)(x - r_3)...(x - r_n) \text{ and } r_1, r_2, r_3,...r_n \text{ are real}$$
numbers, then $r_1, r_2, r_3, ... r_n$ are known as the real zeros of the polynomial function. They are also the x-intercepts of the graph of the function and the real roots of the equation $a(x - r_1)(x - r_2)(x - r_3)...(x - r_n) = 0$.

Consider the graphs of a polynomial function as the degree increases, beginning with degree 0 (the constant function). The sketches in this lesson will focus on the general shape of a graph and the x- and y-intercepts. This is often the only information required to understand the main properties of a graph. The sketches can usually be drawn freehand more quickly than by using a graphing calculator. Adjusting the window settings to appropriate values often slows down the calculator method. However, when a more exact graph is required, using a calculator or computer is the best approach.

THE CONSTANT FUNCTION $f(x) = c$

The graph of the constant function $f(x) = c$ is a horizontal line. The value of c is the y-intercept.

Example

Sketch the graph of $f(x) = -3$.

Solution

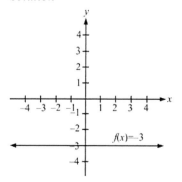

Copyright Protected

THE LINEAR FUNCTION $f(x) = ax + b$

If $a \neq 0$ in the linear function $f(x) = ax + b$, the graph is an oblique (slanted) line with a slope equal to a and a y-intercept equal to b.

NOTES

If $a = 0$, the function is a constant function.

Example

Graph the line defined by the function $f(x) = \dfrac{2}{3}x - 4$.

Solution

Step 1
Determine the slope and the y-intercept of the line.

Using the information in the given equation, the slope of the line is $a = \dfrac{2}{3}$, and the y-intercept is $b = -4$.

Step 2
Plot the y-intercept, $b = -4$.

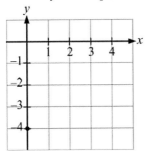

Step 3
Use the slope to locate a second point on the line.

The slope of the line is $m = \dfrac{2}{3}$. Therefore, from the y-intercept, a rise of 2 and a run of 3 in the positive direction will locate another point on the line at $(3, -2)$.

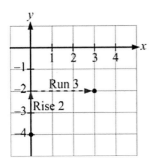

NOTES

Step 4

Draw a line that passes through both points. Add arrows to each end of the line to show that it continues infinitely in both directions.

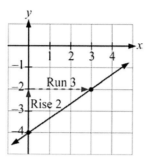

Class Exercise 1

Graph the line defined by the function $f(x) = -\dfrac{2}{5}x - 1$.

THE QUADRATIC FUNCTION $f(x) = ax^2 + bx + c$

The factored form of a quadratic function can be used to sketch the graph of a quadratic function. The graph is a parabola opening upward or downward. If $a > 0$, then the parabola opens upward, and if $a < 0$, the parabola opens downward. The c-value is the y-intercept, and the zeros of the function are the x-intercepts.

Example

Sketch the graph of $f(x) = x^2 + 2x - 15$.

Solution

When written in factored form, this function is $f(x) = (x-3)(x+5)$.

The useful information that can be obtained from this form is that the x-intercepts are 3 and –5. The x-intercepts are the solutions to $0 = (x-3)(x+5)$. You now have the following information:

- The x-intercepts are 3 and –5.
- The parabola opens upward because $a > 0$.
- The y-intercept is –15 because it is the constant term and the result when $x = 0$.

306 Copyright Protected

Using the two *x*-intercepts and the *y*-intercept to sketch the graph, the result is as shown:

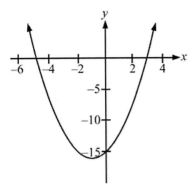

Class Exercise 2

Use the factored form to sketch the graph of $y = 2x^2 - 7x - 4$.

THE CUBIC FUNCTION $f(x) = ax^3 + bx^2 + cx + d$

It is an easy task to sketch the graph of a cubic function if the function is in factored form or if it can easily be put in factored form. The graph forms a smooth curve. If $a > 0$, the extreme ends of the graph are in quadrants III and I, and if $a < 0$, then the extreme ends of the graph are in quadrants IV and II. The *c*-value is the *y*-intercept, and the zeros of the function are the *x*-intercepts.

Example

Sketch the graph of $f(x) = x^3 + x^2 - 9x - 9$.

Solution

This function can be factored by grouping as follows:

$f(x) = x^3 + x^2 - 9x - 9$

$f(x) = x^2(x+1) - 9(x+1)$

$f(x) = (x^2 - 9)(x+1)$

$f(x) = (x+3)(x-3)(x+1)$

From the original form and the factored form, the following information about the intercepts of the graph can be obtained:

- The x-intercepts are -3, 3, and -1 (the solutions to $0 = x^3 + x^2 - 9x - 9$).
- The y-intercept is -9 (the constant term).
- The graph begins in quadrant III and ends in quadrant I because $a > 0$.

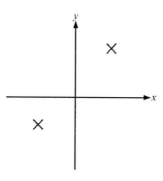

The significant points and information of the function are summarized in the following table:

x	$-\infty$	-3	-1	0	3	$+\infty$
y	$-\infty$	0	0	-9	0	$+\infty$

Place the significant points on the graph, and draw a smooth curve through these points.

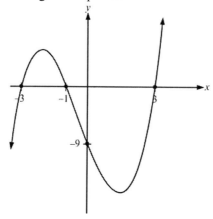

Copyright Protected

The general shape of the graph can be verified by using a graphing calculator.

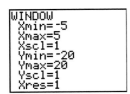 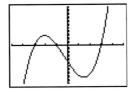

Class Exercise 3

Sketch the graph of $f(x) = (x-2)(x+3)^2$ without using a calculator, and then verify your graph by using a calculator.

Class Exercise 4

Sketch the graph of $y = -2(x+1)^3$ without using a calculator, and then verify your graph by using a calculator.

PRACTICE EXERCISES

Sketch the graphs of each of the following functions without using a calculator. Show the general shape of each graph and the intercepts.

1. $y = 2x + 6$

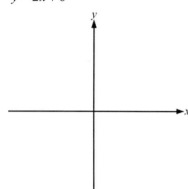

2. $y = 4$

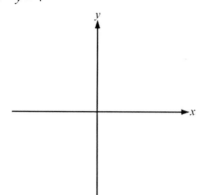

3. $f(x) = -x^2 - 7x$

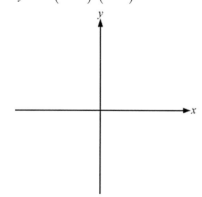

4. $y = (x-1)^2(x+3)$

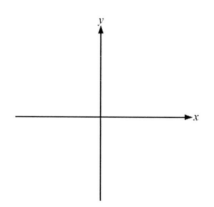

5. $y = -2(x+2)^2(x-1)$

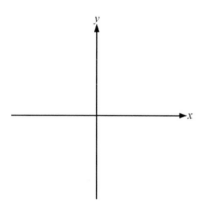

6. $y = (3x-2)(x+4)$

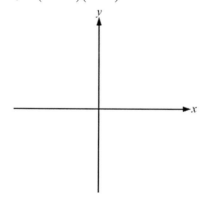

Copyright Protected

7. $f(x) = (x+1)^3$

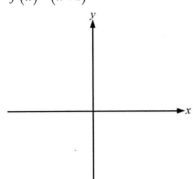

8. $y = x^3 + 5x^2 - x - 5$

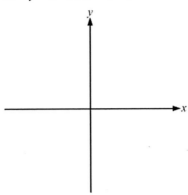

Lesson 3 SOLVING PROBLEMS WITH POLYNOMIAL FUNCTIONS

NOTES

Many problems that occur daily can be modelled using polynomial functions. The graphs of these functions can be interpreted to answer questions about these situations.

Example

To host a concert, it costs the owners of an amphitheatre $200 000.00. Currently, ticket prices are $40.00. The owners plan to increase the price of each ticket in order to maximize the profits. The following graph represents the quadratic relation between the gross revenue as the ticket price increases.

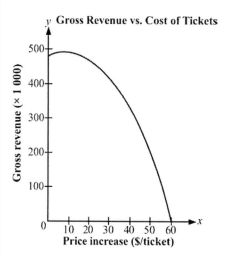

What is the maximum profit that can be generated from the concert?

Solution
Find the maximum on the graph.

The maximum gross revenue will be $500 000; therefore, the maximum profit is 500 000 – 200 000 = 300 000.

Therefore, the maximum profit that can be generated from the concert is $300 000.

Class Exercise 1

A ball is thrown off a cliff that is 25 m high, and its flight can be represented by the parabola shown in the following graph.

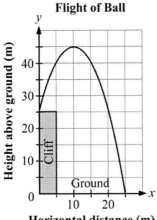

Flight of Ball

a) When the ball strikes the ground, how far from the base of the cliff will it be located?

b) What is the total vertical distance travelled by the ball during its flight?

If the graph of a polynomial function is not given, a TI-83 or similar calculator can be used to generate the graph. The problems related to the polynomial function can then be solved using the calculator functions.

Example

A student throws a ball in the air from the balcony of an apartment building and watches it fall to the ground. The height, y, in metres, of the ball in relation to the ground x seconds after being thrown is given by the equation $y = -4.9x^2 + 24.5x + 6$.

a) What is the maximum height, to the nearest tenth, that the ball reaches before falling to the ground?

Solution

The maximum height that the ball reaches before falling to the ground corresponds with to the y-coordinate of the vertex (the highest point on the parabola). The vertex can be determined graphically using the Maximum feature on the graphing calculator.

Begin by graphing the equation $y = -4.9x^2 + 24.5x + 6$, using a window setting such as x:[0,7,1] y:[0,50,5].

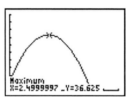

The coordinates of the vertex are (2.5, 36.625). To the nearest tenth, the maximum height that the ball reaches is 36.6 m.

b) To the nearest tenth of a second, how long is the ball more than 25 m above the ground?

Solution

To determine the number of seconds that the ball is more than 25 m above the ground, use a TI-83 or similar calculator.

Using an appropriate window setting, such as x:[0,7,1] y:[0,50,5], graph $y = -Y_1 = 4.9x^2 + 24.5x + 6$ and $Y_2 = 25$.

Next, use the Intersection feature to find the x-coordinate of each point at which the two graphs intersect.

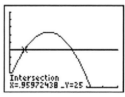 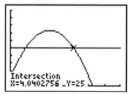

The difference of these two values is the number of seconds that the ball is more than 25 m above the ground. The x-coordinates of the two intersection points are about 4.04 and 0.96.
4.04 – 0.96 = 3.08
To the nearest tenth, the ball is more than 25 m above the ground for 3.1 s.

Copyright Protected

NOTES

Class Exercise 2

The field-goal kicker for the Edmonton Eskimos attempts a 50 yd field goal. If the kicker succeeds, the Eskimos win the football game. A diagram portraying the flight of the ball is shown.

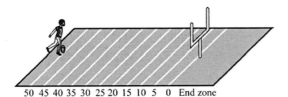

50 45 40 35 30 25 20 15 10 5 0 End zone

The quadratic function representing the parabolic flight of the ball is given by $h(x) = -0.019x^2 + 1.026x + 0.049$, where $h(x)$ is the height of the ball, in yards, and x is the horizontal distance covered by the ball, in yards.

Use a TI-83 or similar calculator to answer the following questions.

a) What is the maximum height of the ball during its flight?

b) What is the total horizontal distance the ball travelled before it hit the ground?

c) If the height of the crossbar of the uprights is exactly 3 yd above the ground at the goal line (the 0 yd line), does the kicker make the field goal and win the game?

Sometimes, you can translate the words of a real-world problem into a function. When modelling a problem using a polynomial function, follow these general steps:
1. Identify the independent and dependent variables.
2. Draw a diagram, if necessary.
3. Determine a function that models the problem.

Example

Jessica recently got married and has to decide on a frame for her favourite wedding picture. The wedding picture is 40 cm by 50 cm.

a) If a picture frame has a border of uniform width, determine a function that models the total area of the picture and picture frame.

Solution

Step 1
Determine the independent and dependent variables.

The independent variable, x, is the width of the border of the frame, and the dependent variable, $A(x)$, is the total area of the picture and border.

Step 2
Draw a diagram.

Let x equal the width of the picture frame.

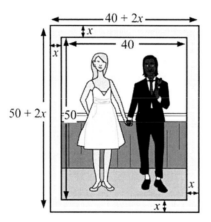

Step 3
Determine a function that models the total area.
total area = length × width
$$A(x) = (40 + 2x)(50 + 2x)$$

Therefore, the function that models the total area of the picture and picture frame is $A(x) = (40 + 2x)(50 + 2x)$, where x is the width of the picture frame.

b) Jessica has a choice of three frames that have uniform borders of 2.5 cm, 5 cm, and 7.5 cm. Which picture frame should Jessica get if she wants the total area to be between 3 500 cm^2 and 4 000 cm^2?

Solution

Determine the total area for each picture frame graphically using a TI-83 or similar calculator.

Press $\boxed{Y=}$, and input the function as $Y_1 = (40 + 2X)(50 + 2X)$. Use the window settings of x: [0, 10, 1] and y: [0, 5000, 500], and press $\boxed{GRAPH}$ to obtain this window.

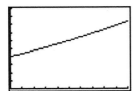

Find the total area when the frame is 1 cm wide.

Press $\boxed{2nd}$ $\boxed{TRACE}$, and select 1:value. Input 2.5, and press $\boxed{ENTER}$ to obtain this window.

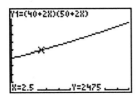

Therefore, the total area when the picture frame is 2.5 cm wide is 2 475 cm^2.

Repeat this process for the widths of 5 cm and 7.5 cm.

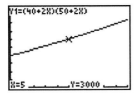 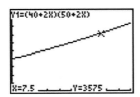

The total area when the picture frame is 5 cm wide is 3 000 cm^2, and the total area when the picture frame is 7.5 cm wide is 3 575 cm^2.

Therefore, Jessica should get the picture frame that is 7.5 cm wide.

Negative x- and y-values are negligible since length, width, and area are only positive values.

Class Exercise 3

Angela is constructing a storage bin in the shape of a rectangular prism. The length of the storage bin is 1 m more than the width. The height of the bin is 1 m less than twice the width of the bin.

a) Determine a function that models the volume as a function of the width of the storage bin.

b) If the volume of the bin is 7.5 m^3, determine the dimensions of the storage bin.

If a data set models a linear, quadratic, or cubic function, a regression can be performed to find the equation of the line or curve of best fit that best models the data. On a TI-83 or similar calculator, a **linear regression** produces a line that is defined by the equation $y = ax + b$. A **quadratic regression** produces a parabolic curve that is defined by the equation $y = ax^2 + bx + c$. A **cubic regression** produces a curve that is defined by the equation $y = ax^3 + bx^2 + cx + d$.

Example

A table of values is given.

x	y
0	23
2	32
4	20
6	13
8	19
10	26
12	38

Determine the cubic regression function that best approximates the given data.

Solution

Step 1
Enter the data values into the calculator.

Start by clearing any lists already present.
Press $\boxed{\text{2nd}}$ $\boxed{+}$, select 4:ClrAllLists, and press $\boxed{\text{ENTER}}$.
Press $\boxed{\text{STAT}}$, and select 1:Edit…. Enter the x-values into list L_1 and the y-values into list L_2.

L1	L2	L3	1
0	23	------	
2	32		
4	20		
6	13		
8	19		
10	26		
12	38		

L1(1)=0

Copyright Protected

Step 2
Perform the cubic regression.

Press $\boxed{\text{STAT}}$ $\boxed{\triangleright}$ to highlight CALC. Select 6:CubicReg, and press $\boxed{\text{ENTER}}$ to obtain the following window.

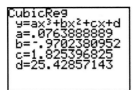

Step 3
Determine the cubic regression function.
Substitute the values of a, b, c, and d into the cubic function $y = ax^3 + bx^2 + cx + d$.

$$y = ax^3 + bx^2 + cx + d$$
$$y \approx 0.08x^3 - 0.97x^2 + 1.83x + 25.43$$

The cubic regression function that best approximates the given data is $y = 0.08x^3 - 0.97x^2 + 1.83x + 25.43$.

Example

Teresa is preparing to open a hot-dog stand. To determine how much people are willing to pay for a hot dog, Teresa surveyed a number of potential customers. The results of the survey are shown in the given table.

Cost of Hot Dog ($)	Resulting Revenue ($)
1.00	160
2.00	216
3.00	177
4.00	12

Teresa believes that the resulting revenue can be modelled by a quadratic equation.

Given the results of the survey, what should Teresa charge for a hot dog to acquire the maximum revenue?

Solution

Step 1
Determine the equation that defines the given data.

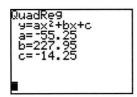

A possible equation that defines the data is
$R = -55.25c^2 + 227.95c - 14.25$, where R is the total revenue, in dollars, and c is the cost of one hot dog, in dollars.

Step 2
Graph the function, and determine the maximum point of the parabola in order to solve the given problem.

Enter the resulting equation in Y_1, and use the Maximum feature to determine the maximum point on the graph.

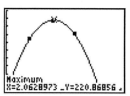

The maximum point is at approximately (2.06, 220.87).

Teresa should achieve a maximum revenue of \$220.87 if the hot dogs are sold for \$2.06 each.

Class Exercise 4

The given table shows the height of a ball, in metres, with respect to time, in seconds, after a football player kicked it.

Time (s)	Height (m)
0	0.25
1	15.85
2	21.15
3	16.62
4	2.35

The height of the ball can be modelled by a quadratic equation.

Determine the height of the ball at 2.7 s, to the nearest hundredth of a metre.

PRACTICE EXERCISES

Use the following information to answer the next question.

The trajectory of a baseball is represented by the given graph.

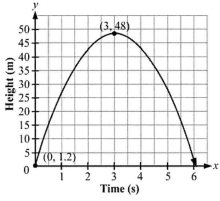

1. a) What is the maximum height of the baseball's trajectory?

b) What was the initial height of the baseball when it was hit?

c) How long does the baseball remain in the air?

Use the following information to answer the next question.

Pauline throws a ball in the air from the balcony of an apartment building and watches it fall to the ground. The height, y, in metres, of the ball in relation to the ground x seconds after being thrown is given by the equation $y = -4.9x^2 + 24.5x + 6$.

2. What is the maximum height, to the nearest tenth, that the ball reaches before falling to the ground?

Use the following information to answer the next question.

A football kicked during a football game follows a parabolic path. This path can be modelled by graphing the equation $h = -2t^2 + 11t - 3$, $t \geq 1$, where t is the number of seconds that have elapsed since the football was kicked and h is the height of the football above the ground in yards.

3. To the nearest tenth of a second, how long did it take the football to reach a height of 12 yd above the ground after it was kicked?

Use the following information to answer the next question.

Irene is constructing a storage box with no lid. She has a 3.2 m by 3.2 m sheet of cardboard, and she will form the box by cutting and removing a square of equal size from each corner. She will then fold up the corners and tape them together to form the box.

4. a) If x represents the side length of the squares cut out from each corner, determine a function, $V(x)$, that models the volume of the box in terms of x.

 Copyright Protected

b) If $0 < x < 1.6$, determine the dimensions, rounded to the nearest hundredth, that will produce a box with a maximum volume.

Use the following information to answer the next question.

The given scatter plot compares the incidence of cavities per 100 children and the fluoride content of water in parts per million (ppm) in a particular area.

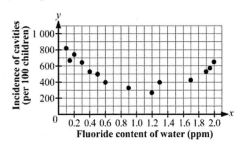

5. Explain whether the **most appropriate** regression equation for the given data is linear, quadratic, sinusoidal, or exponential.

Use the following information to answer the next question.

The owner of a 300-seat theatre sells tickets for $20 each. He believes that for every dollar he increases the price of a ticket, he will lose 10 customers. He charts his resulting revenue for each $1 increase in ticket price:

Increase in Price ($)	Revenue ($)
0	6 000
1	6 090
2	6 160
3	6 210
4	6 240
5	6 250
6	6 240

The owner believes that the data can be modelled by an equation in the form $y = ax^2 + bx + c$.

6. a) What is the ticket price at which the owner should earn the maximum revenue?

   b) If the owner's revenue after raising the ticket price is $5 760, what is the most likely price per ticket?

   c) What is the **greatest** increase in price of each ticket that would result in a total revenue of $6 120?

Use the following information to answer the next question.

A motion detector is used to identify the position of motorcycle during a stunt demonstration.

The motion detector measures the distance, in metres, separating the motorcycle from the motion detector's sensor.

A mechanic records the position of the motorcycle every four seconds. The results from the first 20 s of the demonstration are given.

Time (s)	Distance (m)
0	200.5
4	295.7
8	224.6
12	110.5
16	76.5
20	246.1

After performing a regression on the data, the mechanic found that it could be modelled by a function of the form $D(t) = at^3 + bt^2 + ct + d$, where the values of a, b, c, and d are rounded to the nearest thousandth.

7. After 24 s, what distance should the mechanic expect that the distance separating the motorcycle from the sensor will be, rounded to the nearest metre?

REVIEW SUMMARY

- The general form of a polynomial function is written as

  $f(x) = a_n x^n + a_{n-1} x^{n-1} + a_{n-2} x^{n-2} + \ldots + a_2 x^2 + a_1 x + a_0$, where a_0, a_1, a_2, $\ldots a_n$ are the coefficients,

  a_n is the leading coefficient, n is the degree of the function, and a_0 is the y-intercept of the graph of the function. The terms are usually written in order from highest to lowest degree.

- Polynomial functions must have real-number coefficients, and the value of n must be a positive whole number.

- The factored form of a function is $f(x) = a(x - r_1)(x - r_2)(x - r_3)\ldots(x - r_n)$, where r_1, r_2, r_3, $\ldots r_n$ are real numbers and represent the zeros of the function and roots of the equation

  $0 = a(x - r_1)(x - r_2)(x - r_3)\ldots(x - r_n)$.

- The repeated zeros of the corresponding function are referred to in terms of their multiplicity. The degree of a polynomial function is equal to the sum of the multiplicities of its zeros.

- If the multiplicity of a zero is 1, the graph of the function passes straight through the x-axis. If the multiplicity of a zero is an odd number greater than 1, the graph of the function is tangent to and crosses the x-axis in the form of an S curve. If the multiplicity of a zero is even, the graph is tangent to, or touches, the x-axis with a downward curve or an upward curve.

- If the degree of a function is odd and the leading coefficient is positive, the extreme ends of the graph are in quadrants I and III. If the degree of a function is odd and the leading coefficient is negative, the extreme ends of the graph are in quadrants II and IV.

- If the degree of a function is even and the leading coefficient is positive, the extreme ends of the graph are in quadrants I and II. If the degree of a function is even and the leading coefficient is negative, the extreme ends of the graph are in quadrants III and IV.

- The zeros, multiplicities of the zeros, degree, leading coefficient, and y-intercept can all be used to help sketch the graph of a polynomial function written in factored form.

- Many problems that occur daily can be modelled using polynomial functions. The problems related to the polynomial function can be solved graphically.

PRACTICE TEST

Explain why each of the following functions is not a polynomial function.

1. $f(x) = 2x^4 - \dfrac{3}{x^2} + 4x - 1$

2. $f(x) = 5x^3 - 2x^2 + \sqrt{3x} - 4$

3. $f(x) = x^2 - \sqrt{3}x^3 + x^{-4} + 5x^{\frac{5}{4}}$

4. Identify the leading coefficient, degree, and constant term of the polynomial $f(x) = \dfrac{24x - 12x^3 + 15x^2 + 8}{3}$.

5. For the function $g(x) = 24x - 3$, what is the value of $g\left(\dfrac{1}{3}\right)$?

6. For the function $f(x) = 8x^2 - 10x + 5$, what is the value of $f\left(-\dfrac{1}{2}\right)$?

7. For the function $g(x) = 2x^2 - 5x - 14$, what x-values result in an output value of $g(x) = -2$?

8. Given the linear function $f(x) = -2(x+3)+5$, what is the input value of x if $f(x) = 21$?

9. Given the linear function $f(x) = \dfrac{ax}{4} + \dfrac{11}{4}$, what is the value of a if $f(1) = 2$?

10. For the function $f(x) = 5x^2 - 6x + 25$, what is the sum of $f(-4)$ and $f(1)$?

Sketch the graphs of each of the following functions without using a calculator. Show the general shape of each graph and the intercepts.

11. $f(x) = -x + 1$

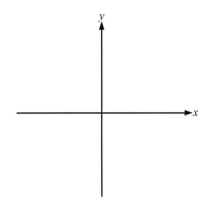

12. $f(x) = x^2 - x - 12$

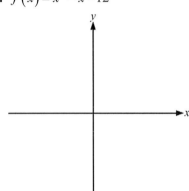

13. $y = (x-2)^2(x+1)$

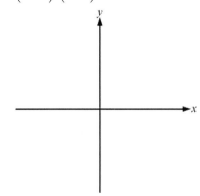

Copyright Protected

14. $y = x^3 + 2x^2 - 4x - 8$

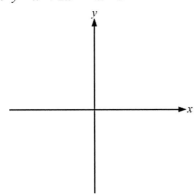

Use the following information to answer the next question.

An efficiency consultant records the daily production costs at an industrial rubber manufacturing plant. The consultant records the daily cost of production, in dollars, on several days when a different number of units were produced.

The results are shown in the given scatter plot.

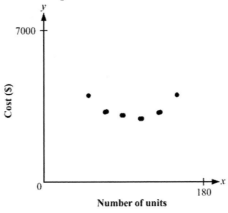

15. If *C* is the daily cost of production and *p* is the number of units produced on a given day, which of the following quadratic equations could represent a reasonable model for production costs?

A. $C = 0.55p^2 - 110p$

B. $C = -0.55p^2 - 110p$

C. $C = 0.55p^2 - 110p + 9000$

D. $C = -0.55p^2 - 110p + 9000$

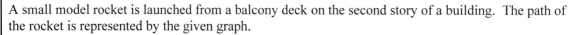

Use the following information to answer the next question.

A small model rocket is launched from a balcony deck on the second story of a building. The path of the rocket is represented by the given graph.

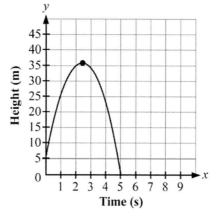

16. Once it is launched, how much time does the rocket take to strike the ground?

Use the following information to answer the next question.

A city's population can fluctuate. A small Ontario city that has a declining population is expecting the population to begin increasing in the near future because of the introduction of several industrial development initiatives. The city planners predict that the city's population can be modelled by the quadratic function $P = 150t^2 - 1\,200t + 14\,900$, $t \geq 0$, in which t represents the time in years since January 1, 2006, and P represents the population.

17. a) Using a graphing calculator, determine the year the city's population will be the lowest.

 Copyright Protected

b) Using a graphing calculator, determine the first year that the city's population will be more than 24 000.

Use the following information to answer the next question.

A scientist studying a new antibiotic drug carefully monitors the weight of a rat over a number of weeks.

The weight of the rat during the course of the six-week study can be modelled by the equation $y = 0.38x^3 - 3.81x^2 + 10.92x + 450.02$, where y is the weight of the rat, in grams, and $0 \leq x \leq 7$ is the number of weeks since the study began.

18. a) What characteristics of the weight function should be analyzed in order to determine the weight of the rat when the study began?

b) How long did it take for the rat's weight to first reach 458 g?

c) After 7 weeks, what should the researcher expect the rat's weight to be, to the nearest hundredth gram?

Use the following information to answer the next question.

A trader recorded the share value in Canadian dollars for the first seven days of September, as shown in the given table.

Date	Unit Stock Value (CAD)
1	79
2	64
3	54
4	49
5	51
6	55
7	67
8	79

The trader believes that the unit value of the stock approximated a quadratic pattern during that week in September.

19. a) Which feature of the given data suggests to the trader that the values of the stock approximate a quadratic pattern?

b) If the unit stock value is modelled using an equation of the form $V = at^2 + bt + c$, where V is the value of the stock in Canadian dollars and t is the date of the month, what is the value of c, to the nearest tenth?

Use the following information to answer the next question.

A model rocket is launched upward from a platform. The height of the rocket, h, in metres, with respect to time, t, in seconds, is recorded in the given table.

Time (s)	Height (m)
0	3
1	148
3	410
8	890
14	1140
20	1025
25	700

20. Assuming that the flight of the rocket can be modelled by a quadratic relationship, what is the total time that the rocket was in the air?

Use the following information to answer the next two questions.

Tom constructs a tent in the shape of a triangular prism. The width of the floor of the tent is represented by x. The height of the tent is 0.5 m more than the width of the floor. The length of the tent is double the width of the floor.

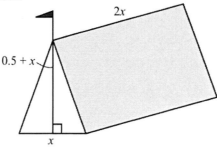

21. Determine a function, $V(x)$, that represents the volume of the tent as a function of the width, x, if the volume of a triangular prism is $\text{volume} = \dfrac{(\text{width})(\text{height})}{2} \times \text{length}$.

22. If the volume of the tent is 4.5 m³, determine the dimensions of the tent using technology.

SINUSOIDAL FUNCTIONS

When you are finished this unit, you will be able to...
• Recognize the characteristics of a sinusoidal curve
• Identify the characteristics of a sinusoidal curve given the equation or the graph of a sinusoidal function
• Recognize the connection between the key values of the sinusoidal regression function and the characteristics of the sinusoidal curve
• Use the sine regression to draw sine curves and solve problems
• Use the sine function and its characteristics to solve problems

PREREQUISITE SKILLS AND KNOWLEDGE

Prior to starting this unit, you should be able to...
• Sketch and interpret a graph given a table of values and/or an equation
• Change between degrees and radians on a calculator
• Use a graphing calculator to determine a regression equation
• Use the features of a graphing calculator to view and determine the characteristics of a graph

Lesson 1 GRAPHS OF SINUSOIDAL FUNCTIONS

NOTES

The graphs of **periodic functions** repeat the same y-value for some consistent increase in the domain value. For example, consider the graph of the given periodic function. The y-value of 3 at $x = -6$ occurs 7 units to the right at $x = 1$ and reoccurs 14 units to the right at $x = 8$.

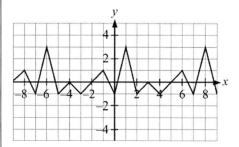

Some periodic or repetitive data can be modelled using sine or cosine functions. Any data that can be modelled using one of these functions is called a **sinusoidal function.** The graph of $y = \sin x$ is an example of a sinusoidal graph.

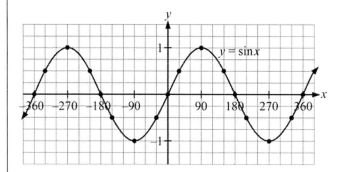

The **period** is the length of the shortest repeating section of a periodic function. The graph of $y = \sin x$ shows that the y-value of the function is the same every 360°. Therefore, the function $y = \sin x$ has a period of 360°.

The **horizontal midline axis** is the equation of the horizontal line that is located halfway between the maximum and minimum values. A formula used to find the horizontal midline axis is $y = \dfrac{\text{maximum} + \text{minimum}}{2}$.

Therefore, the horizontal midline axis for $y = \sin x$ is $y = \dfrac{1 + (-1)}{2} = 0$, or simply the x-axis.

The **maximum** value is the y-coordinate of the highest point on a sinusoidal graph.
The **minimum** value is the y-coordinate of the lowest point of a sinusoidal graph.

The horizontal midline axis can also be referred to as the median of the graph.

Copyright Protected

The **amplitude** is the vertical distance from the horizontal midline axis of graph to the minimum or maximum value of the function. A formula used to find the amplitude is $\text{amplitude} = \dfrac{\text{maximum} - \text{minimum}}{2}$. Therefore, the graph of $y = \sin x$ has an amplitude of $\dfrac{1 - (-1)}{2} = 1$.

The characteristics of the graphs of $y = \sin x$ and $y = \cos x$ are similar. The graph of $y = \cos x$ can be obtained by translating the graph of $y = \sin x$ to the left $\dfrac{\pi}{2}$ radians, or $90°$.

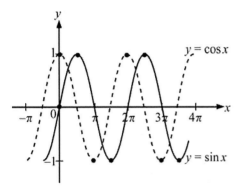

The graphs of $y = \sin x$ and $y = \cos x$ also have the following similarities:

• They are both periodic functions.
• They both have the domain $x \in \mathbb{R}$.
• They both have an amplitude of 1.
• They both have a period of 2π.
• They both have a range of $-1 \le x \le 1$.
• If examined within the domain $0 \le x \le 2\pi$, the main difference between the graphs of $y = \sin x$ and $y = \cos x$ is that the graph of $y = \sin x$ starts at 0 and increases, and the graph of $y = \cos x$ starts at 1 and decreases.

NOTES

Example

A sinusoidal graph is given.

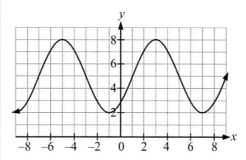

Determine the following characteristics of the graph:

- Period
- Horizontal midline axis
- Amplitude

Solution

Step 1

Determine the period of the graph.

A maximum occurs at $(-5, 8)$ and again at $(3, 8)$. These points are $3 - (-5) = 8$ units apart. Therefore, the period of the graph is 8 units.

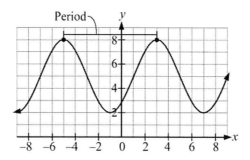

Step 2

Determine the horizontal midline axis.

The horizontal midline axis is $y = \dfrac{8+2}{2} = 5$.

The horizontal midline axis is

$$y = \frac{\text{maximum} + \text{minimum}}{2}.$$

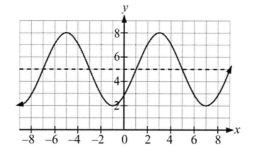

Step 3
Determine the amplitude.

The maximum value is 8, and the minimum value is 2. Therefore, the amplitude is $\frac{8-2}{2} = 3$ units.

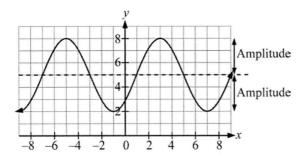

Class Exercise 1

State the period, horizontal midline axis, and amplitude of the given sinusoidal graph.

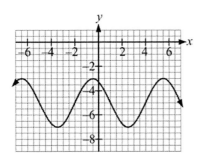

A sinusoidal function can be expressed in the form $y = a\sin(bx + c) + d$, where a, b, c, and d are real numbers and $a, b > 0$. The parameters of a, b, c, and d represent specific features on a sinusoidal graph.

Angles can be in measured in two different ways: degrees and **radians**. There are 360° in one complete revolution. In radians, one complete revolution is equal to 2π rad. The concept of a radian makes the transition to taking the sine or the cosine of a real number possible.

Often, when radian measures are used, the word *radians* is abbreviated as *rad*.

NOTES

APPLYING PARAMETER *a* IN $y = a\sin x$

To examine the effect of changing the value of parameter a, compare the primary function $y = \sin x$ with the graphs of $y = 3\sin x$ and $y = \frac{1}{2}\sin x$.

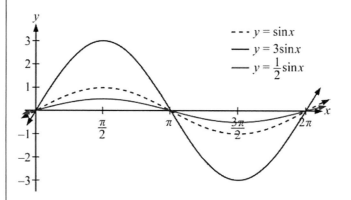

The range of $y = 3\sin x$ is $-3 \le y \le 3$, and the amplitude is 3. The range of $y = \frac{1}{2}\sin x$ is $-\frac{1}{2} \le y \le \frac{1}{2}$, and the amplitude is $\frac{1}{2}$. For both graphs, the domain is $x \in R$, the period is 360°, or 2π, and the horizontal midline axis is $y = 0$.

Therefore, parameter a creates a change in amplitude and range. The amplitude is $|a|$, and the range is $-|a| \le y \le |a|$. Parameter a has no effect on the on the domain, period, and horizontal midline axis.

The range of a sinusoidal function is equal to
$d - |a| \le y \le d + |a|$.

APPLYING PARAMETER *b* IN $y = \sin(bx)$

To examine the effect of changing the value of parameter b, compare the primary function $y = \sin x$ with the graph of $y = \sin(2x)$.

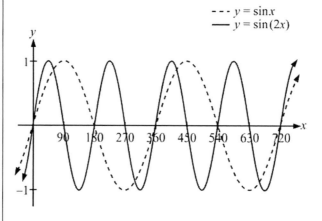

The period of $y = \sin(2x)$ is 180°. The domain is $x \in R$, the range is $-1 \le x \le 1$, the amplitude is 1, and the horizontal midline axis is $y = 0$.

Copyright Protected

Compare the primary function $y = \sin x$ with the graph of $y = \sin\left(\dfrac{1}{2}x\right)$.

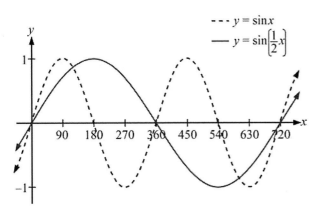

The period of $y = \sin\left(\dfrac{1}{2}x\right)$ is $720°$. The domain is $x \in R$, the range is $-1 \le x \le 1$, the amplitude is 1, and the horizontal midline axis is $y = 0$.

Therefore, parameter b creates a change in period. The period is $\dfrac{2\pi}{b}$, or $\dfrac{360}{b}$. Parameter b has no effect on the on the domain, range, amplitude, or horizontal midline axis.

APPLYING PARAMETER c IN $y = \sin(x + c)$

To examine the effect of changing the value of parameter c, compare the graph of $y = \sin x$ with the graph of $y = \sin(x + 45°)$.

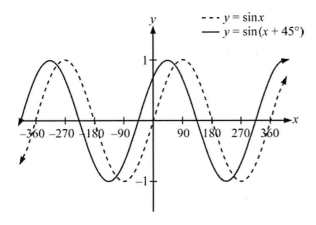

The graph of $y = \sin(x + 45°)$ is obtained from the graph of $y = \sin x$ by a horizontal translation of $45°$ left. The horizontal translation of a sinusoidal graph is called a **phase shift**. A phase shift occurs when $c \ne 0$. There is no change in the domain, range, location of the horizontal midline axis, amplitude, or period.

A horizontal translation involves taking the graph of a function and moving it left or right.

APPLYING PARAMETER d IN $y = \sin x + d$

To examine the effect of changing the value of parameter d, compare the graph of $y = \sin x$ with the graphs of $y = \sin x + 2$ and $y = \sin x - 3$.

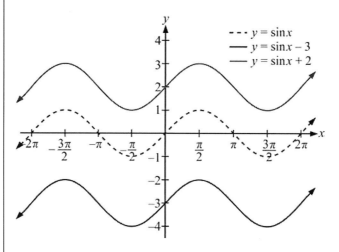

The range of $y = \sin x + 2$ is $1 \le y \le 3$, and the horizontal midline axis is $y = 2$. The range of $y = \sin x - 3$ is $-4 \le y \le -2$, and the horizontal midline axis is $y = -3$. For both graphs, the domain, amplitude, and period remain unchanged.

Therefore, parameter d affects the location of the horizontal midline axis and the range. The equation of the horizontal midline axis is $y = d$, and the range is $d - 1 \le y \le d + 1$. The domain, amplitude, and period remain unchanged.

Recall that the range of a sinusoidal function is equal to
$d - |a| \le y \le d + |a|$.

The graph of $y = a \sin(bx + c) + d$ can be summarized as follows:

• The amplitude is $|a|$.

• The period is $\dfrac{2\pi}{b}$, or $\dfrac{360°}{b}$.

If $c > 0$, then the graph of $y = a \sin(bx + c) + d$ shifts $\dfrac{c}{b}$ units to the right.

If $c < 0$, then the graph shifts $\dfrac{c}{b}$ units to the left.

• A phase shift occurs if $c \ne 0$.

• The horizontal midline axis is $y = d$.

• The maximum value is $d + |a|$. The minimum value is $d - |a|$.

Copyright Protected

Example

Determine a function in form $y = a\sin(bx) + d$, where x is in radians, that represents the given graph.

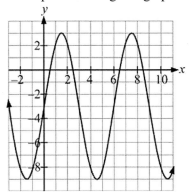

Solution

Step 1

Determine the value of a.

The graph has a maximum of 3 and minimum of –9, so the amplitude is $\dfrac{3 - (-9)}{2} = 6$. Therefore the value of a is 6.

Step 2

Determine the value of b.

A maximum occurs at (1.5, 3) and again at (7.5, 3). Therefore, the period is 7.5 – 1.5 = 6 units. Thus, the value of b is calculated as follows:

$$b = \frac{2\pi}{\text{period}}$$
$$b = \frac{2\pi}{6}$$
$$b = \frac{\pi}{3}$$

NOTES

The value of b is determined using the formula $b = \dfrac{2\pi}{\text{period}}$.

Leave the value of b as a fraction unless stated otherwise.

Step 3

Determine the value of d.

The horizontal midline axis is $y = \dfrac{3 + (-9)}{2} = -3$. Therefore, the value of d is –3.

NOTES

Step 4

Determine the function that represents the graph.

Substitute the values of a, b, and d into the function $y = a\sin(bx) + d$.

$$y = a\sin(bx) + d$$

$$y = 6\sin\left(\frac{\pi}{3}x\right) + (-3)$$

$$y = 6\sin\left(\frac{\pi}{3}x\right) - 3$$

The function that represents the graph is $y = 6\sin\left(\frac{\pi}{3}x\right) - 3$.

Class Exercise 2

State the period, amplitude, horizontal midline axis, and range of the graph of the function $y = 9\sin(3x + \pi) + 12$.

PRACTICE EXERCISES

For the following sinusoidal graphs, state the period, amplitude, horizontal midline axis, and range.

1.

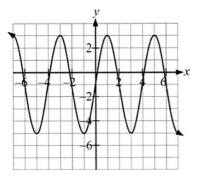

2.

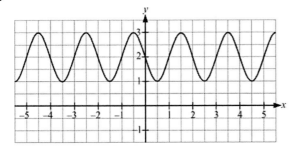

3.

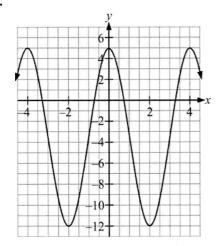

For the following functions, state the amplitude, period, equation of the horizontal midline axis, and maximum and minimum values.

4. $y = 5\sin(9x + 4) + 11$

5. $y = \dfrac{1}{2}\sin(x + 9) + 8$

6. $y = 4\sin\left(\dfrac{1}{4}x + \dfrac{\pi}{6}\right) - 2$

Determine a function in form $y = a\sin(bx) + d$, where x is in radians, that represents each of the following graphs.

7.

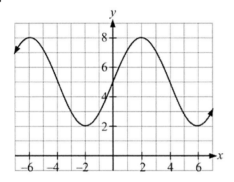

8.

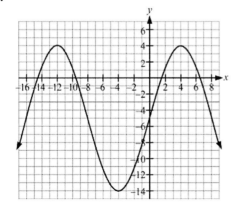

348   Copyright Protected

9.

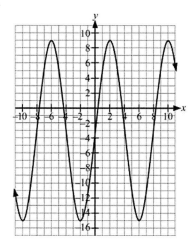

10.

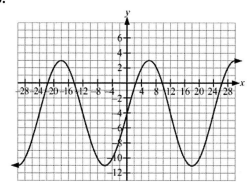

Lesson 2 *SOLVING CONTEXTUAL PROBLEMS INVOLVING SINUSOIDAL FUNCTIONS*

NOTES

Numerous real-world situations can be modelled using the sinusoidal function $y = a\sin(bx + c) + d$. For example, the time the sun rises, the depth of water caused by the tides, and the position of a clock pendulum during each swing can each be modelled using a sinusoidal function.

SOLVING PROBLEMS USING A GRAPH

Real-life situations modelled by sinusoidal functions can be represented graphically. Problems involving graphically represented sinusoidal functions can be solved by interpreting values from the graph.

Example

A stone is stuck in the wheel of a cart. The height of the stone, *h*, in centimetres, *t* seconds after it gets stuck in the wheel is represented by | the given graph.

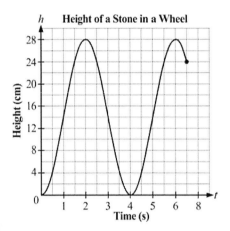

a) What is the diameter of the wheel?

Solution

The diameter corresponds to the maximum value of the graph.

The highest point reached by the stone is 28 cm. Therefore, the diameter of the wheel is 28 cm.

b) How far above the ground is the axle (centre of the wheel) located?

Solution

The axle corresponds to the horizontal midline axis of the graph.

The axle is located halfway between the minimum, 0 cm, and the maximum, 28 cm. Therefore, the axle is located 14 cm above the ground.

c) How long does it take for the wheel to complete one revolution?

Solution

The graph shows a period of 4 (the amount of time until the graph repeats itself). Therefore, the time for one complete revolution is 4 s.

d) How would the graph change if the stone were stuck in a wheel with a larger diameter?

Solution

If the diameter of the wheel were larger, the maximum value on the wheel would be higher. Also, the amplitude (radius) would be larger, and the horizontal midline axis (location of axle) would be higher on the graph. If the cart continued to travel at the same speed, the amount of time for the wheel to make a complete revolution would increase, so the period would be longer than 4 s.

Class Exercise 1

The height above ground level of a rider on a ferris wheel is given by the following graph, where $h(t)$ is the height in metres of the rider t seconds after the ride begins.

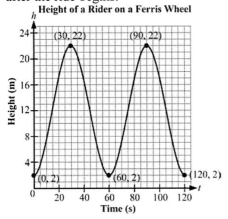

a) What are the maximum and minimum heights of the rider on the ferris wheel?

b) How long after the ride begins does it take the rider to reach the height of the axle of the ferris wheel?

c) How long does it take the ferris wheel to make one complete revolution?

d) How would the graph change if the time for one revolution were increased?

NOTES

The concept of a radian allows for the transition from working with degree measures to real numbers.

SOLVING PROBLEMS USING AN EQUATION

Often, solving sinusoidal function problems requires solving for a particular value of a variable when given the function in the form of an equation. Remember that the input of a trigonometric function will not always be an angle measurement in degrees. For example, it is possible to calculate the sine of a real number. For problems involving the function $y = a\sin(bx + c) + d$, assume the value of x is in radians unless stated otherwise.

Example

The average monthly temperature of a certain city is given by function $T(m) = 18.21\sin(0.52x - 1.63) + 13.11$, where $T(m)$ is the average temperature in degrees Celsius and m is the number of the month.

a) What is the period of the sinusoidal function, rounded to the nearest month?

Solution

The value of b in the function $T(m) = 18.21\sin(0.52m - 1.63) + 13.11$ is 0.52. Therefore, the period is calculated as follows:

$$\text{period} = \frac{2\pi}{b}$$
$$\text{period} = \frac{2\pi}{0.52}$$
$$\text{period} \approx 12.1$$

The period is approximately 12 months. This is logical because temperatures tend to repeat at about the same time each year.

b) What is the maximum average temperature for the city?

Solution

The maximum value is $d + a$. The amplitude is 18.21, and the horizontal midline axis is 13.11. Therefore, the maximum average temperature for the city is $13.11 + 18.21 = 31.32°C$.

Make sure your calculator is in radian mode.

c) What is the average monthly temperature in the city for the month of September, rounded to the nearest tenth of a degree?

Solution

September is the ninth month of the year. Using the given function, find the value of $T(9)$.

$$T(m) = 18.21\sin(0.52m - 1.63) + 13.11$$
$$T(9) = 18.21\sin(0.52(9) - 1.63) + 13.11$$
$$T(9) \approx 14.8$$

In this example, the input is the month number, and the output is the average temperature in a particular month.

The average monthly temperature for September is 14.8°C.

 Copyright Protected

Class Exercise 2

The height of the tide in a particular area is given by the function $h(t) = 5.08\sin(0.51t + 2.02) + 6.48$, where $h(t)$ is the height of the tide in metres over time, t, in hours.

a) What is the maximum height of the tide?

b) What is the period of the tide?

c) How many metres taller is the tide at 2 h than at 5 h? Round your solution to the nearest tenth of a metre.

Some problems will require you to create an equation that models a given contextual situation. You will need to analyze the given problem carefully and pick out key features that relate to the sinusoidal function $y = a\sin(bx + c) + d$.

Example

A ferris wheel has a radius of 25 m, and its axle is located 28 m above ground level. The wheel completes one rotation in 35 s.

a) If the rider is 28 m above the ground at $t = 0$, determine the function $h(t) = a\sin(bt) + d$, where $h(t)$ represents the rider's height above ground after time, t, in seconds.

Solution

Step 1
Determine the value of a.

The value of a represents the amplitude. The amplitude of the ferris wheel is given by the radius of the ferris wheel. Therefore, the value of a is 25.

Step 2
Determine the value of b.

The value of b is given by the formula $b = \dfrac{2\pi}{period}$. Since it takes 35 s for the wheel to complete one rotation, the value of b is $\dfrac{2\pi}{35}$.

When the y-intercept of a sine function falls on the horizontal midline axis, there is no phase shift, and $c = 0$.

Note: Remember to leave the value of b as a fraction unless stated otherwise.

Step 3

Determine the value of d.

The value of d represents the horizontal midline axis, or median. The middle of the ride is located at the axle of the wheel, which is 28 m above ground level. Therefore, the value of d is 28.

Step 4

Determine the function that models the height of the rider.

Substitute the values of a, b, and d into the function $h(t) = a\sin(bt) + d$.

$$h(t) = a\sin(bt) + d$$
$$h(t) = 25\sin\left(\frac{2\pi}{35}t\right) + 28$$

Therefore, the function that represents the height of a rider on the ferris wheel is $h(t) = 25\sin\left(\frac{2\pi}{35}t\right) + 28$.

b) Using the function $h(t) = 25\sin\left(\frac{2\pi}{35}t\right) + 28$, which was determined in part a), determine the height of rider after 45 s. Round your solution to the nearest tenth of metre.

Solution

Using the function $h(t) = 25\sin\left(\frac{2\pi}{35}t\right) + 28$, determine the value of $h(45)$.

$$h(t) = 25\sin\left(\frac{2\pi}{35}t\right) + 28$$
$$h(45) = 25\sin\left(\frac{2\pi}{35}(45)\right) + 28$$
$$h(45) \approx 52.4$$

Therefore, the rider is 52.4 m above the ground after 45 s.

c) How long does it take the rider to complete $\frac{1}{4}$ of a revolution?

Solution

It takes the ferris wheel 35 s to complete one revolution. Therefore it will take $\frac{1}{4} \times 35 = 8.75$ s to complete $\frac{1}{4}$ of a revolution.

Copyright Protected

Class Exercise 3

A bucket is attached to a water wheel that has a diameter of 2.4 m. The wheel makes half a rotation in 20 s, and the centre of rotation is 1.5 m above ground level.

a) If the height of the bucket is 1.5 m at the start of the rotation, determine the function $h(t) = a\sin(bt) + d$, where $h(t)$ represents the height of bucket above ground after time, t, in seconds.

b) What is the height of bucket at 9 s?

SOLVING PROBLEMS USING TRIGONOMETRIC REGRESSION

Sometimes, graphed data appears to follow a sinusoidal pattern. In cases like this, the data can be entered into a TI-83 or similar calculator to obtain a **sinusoidal regression** function to best represent the data. Once the equation of the function is acquired, it can be used to solve various problems.

The sinusoidal regression function given on a TI-83 or similar calculator is of the form $y = a\sin(bx + c) + d$, where x is in radians.

Example

Kevin recorded the sunrise times on the first day of each month in 2012 for a certain city in Alberta. His data is given in the following table:

Date	Day Number	Sunrise Time (A.M.)
Jan 1	1	8:49
Feb 1	32	8:19
Mar 1	61	7:20
Apr 1	92	7:06
May 1	122	5:58
June 1	153	5:11
July 1	183	5:10
Aug 1	214	5:51
Sept 1	245	6:44
Oct 1	275	7:36
Nov 1	306	8:34
Dec 1	336	8:27

a) Determine the sunrise times in decimal form.

Solution

First, convert the sunrise time 8:49 A.M. into decimal form. There are 60 min in 1 h, so 49 min is equivalent to $49\,\text{min}\times\dfrac{1\,\text{h}}{60\,\text{min}}\approx 0.82\,\text{h}$.

Therefore, 8:49 A.M. can be written as a decimal as $8 + 0.82 = 8.82$.

The rest of the sunrise times can be converted to decimals by applying the same procedure.

Date	Day Number	Sunrise Time in Decimal Form
Jan 1	1	8.82
Feb 1	32	8.32
Mar 1	61	7.33
Apr 1	92	7.10
May 1	122	5.97
June 1	153	5.18
July 1	183	5.02
Aug 1	214	5.85
Sept 1	245	6.73
Oct 1	275	7.60
Nov 1	306	8.57
Dec 1	336	8.45

b) Determine a sinusoidal regression function that best approximates sunrise time, $T(d)$, on a particular day of the year, d. Round your values for a, b, c, and d to the nearest hundredth.

Solution

Step 1
Enter the data values into the calculator.

Start by clearing any lists already present. Press $\boxed{\text{2nd}}$ $\boxed{+}$, select 4:ClrAllLists, and press $\boxed{\text{ENTER}}$. Press $\boxed{\text{STAT}}$, and select 1:Edit.... Enter the day numbers into list L_1, and enter the sunrise times into list L_2.

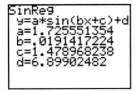

Step 2
Perform the sinusoidal regression.
Press $\boxed{\text{STAT}}$ $\boxed{\triangleright}$ to highlight CALC. Select C:SinReg, and press $\boxed{\text{ENTER}}$ to obtain the following window.

```
SinReg
y=a*sin(bx+c)+d
a=1.725551354
b=.0191417224
c=1.478968238
d=6.89902482
```

Step 3
Determine the sinusoidal regression function.
For the data entered, $a \approx 1.73$, $b \approx 0.02$, $c \approx 1.48$, and $d \approx 6.90$.
Therefore, the sinusoidal function that best approximates the data is
$T(d) = 1.73\sin(0.02d + 1.48) + 6.90$, where $T(d)$ is the sunrise time on a particular day, d.

c) Using the sinusoidal regression function, determine the time of sunrise on March 5.

Solution

Step 1
Determine the time of sunrise on March 5 in decimal form.
There are 4 days between March 1 and March 5. Since March 1 corresponds to day 61, March 5 corresponds to day $(61 + 4) = 65$.
Using the function, determine the value of $T(d)$.

$T(d) = 1.73\sin(0.02d + 1.48) + 6.90$

$T(65) = 1.73\sin(0.02(65) + 1.48) + 6.90$

$T(65) \approx 7.51$

NOTES

Step 2
Convert 7.51 to time format.
Since there are 60 min in 1 h, 0.51 h is equivalent

to $0.51\,\mathrm{h} \times \dfrac{60\,\mathrm{min}}{1\,\mathrm{h}} \approx 31\,\mathrm{min}$. Therefore, the time of sunrise on March 5

is approximately 7:31 A.M.

d) Graph the unrounded regression function using a TI-83 or similar calculator.

Solution

Press $\boxed{\text{Y=}}$, and input the unrounded exponential regression function by pressing $\boxed{\text{VARS}}$ $\boxed{5}$ $\boxed{\triangleright}$ $\boxed{\triangleright}$ and selecting 1:RegEQ.

When graphing a sinusoidal regression function, make sure your calculator is in radian mode.

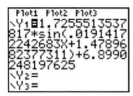

Use the window settings x: [0, 370, 20] and y: [0, 9, 1].
Press $\boxed{\text{GRAPH}}$ to obtain the following window.

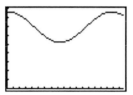

e) Use your graph to determine the date of the earliest sunrise of the year.

Solution
The day when the sun rises the earliest is the x-coordinate of the minimum of the graph.

Step 1
Determine the minimum of the graph.
Press $\boxed{\text{2nd}}$ $\boxed{\text{TRACE}}$, and select 3: minimum. When asked for a left bound, position the cursor just left of the minimum, and press $\boxed{\text{ENTER}}$.

Copyright Protected

When asked for a right bound, position the cursor just right of the maximum, and press ENTER .

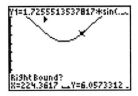

After the "Guess?" prompt, press ENTER . The result gives the coordinates of the minimum of the graph.

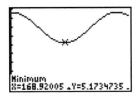

Step 2
Determine the date of the earliest sunrise of the year.

The *x*-coordinate of the minimum is approximately 169 days. Since June 1 is day 153 of the year, day 169 corresponds to June 17. Therefore, according to the model, the date of the earliest sunrise of the year was June 17.

Class Exercise 4

This data represents the change in the pitch of a siren over time.

Time (s)	Frequency (Hz)
0	640.0
1	706.6
2	681.1
3	598.9
4	573.4
5	640.0
6	706.6
7	681.1
8	598.8
9	573.4
10	640.0

a) Determine the sinusoidal regression equation that represents the given data. Round the values of *a*, *b*, *c*, and *d* to the nearest hundredth.

b) Determine the period of the equation of the siren rounded to the nearest tenth of a second.

c) Determine the frequency of the siren at 12 s. Round the solution to the nearest tenth of a hertz.

PRACTICE EXERCISES

Use the following information to answer the next three questions.

A stone is stuck in the tread of the back tire of a tricycle. The given graph represents the height, *h*, in centimetres of the stone relative to the ground with respect to the angle, *x*, in degrees through which the tire is rotating.

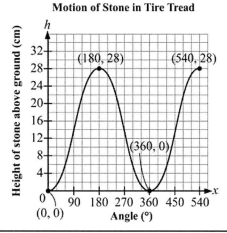

Motion of Stone in Tire Tread

1. What is the period of the given graph?

2. What is the diameter of the tire?

3. What is the height of the stone after the tire has made $1\frac{1}{2}$ revolutions?

Use the following information to answer the next three questions.

The following graph shows the height of the tide over 24 h of a certain bay in Northern Canada.

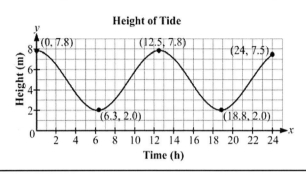

4. What is the period of the tide?

5. At what time does the tide first reach its minimum height if it is midnight when $t = 0$?

6. How would the graph change if the average height of the tide were larger?

Use the following information to answer the next three questions.

A piston in the engine of a car moves up and down in its cylinder in a periodic fashion. The motion of the piston can be described by the function $h = 5\sin(157.08t) + 15$, where h is the height of the piston head from the bottom of the cylinder in centimetres, and t is the time in seconds.

7. Determine the minimum and maximum heights of the piston head.

8. Determine how long it takes for the piston to go up and down through one cycle within the cylinder. Round your answer to the nearest hundredth of a second.

9. Calculate the number of complete cycles the piston makes if the piston operates at a constant speed for one hour.

Use the following information to answer the next three questions.

The height above ground level of a rider on a ferris wheel is given by the function $h(t) = 4\sin(0.26t + 4.71) + 6$, where $h(t)$ is the height in metres of the rider t seconds after the rider gets on.

10. What are the maximum and minimum heights of the rider on the ferris wheel?

11. How long does it take for the ferris wheel to complete one revolution? Round your solution to the nearest second.

12. What is the height of the rider after 13 s? Round your solution to the nearest hundredth of a metre.

Use the following information to answer the next two questions.

Pierre lives on a small farm that gets its water supply from a well that has a pump. Pierre notices that the water pressure in his farmhouse is not consistent. He decides to test it by hooking up a tester to measure the pressure of the water. He measures the pressure every hour and gets the following results:

Time (h)	Pressure (PSI)
0	22.2
1	19.0
2	18.3
3	16.8
4	16.0
5	17.5
6	18.1
7	20.2
8	23.0
9	23.5
10	21.4
11	19.5
12	17.0

13. Determine the sinusoidal regression equation that best fits the given data. Round the values of a, b, c, and d to the nearest hundredth.

14. What is the water pressure after 17 h? Round your answer to the nearest tenth of a PSI.

15. Will Pierre consistently have good water pressure at the same times each day? Explain your answer.

 Copyright Protected

REVIEW SUMMARY

- A periodic function is a function whose y-values repeat at regular intervals.
- One kind of periodic function is a sinusoidal function. Sinusoidal functions all have the following characteristics:
- Period: The length of the shortest repeating section of a periodic function.
- Horizontal midline axis: The horizontal line that is located halfway between the maximum and minimum values.
- Amplitude: The vertical distance from the horizontal midline axis of graph to the minimum or maximum value of the function.
- A phase shift occurs when the graph of the function is translated horizontally to the left or right.
- The equation of a sinusoidal function can be written in the form $y = a\sin(bx + c) + d$. Each of the variables has a specific effect on the graph of the function:
  - The amplitude is a.
  - The period is $\dfrac{2\pi}{b}$, or $\dfrac{360°}{b}$.
  - A phase shift occurs if $c \neq 0$.
  - The horizontal midline axis is $y = d$.
  - The maximum value is $d + a$. The minimum value is $d - a$.
  - To calculate the value of b when given the period, use the formula $b = \dfrac{2\pi}{\text{period}}$.
- Situations modelled by sinusoidal functions can be represented graphically. Problems involving graphically represented sinusoidal functions can be solved by interpreting values from the graph.
- Sinusoidal function problems may require using the function in the form of an equation. This may involve interpreting the values of a, b, c, or d in the given equation, or it may involve substituting a value for the variable and then solving.
- Trigonometric regressions are often performed on a TI-83 or similar calculator to model sinusoidal data. A sinusoidal regression function is of the form $y = a\sin(bx + c) + d$.
- Some problems will require you to create a table of values in order to perform a sinusoidal regression. Use key points with respect to the given context to determine the characteristics of the graph. These can then be used to create the table of values.

PRACTICE TEST

For the following sinusoidal functions, state the period, amplitude, horizontal midline axis, and range.

1. $y = 3\sin(5x) - 2$

2. $y = 7\sin\left(12x + \dfrac{1}{2}\pi\right) + 3$

Determine a function in form $y = a\sin(bx) + d$, where x is in radians, that represents each of the following graphs.

3.

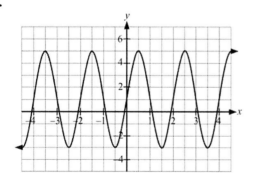

4.

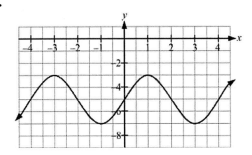

Sketch a graph representing each of the following functions.

5. $y = 6\sin(2x)$

6. $y = 3\sin\left(\dfrac{\pi}{4}x\right) + 4$

Use the following information to answer the next four questions.

The amount of the monthly heating bill of a particular Calgary family can be modelled using the function $f(m) = 59\sin(0.5m + 1.3) + 136$, where $f(m)$ represents the amount of the monthly heating bill in dollars and m represents the number of the month.

7. What is the average monthly heating bill according to the model?

8. What is the highest bill that the family would expect to receive?

9. How much should the family expect to pay in May?

10. During which month are heating costs the lowest?

Use the following information to answer the next four questions.

The horses on a particular merry-go-round are suspended from a mechanism that is 3.2 m above the platform, as shown.

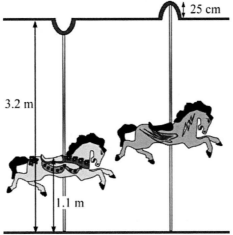

The mechanism makes 20 complete rotations in one minute, moving the horses up and down as it turns. The seat of each horse at the lowest point in the rotation is 1.1 m from the platform.

The distance between the platform of the merry-go-round and the seat of a horse can be modelled using a sinusoidal function in the form $h = a\sin(bt - \frac{\pi}{2}) + d$, where h is the height of the seat of the horse in centimetres and t is the time in seconds.

11. Determine the amplitude, horizontal midline axis, minimum, maximum, and period of the function.

12. Sketch the graph showing the height of the seat from the platform over the first 6 s, given that the horse is at the lowest possible point at $t = 0$.

13. Determine the equation of the function.

Use the following information to answer the next three questions.

There is a straight fence touching one edge of the platform of the merry-go-round.

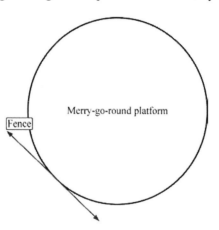

The distance, *d*, in metres, between the fence and a girl riding one of the horses *s* seconds after the ride begins is represented by the given graph.

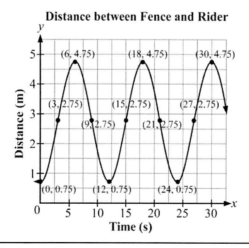

14. If the ride continues for 3 min, how many times will the girl go around?

15. What is the radius of the merry-go-round platform?

16. How far away is the girl from the fence after 9 s?

Use the following information to answer the following three questions.

The following table shows the number of hours of daylight for an area in central Alberta on certain days of the year 2011.

Date	Day Number	Hours of Daylight
January 1	1	8.00
February 12	43	9.87
March 15	74	11.83
April 27	117	14.59
May 8	128	15.20
June 28	179	16.53
July 18	199	16.00
August 10	222	14.87
September 8	251	13.10
October 17	290	10.62
November 6	310	9.42
December 22	356	7.90

17. What is a sine regression function that gives the number of hours of daylight, $H(d)$, with respect to the day number, d, of the year 2011? Round the values for a, c, and d to the nearest hundredth, and round the value for b to the nearest thousandth.

18. The summer solstice occurs on the day of the year that has the greatest number of daylight hours. According to the model, on which day of the year 2011 did the summer solstice occur?

19. According to the model, on which days do the number of hours of daylight equal the number of hours of darkness?

Use the following information to answer the next five questions.

A wind turbine has four blades mounted on a concrete tower.

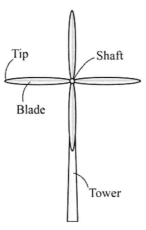

The following table shows the height of the tip of one of the blades of the turbine as it turns through two rotations.

Time (s)	Height (m)
1	10.2
2.5	9.1
4	4.8
5.5	5.9
7.5	10.7
9	7.5
10.5	4.4

20. What is a sine function that represents the height above the ground, $h(t)$, of the tip of the blade with respect to time, t, in seconds? Round the values of a, b, c, and d to the nearest hundredth.

21. What is the height of the tip of the blade after 45 s of rotation? Round your answer to the nearest tenth of a metre.

22. What is the length of one of the turbine blades?

23. What is the height of the tower?

24. To the nearest second, how long does it take the turbine to make one complete rotation?

Student Notes and Problems

ANSWERS AND SOLUTIONS

CASTLE ROCK
RESEARCH CORP

LOGICAL REASONING AND PROBLEM STRATEGIES

Lesson 1—Completing Patterns

CLASS EXERCISES
ANSWERS AND SOLUTIONS

1. **Step 1**
    Look at the order of the shapes.

    Each figure has a square, a triangle, and a circle appearing in the same order. The next figure will probably have the same three shapes in the same order.

    Step 2
    Look at the direction of the arrows.

    In each new figure, the arrow on the square rotates a quarter turn clockwise, the arrow on the triangle rotates a half turn, and the arrow on the circle rotates an eighth of a turn counterclockwise.

    If this pattern continues, in the next figure, the arrow on the square and the arrow on the triangle will both point down, and the arrow on the circle will point to the left.

    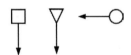

    Note: This solution is based on the assumption that each of the shapes will continue to change in exactly the same way. For example, if the arrow on the circle behaved like a pendulum, then the fourth figure would have all three arrows pointing down. However, when answering these types of questions, it is usually safer to assume that the same kind of change that took place in previous terms will continue in future terms.

2. a) **Step 1**
        Look at the relationship between the numbers in each line.

        In each line, the second number is always 9, and the first and third numbers are the same, but in reversed order.

    Step 2
    Look at how the numbers change from one line to the next.

    In each line, an additional 9 is inserted after the 0 in the first number. The first number in the fourth line has three 9s, so the first number in the fifth line will have four 9s. The second number will be 9, and the third number will have the same digits as the first, but in reversed order.

    Therefore, the next line will be
    $10\ 999\ 989 \times 9 = 98\ 999\ 901$.

    b) According to the given pattern, if a number with any number of 9s inserted between the 0 and the 8 of 1 089 is multiplied by 9, the product will have the same digits, but in reversed order.

        The number 1 099 999 989 has six 9s inserted between the 0 and the 8 of 1 089, so this pattern can be applied. The product is 9 899 999 901.

PRACTICE EXERCISES
ANSWERS AND SOLUTIONS

1. **Step 1**
    Determine the colour of the triangle.

    In the first figure, the triangle is black. In the second figure, the triangle is white, and in the third figure, the triangle is black again. The colour appears to be alternating between black and white, so the next triangle will probably be white.

    Step 2
    Determine the location of the triangle.

    In each figure, the triangle moves two sides around the pentagon in a counterclockwise direction. Therefore, in the fourth figure, it will move two more sides.

Note: The triangle can also be seen as moving three sides clockwise with each new figure.
If the motion of the triangle is interpreted this way, the result will be the same.

3. **Step 1**
Determine what the two identical diagonal shapes will be.

In the second figure, the two diagonal shapes are circles. The circle was in the top right position in the first figure. In the third figure, the two diagonal shapes are squares, and a square was the top right shape in the previous figure.

The shape in the top right of the third figure is an X, so the two diagonal shapes in the fourth figure are probably X's.

Step 2
Determine what the top right shape will be.

The top right shape in each figure is the same as the bottom left shape in the previous figure. The bottom left shape in the third figure is a triangle, so the top right shape in the fourth figure should be a triangle.

Step 3
Determine what the bottom left shape will be.

In each figure, the shape on the bottom left is a shape that did not appear in the previous figure. In the first three figures, the shapes that appear are a triangle, a circle, a square, and an X. Of these four shapes, only the circle did not appear in the third figure, so the bottom left shape in the fourth figure must be a circle.

5. Each letter on the grid is moving according to a different rule. Find the rule for each letter separately.

Step 1
Find the rule for the black letter O.

The black letter O is alternating between the top middle space and the bottom middle space. In the third figure, it is in the top middle space. Therefore, in the fourth figure, it must be in the bottom middle space.

Step 2
Find the rule for the grey letter O.

The grey letter O is in the middle space in each figure, so it probably stays in the middle space in the fourth figure.

Step 3
Find the rule for the black letter X.

The black letter X is alternating between the bottom left space and the top right space. In the third figure, it is in the bottom left space. Therefore, in the fourth figure, it must be in the top right space.

Step 4
Find the rule for the grey letter X.

The grey letter X is moving around the outside of the box in a counterclockwise direction. In the third figure, it is in the bottom middle space. Therefore, in the fourth figure, it should be in the bottom right space.

7. **Step 1**
Analyze the pattern.

Each time an extra 9 is appended to the number being squared, an extra 9 is inserted at the beginning of the square, and an extra 0 is inserted before the digit 1.

In each row, if the number being squared has n digits, the perfect square has $(n - 1)$ 9s and $(n - 1)$ 0s.

Step 2
Apply the pattern to solve $9\ 999^2$.

There are four 9s in the number being squared, so the square will have three 9s and three 0s.

Therefore, $9\ 999^2 = 99\ 980\ 001$.

9. Step 1

Analyze the pattern.

In each row, a number whose digits are the first n consecutive numbers is multiplied by 9 and then added to $n + 1$, and the result is a number composed of $(n + 1)$ 1s.

For example, in the third line, 123 is multiplied by 9 and then added to 4, and the result is 1 111.

Step 2

Apply the pattern to solve 12 345 × 9 + 6.

The number 12 345 is composed of the first 5 consecutive digits. It is multiplied by 9 and added to 6, so the result will have six 1s.

Therefore, 12 345 × 9 + 6 = 111 111.

Lesson 2—Logical Reasoning Games

CLASS EXERCISES
ANSWERS AND SOLUTIONS

1. Only one guess includes the digit 1, but each of the other digits was guessed in each of the four possible places. Start by looking for the locations of 2, 4, and 5, and then go back to the digit 1.

Step 1

Look for the location of the digit 2.

The digit 2 was included in five of the guesses:

		Guess	Bulls	Cows
→	1	1234	0	3
→	2	2345	0	3
	3	3456	1	1
→	4	4572	0	3
→	5	5728	2	0
→	6	7289	0	1

There were no bulls for the guesses with 2 in the first, second, or fourth place. This means that the only possible location for 2 is in the third place.

Step 2

Look for the location of the digit 4.

The digit 4 was in four of the guesses.

		Guess	Bulls	Cows
→	1	1234	0	3
→	2	2345	0	3
→	3	3456	1	1
→	4	4572	0	3
	5	5728	2	0
	6	7289	0	1

There were no bulls for the guesses with 4 in the first, third, or fourth place. This means that the only possible location for 4 is in the second place.

Step 3

Look for the location of the digit 5.

The digit 5 was in four of the guesses.

		Guess	Bulls	Cows
	1	1234	0	3
→	2	2345	0	3
→	3	3456	1	1
→	4	4572	0	3
→	5	5728	2	0
	6	7289	0	1

There were no bulls for the guesses with 5 in the second or fourth places, and the digit 2 is already in the third place. The only possible location for the digit 5 is in the first place.

Step 4

Determine the secret number.

The digit 2 is in the third place, 4 is in the second place, and 5 is in the first place. The only remaining place for 1 is in the fourth place.

Therefore, the secret number is 5 421.

2. Without rotation, the L-shaped figure can only sit in a 3-by-3 grid in four different positions. This means that there are only four ways to arrange the pieces.

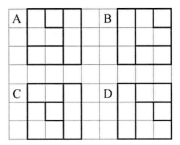

Try each of the options to determine which arrangement does not result in two adjacent identical shapes.

Step 1
Try arrangement A.

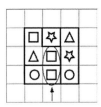

There are two adjacent squares, so this arrangement is incorrect.

Step 2

Try arrangement B.

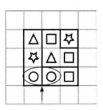

There are two adjacent circles, so this arrangement is incorrect.

Step 3
Try arrangement C.

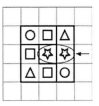

There are two adjacent stars, so this arrangement is incorrect.

Step 4
Try arrangement D.

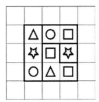

There are no adjacent identical shapes, so this arrangement is correct.

3. **Step 1**
List all the numbers that can go into the squares in the circled box.

The numbers already contained in the box are 1, 2, 4, 7, and 9. This means that each square can contain only the numbers 3, 5, 6, or 8. Numbers also cannot be repeated within the same row or column.

All of the possibilities for each box are shown.

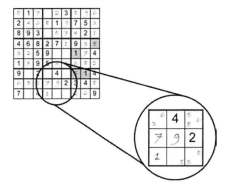

Step 2
Use logical reasoning to determine which number must go in each square.

The circled box needs to have each of the digits from 1 though 9, but the square on the top left is the only one that can contain the number 3. If the top left square is 3, then the top right square is the only square that can contain 6.

The only number that can possibly go in the bottom middle square is 8, which means that the bottom right square must be 5.

Once the values in this box are filled in, they can be used to complete the rest of the puzzle.

See Puzzle Solutions at the back of the book for the completed puzzle.

PRACTICE EXERCISES
ANSWERS AND SOLUTIONS

1. **Step 1**
Make an ordered list of the letters that can go in the circle on the left.

The column on the left already has an A and a C. Also, the string of circles already contains the letter E. The only possibilities are B and D.

Step 2
Make an ordered list of letters that can go in the second circle.

The second column already has an E and an A. Also, the string of circles already contains a C and a B. The only possibility is D.

Step 3
Make an ordered list of letters that can go in the third circle.

The string of circles already contains a B and a C, so the only possibilities are A, D, and E.

Step 4
Make an ordered list of letters that can go in the fourth circle.

The fourth column already has a B and a D. Also, the string of circles already contains an A, so the only possibilities are C and E.

Step 5
Make an ordered list of letters that can go in the circle on the right.

The right column already has a C and an A. Also, the string of circles already contains a D. The only possibilities are B and E.

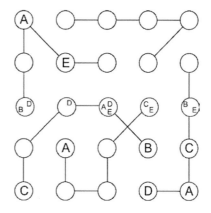

3. **Step 1**
Determine the shapes that could go in the top left square.

The shape in the top left square is black. There is already a black square, so the top left square may contain a triangle or a circle.

---

382 Copyright Protected

Step 2
Examine the puzzle to see if more information can be found.

Three triangles are given. Since one triangle is grey, and one triangle is spotted, the third triangle must be black.

Step 3
Determine the shape contained in the top left square.

The grid now contains a black triangle and a black square. This means that the only shape that can go into the top left square is a black circle. Therefore, Samia's statement was incorrect.

See Puzzle Solutions at the back of the book for the completed puzzle.

5. **Step 1**
Determine the location of the number 2.

According to the clue at the top right, the number 2 is contained in one of the squares along the diagonal. Only one of those squares is adjacent to the number 1, so that is the place to put the number 2.

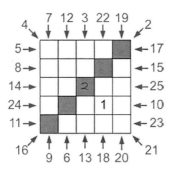

Lucy placed the number 2 correctly.

Step 2
Determine the location of the number 3.

According to the clue on the top, the number 3 is contained in one of the squares in the centre column. There are two squares in the centre column that are adjacent to the number 2, so 3 must go in one of those two squares.

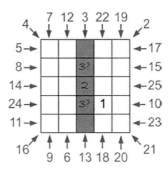

Step 4
Determine the location of the number 4.

According to the clue at the top left, the number 4 is contained in one of the squares along the diagonal. Only one of those squares is adjacent to either 3, so that is the correct square for the number 4.

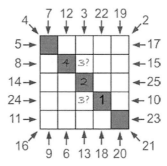

In order for 4 to be adjacent to 3, the number 3 must be placed above the number 2.

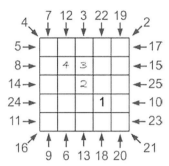

Lucy was incorrect because her placement of the number 3 did not allow for correct placement of the number 4.

See Puzzle Solutions at the back of the book for the completed puzzle.

Lesson 3—Strategy Games

CLASS EXERCISES
ANSWERS AND SOLUTIONS

1. Determine whether moving each piece will allow Carrie to capture one of Adam's pieces:
   - Piece 1—Can be moved
   - Piece 2—Moving piece 2 allows the capture of piece 3.
   - Piece 3—Can be moved
   - Piece 4—Can be moved
   - Piece 5—Moving piece 5 puts it in a position where it can be captured.
   - Piece 6—Moving piece 6 allows the capture of piece 7.
   - Piece 7—Moving piece 7 puts it in a position where it can be captured.

   Therefore, Adam should move piece 1, 3, or 4.

PRACTICE EXERCISES
ANSWERS AND SOLUTIONS

1. There are two possible moves that white can make to protect both rows. Either move is equally valid.

   Step 1
   Identify which black checkers may attack the rows.

   The black checker at B5 can move to C5 to capture the vertical line of checkers, or the black checker at B6 could move to C5 to capture the diagonal line of checkers.

   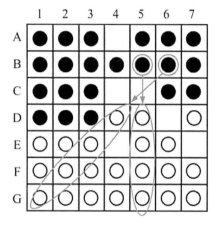

   Step 2
   Plan a move that will prevent both captures.

   There are several moves that will prevent one capture but not the other. For example, moving the white checker at D4 to C4 captures a black checker and prevents the capture of the diagonal row of white checkers but still allows the vertical row to be captured.

   The best way to prevent both captures is to block C5, as that is the empty square that black needs to move into for either capture.

White can move either D4 or D5 into C5, and either move will both capture two black checkers and block both captures. The following boards show the results of both moves.

D4 to C5

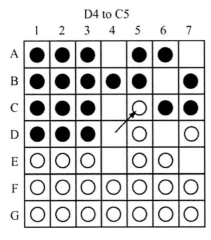

D5 to C5

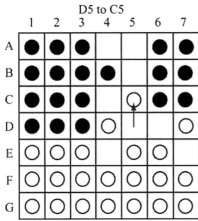

Either of these two moves will prevent black from capturing a row of four.

3. **Step 1**
Test to see if Tamia will win if she goes next.

If Tamia goes next, she can write her initial in square E3.

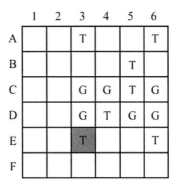

If she does this, she will be able to win on the following turn by playing on square B6 or F2. Genevieve will not be able to block both squares, so if Tamia goes next, she will win.

Step 2
Test to see if Genevieve will win if she goes next.

If Genevieve goes next, she can write her initial in square B3.

	1	2	3	4	5	6
A			T			T
B			G		T	
C			G	G	T	G
D			G	T	G	G
E						T
F						

If she does this, she will be able to win on the following turn by playing on square A2 or E3. Tamia will not be able to block both squares, so if Genevieve goes next, she will win.

Therefore, Genevieve was correct. The order of play does matter because whoever goes next can win the game.

5. Label the three available points A, B, and C. Use trial and error to determine which connections will result in a win.

Step 1
Try connecting A and B.

This move could result in player 1 drawing the last line, thereby losing the game.

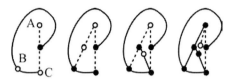

Step 2
Try connecting A and C.

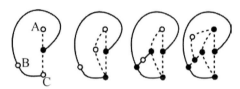

This move could result in player 1 drawing the last line, thereby losing the game.

Step 3

Try connecting A and B on the inside of the loop.

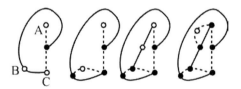

This move could result in player 1 drawing the last line, thereby losing the game.

Step 4
Try connecting B and C on the outside of the loop.

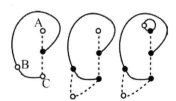

This move forces player 2 to draw the last possible legal line, resulting in a win for player 1.

1. Step 1
Analyze the pattern.

In each line, 999 999 is multiplied by a number, x, to result in a product that has $x - 1$ millions and $10 - x$ ones.

For example, in the third line, 999 999 is multiplied by 3, and the result has 2 millions and 7 ones.

Step 2
Apply the pattern.

The product 6 999 993 has 6 millions and 3 ones. The sum of $6 + 1$ is 7, and the difference of $10 - 3$ is 7, so $999\ 999 \times 7 = 6\ 999\ 993$.

3. Step 1
Determine the location of the cars in the fourth figure.

Each figure has a total of five cars, but the distribution of the cars changes. Each figure has 1 more car on the bottom than in the previous figure. The third figure has 2 cars on the top and 3 on the bottom, so the fourth figure will have 1 car on top and 4 cars on the bottom.

Step 2
Determine the location of the truck in the fourth figure.

Each figure has only one truck, so the fourth figure will likely also have only one truck. The location of the truck is alternating between the top and the bottom. Since the truck was on the top in the third figure, it will be on the bottom in the fourth figure.

Copyright Protected

5. There is more than one way to arrive at a solution; only one way is shown here.

Use the process of elimination.

The grid has three missing shapes: one in the top left, one in the bottom right, and the white one.

There are already four clubs in the grid, so the missing three shapes must be a heart, a spade, and a diamond.

Three of the diamonds are given with their colours: black, grey, and spotted. This means that the fourth diamond must be hatched. The missing shape in the top left corner is black, and the missing shape in the bottom right corner is spotted. This means that the only possible place to put the missing hatched diamond is in the square with the white star.

See Puzzle Solutions at the back of the book for the completed puzzle.

7. Step 1
Identify the numbers that are correctly circled.

The only way for the numbers in the bottom row to have a sum of 8 is by circling 1, 3, and 4, so those circles must be correct.

If 1 is circled in the bottom left, then the only way for the numbers in the left column to have a sum of 6 is to circle 4 and both 1s, so those circles are also correct.

If 3 in the bottom row is circled, then there are still two ways for the numbers in the second column to have a sum of 6: both 3s or 3, 2, and 1 could be circled. It is not certain that 3 in the top row of the second column is correctly circled.

If 4 in the bottom right is circled, then the only way for the numbers in the right column to have a sum of 5 is to circle 1 and 4, so both of those circles are correct.

The circles that have been identified as definitely being correct are shaded in the following diagram.

2	③	3	①	4
④	1	3	2	5
①	2	4	2	7
①	③	2	④	8
6	6	7	5	

Step 2
Correct the error.

If 4 in the first column is circled, then the only way for the numbers in the second row to have a sum of 5 is to circle 1 in the second row. This means that 2 and 3 in the second row may not be circled.

2	3	3	①	4
④	①	✗	✗	5
①	2	4	2	7
①	③	2	④	8
6	6	7	5	

Because 3 in the second row of the third column cannot be circled, the only way for the numbers in the third column to have a sum of 7 is to circle 3 in the top row and 4 in the third row.

2	3	③	①	4
④	①	✗	✗	5
①	2	④	2	7
①	③	2	④	8
6	6	7	5	

Therefore, Darcy's error was circling the incorrect 3 in the top row. He should correct it by circling the number 3 in the third column of the top row.

See Puzzle Solutions at the back of the book for the completed puzzle.

9. Step 1

Look for a move with a positive rating.

A move with a positive rating is one in which Tyler completes one or more triangles. Tyler can complete a triangle if he can find two line segments that join at an acute angle, as shown here.

There are no segments that join at an acute angle, so Tyler will not be able to complete any triangles, and the rating will not be greater than 0.

Step 2

Look for a move with a rating of 0.

A move has a rating of 0 if it does not allow Matt to complete a triangle. Every possible line that Tyler could draw forms an acute angle with another segment, so the rating will be less than 0.

Step 3

Look for a move with a rating of –1.

If Tyler draws either of the lines shown, it will allow Matt to draw exactly 1 triangle. This is his best move.

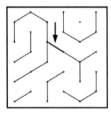

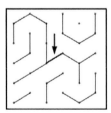

Therefore, Tyler's best move has a rating of –1.

SET THEORY

Lesson 1—Understanding Sets and Set Notation

CLASS EXERCISES
ANSWERS AND SOLUTIONS

1. The days of the week are Sunday, Monday, Tuesday, Wednesday, Thursday, Friday, and Saturday. In roster form, each of the elements of a set is listed inside a set of curly brackets, separated by commas.

   Therefore, D = {Sunday, Monday, Tuesday, Wednesday, Thursday, Friday, Saturday}.

2. Set P has an infinite number of elements, so an ellipsis must be used. List the first three elements of the set, and then use an ellipsis to show that the set continues indefinitely.
   $P = \{1, 2, 3, ...\}$

3. **Step 1**
   Assign a variable to the elements of the set.

   Any variable may be assigned. In this case, use x.

   Step 2
   Use a formula to define x.

   All of the possible values of x are multiples of 10, so all values of x are equal to 10 multiplied by another number, n, as long as n is an integer. Therefore, $x = 10n$.

   Step 3
   List any other restrictions on n.

   All of the values of x are from 10 to 500, inclusive. Since $x = 10n$, the values of n must be from 1 to 50, inclusive.

   Step 4
   Express $M = \{10, 20, 30, ... , 500\}$ using set builder notation.

   Set M contains all the values of x such that $x = 10n$, where n is an integer with a value from 1 to 50, inclusive.
   $M = \{x : x = 10n, n \text{ is an integer}, 1 \leq n \leq 50\}$

Note: The definition
$M = \{10x : x \text{ is an integer}, 1 \le x \le 50\}$ is also correct.

4. **Step 1**
Express the definition in descriptive language.

Set F contains all values of p such that p is the perfect cube of x, where x is an integer less than or equal to -1.

Step 2
Make a table showing some of the possible values of x and corresponding values of p.

Set F contains an infinite number of elements. Choose the four values that are easiest to calculate.

x	p
-1	-1
-2	-8
-3	-27
-4	-64

Step 3
Express F in roster form.

Because F contains an infinite number of elements, it is impossible to list all of the elements in roster form. Therefore, an ellipsis must be used to replace some of the elements. By convention, numbers are listed in ascending order, although listing the same numbers in descending order would also be correct.
$F = \{\ldots -64, \ -27, \ -8, \ -1\}$

5. **Step 1**
Make a list of Canadian coins with values that are not multiples of 2.

The three coins that are not multiples of 2 are pennies (1¢), nickels (5¢), and quarters (25¢).

Step 2
List the elements of set D.

Set D is contained in universe C, which consists of Canadian coins with a value equal to or less than 10¢. This means that quarters, which have a value greater than 10¢, do not exist in the universe. Therefore, they are not contained in set D, and $D = \{\text{penny, nickel}\}$.

6. The universe P contains the one-digit numbers 0, 1, 2, 3, 4, 5, 6, 7, 8, and 9. The complement of a set contains all of the elements in the universe that are not also contained in that set.

Therefore, $C' = \{0, 1, 3, 5, 7, 9\}$.

7. A set is a subset of W if all of its elements are also contained in W. Set W has the following seven subsets:
$\varnothing, \{1\}, \{2\}, \{3\}, \{1, 2\}, \{1, 3\}, \{2, 3\}$

Note: The set $\{1, 2, 3\}$ is not a proper subset of W because it contains exactly the same elements as W.

8. **a) Step 1**
Find $V \cup W$.

Set V contains the numbers 1, 2, and 3, and set W contains 1, 3, and 5. Set $V \cup W$ contains all of the elements that belong to either of the two sets, so $V \cup W = \{1, 2, 3, 5\}$.

Step 2
Find $W \cup X$.

Set W contains the numbers 1, 3, and 5, and set X contains 3, 4, and 6. Set $W \cup X$ contains all of the elements that belong to either of the two sets, so $W \cup X = \{1, 3, 4, 5, 6\}$.

Step 3
Find $V \cup X$.

Set V contains the numbers 1, 2, and 3, and set X contains 3, 4, and 6. Set $V \cup X$ contains all of the elements that belong to either of the two sets, so $V \cup X = \{1, 2, 3, 4, 6\}$.

b) Count the numbers that are elements of each set:
- Set $V \cup W = \{1, 2, 3, 5\}$ has 4 elements.
- Set $W \cup X = \{1, 3, 4, 5, 6\}$ has 5 elements.
- Set $V \cup X = \{1, 2, 3, 4, 6\}$ has 5 elements.

Therefore, $V \cup W$ has the smallest number of elements.

c) The union $V \cup W \cup X$ contains all of the numbers that are elements of sets V, W, or X. Therefore, $V \cup W \cup X = \{1, 2, 3, 4, 5, 6\}$.

9. **Step 1**

List the elements of set O.

The only Canadian cities to have hosted the Olympic Games are Vancouver, Calgary, and Montreal.

Step 2

List the elements of set A that are also elements of set O.

The only city in Alberta that has hosted the Olympic Games is Calgary.

Therefore, $O \cap A = \{Calgary\}$.

10. **Step 1**

Find the sets that share no common elements with set S.

Set S is the set of all animals that swim. There are several types of mammals that swim, including whales, dolphins, and otters. Therefore, sets M and S are not disjoint.

There are several species of sea creatures that lack vertebrae and also swim, including squid and jellyfish. Therefore, sets S and V are not disjoint.

Step 2

Find the sets that share no common elements with set M.

It has already been established that set S shares elements with set M.

Set M is the set of all mammals. There are no mammals without vertebrae, so sets M and V share no common elements, and they are disjoint sets.

Therefore, the only pair of disjoint sets is M and V.

PRACTICE EXERCISES
ANSWERS AND SOLUTIONS

1. a) The universal set contains all of the kinds of items that are sold at any of the four stores. If one kind of item is sold at more than one store, it is still counted only once in the universal set. $U = \{shirts, pants, jackets, skirts, belts, jewellery, shoes, hats, bags\}$

Therefore, the universal set contains 9 elements.

b) The complement of set K contains all of the kinds of items that are not sold at Kaleidoscope but are sold at least one of the other stores in the strip mall.

Therefore, $K' = \{shirts, pants, jackets, skirts\}$.

c) Set $J \cup L$ contains all of the elements contained in sets J or L. Elements found in both sets are not repeated.

$J \cup L = \{shirts, pants, jackets, skirts, belts, bags\}$

d) The complement of $J \cup L$ contains all of the kinds of items that are not sold at either Josie Jay or Leather Land. In other words, it contains all of the items that are not elements of $J \cup L$.

Therefore, $(J \cup L)' = \{jewellery, shoes, hats\}$.

e) Set $J \cap L$ contains only the kinds of items that are sold at both Josie Jay and Leather Land.

Therefore, $J \cap L = \{pants, jackets, belts\}$.

f) Set $K \cap L \cap M$ contains only the kinds of items that are sold at all three stores.

Therefore, $K \cap L \cap M = \{bags\}$.

g) The only store that sells only items that are also sold at one of the other stores is Magnifique. Magnifique sells only shoes and bags, which are both also sold at Kaleidoscope.

Therefore, $M \subset K$.

3. **a)** List all of the elements of the set within a pair of curly brackets. By convention, elements are listed in ascending order, but any other order is also correct.
$A = \{-26, \ -25, \ -24, \ -23, \ -22, \ -21\}$

b) **Step 1**
Express the definition in descriptive language.

Set D contains all values of k such that k is $3n$, where n is an integer from –12 to –6, inclusive.

Step 2
Make a table showing the possible values of n and corresponding values of k.

n	k
–12	–36
–11	–33
–10	–30
–9	–27
–8	–24
–7	–21
–6	–18

Step 3
Express set D in roster form.

List all of the elements of the set within a pair of curly brackets.
$D = \{-36, -33, -30, -27, -24, -21, -18\}$

5. **a)** **Step 1**
Assign a variable to the elements of the set.

Any variable may be assigned. In this case, use x.

Step 2
List any restrictions on x.

All of the values of x are integers from –26 to –21, inclusive.

Step 3
Express A using set builder notation.

Set A contains all the values of x such that x is an integer and $-26 \leq x \leq 21$.
$A = \{x : x \text{ is an integer}, \ -26 \leq x \leq 21\}$

b) **Step 1**
Assign a variable to the elements of the set.

Any variable may be assigned. In this case, use x.

Step 2
List any restrictions on x.

All of the values of x are rational numbers with a denominator of 5. All of these numbers can be expressed in the form $\dfrac{n}{5}$, as long as n is an integer.

Step 3
Express set B using set builder notation.

Set B contains all the values of x such that $x = \dfrac{n}{5}$, where n is any integer.
$B = \left\{ x : x = \dfrac{n}{5}, n \text{ is an integer} \right\}$

c) **Step 1**
Assign a variable to the elements of the set.

Any variable may be assigned. In this case, use x.

Step 2
List any restrictions on x.

Some of the numbers between 0 and 1 are rational numbers, but there are also irrational numbers between 0 and 1. The set of real numbers includes both rational and irrational numbers. Therefore, x can be any real number between 0 and 1.

Step 3
Express C using set builder notation.

The set C contains all the values of x such that x is a real number from 0 to 1, inclusive.
$C = \{x : x \text{ is a real number}, \ 0 \leq x \leq 1\}$

7. The intersection of two sets consists of all of the elements found in both sets. Identify all of the elements that are contained in both B and C.

Step 1
Describe the elements of set C.

Set C contains all of the numbers from 0 to 1, inclusive, but it does not contain any number less than 0 or any number greater than 1.

Step 2
Identify the elements of B that are also contained in C.

All of the elements of set B are fractions with a denominator of 5. The fractions with a denominator of 5 that are equal to or greater than 0 but less than or equal to 1 are $\frac{0}{5}, \frac{1}{5}, \frac{2}{5}, \frac{3}{5}, \frac{4}{5},$ and $\frac{5}{5}$. Therefore, $B \cap C = \left\{ 0, \frac{1}{5}, \frac{2}{5}, \frac{3}{5}, \frac{4}{5}, 1 \right\}$.

9. Step 1
Determine if sets A and B are disjoint.

Any integer can be written as a fraction with a denominator of 5. For example, –21 can be written as $-\frac{105}{5}$. Therefore, $A \cap B \neq \varnothing$, and A and B are not disjoint.

Sets B and D are not disjoint for the same reason.

Step 2
Determine if sets A and C are disjoint.

Set A contains integers from –26 to –21, inclusive, and set C contains only numbers between 0 and 1. Therefore, $A \cap C = \varnothing$, and A and C are disjoint.

Step 3
Determine if sets A and D are disjoint.

The integers –24 and –21 are elements of both A and D. Therefore, $A \cap D \neq \varnothing$, and A and D are not disjoint.

Step 4
Determine if sets B and C are disjoint.

The numbers 0, $\frac{1}{5}, \frac{2}{5}, \frac{3}{5}, \frac{4}{5},$ and 1 are elements of both B and C. Therefore, $B \cap C \neq \varnothing$, and B and C are not disjoint.

Step 5
Determine if sets C and D are disjoint.

Set C contains only numbers between 0 and 1, and set D contains multiples of 3 from –36 to –18, inclusive. Therefore, $C \cap D = \varnothing$, and C and D are disjoint.

Therefore, the two pairs of sets that are disjoint are A and C, and C and D.

Lesson 2—Solving Problems Involving Sets

CLASS EXERCISES
ANSWERS AND SOLUTIONS

1. a) Step 1
Calculate the number of elements in the universal set.

Find the sum of all of the regions in the Venn diagram.
$67 + 11 + 46 + 16 + 18 + 9 + 57 + 31 = 255$

Step 2
Interpret the difference.

The given table provides information about the options chosen on the sale of 129 cars, so the universal set in the Venn diagram should contain only 129 elements. However, the universal set in the Venn diagram contains 255 elements. Therefore, the Venn diagram must contain one or more errors.

b) Step 1
Identify the errors.

According to the table, the following values have been correctly entered in the Venn diagram:

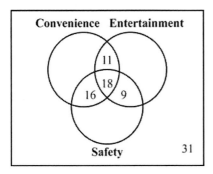

The number 67, which represents the total number of cars with convenience options that were purchased, was incorrectly entered into the region of the Venn diagram that represents cars that were purchased with only convenience options. Similarly, the numbers 57 and 46 were incorrectly entered into the regions representing only safety options and only entertainment options, respectively.

Step 2
Determine the number of cars that were purchased with only convenience options.

A total of 67 cars with convenience options were sold. Of these, 16 cars also had safety options, 11 cars also had entertainment options, and 18 cars had all three kinds of options.
$67 - (16 + 11 + 18) = 22$

There were 22 cars with only convenience options sold.

Step 3
Determine the number of cars that were purchased with only safety options.

A total of 57 cars with safety options were sold. Of these, 16 cars also had convenience options, 9 cars also had entertainment options, and 18 cars had all three kinds of options.
$57 - (16 + 9 + 18) = 14$

There were 14 cars with only safety options sold.

Step 4
Determine the number of cars that were purchased with only entertainment options.

A total of 46 cars with entertainment options were sold. Of these, 9 cars also had safety options, 11 cars also had convenience options, and 18 cars had all three kinds of options.
$46 - (9 + 11 + 18) = 8$

There were 8 cars with only entertainment options sold.

Therefore, the correct Venn diagram is as follows:

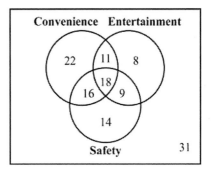

c) This data set has three overlapping categories: convenience options, entertainment options, and safety options. A Carroll diagram is a two-way table, and it can accommodate only two categories.

2. a) The left column represents set S, the set of people who spent money shopping, and the top row represents set F, the set of people who spent money on food.

The number of people who spent money shopping or on food corresponds to $S \cup F$. This can be calculated by finding the sum of the numbers in the shaded regions.

	Spent Money Shopping	Did Not Spend Money Shopping
Spent money on food	28	32
Did not spend money on food	26	14

$28 + 26 + 32 = 86$

Therefore, 86 people spent money shopping or on food.

b) The number of people who spent money shopping and on food corresponds to $S \cap F$. This is equal to the number in the shaded region.

	Spent Money Shopping	Did Not Spend Money Shopping
Spent money on food	28	32
Did not spend money on food	26	14

Therefore, 28 people spent money shopping and on food.

c) The number of people who did not spend money shopping corresponds to S'. This can be calculated by finding the sum of the numbers in the shaded regions.

	Spent Money Shopping	Did Not Spend Money Shopping
Spent money on food	28	32
Did not spend money on food	26	14

$32 + 14 = 46$

Therefore, 46 people did not spend money shopping.

d) The number of people who spent money shopping but not on food corresponds to $S \cap F'$. This is equal to the number in the shaded region.

	Spent Money Shopping	Did Not Spend Money Shopping
Spent money on food	28	32
Did not spend money on food	26	14

Therefore, 26 people spent money shopping but not on food.

3. Answers will vary. If you have a strong preference about which representation is easier, then you may choose to consistently represent data using that graphic organizer. Data that is given as a Venn diagram with two circles can easily be rewritten as a Carroll diagram and vice versa. Keep in mind that data with three categories cannot be represented in a Carroll diagram.

PRACTICE EXERCISES
ANSWERS AND SOLUTIONS

1. **Step 1**
Draw the diagram.

Christa has glass ornaments and angel ornaments. Draw a rectangle to represent the universal set of 47 elements, as well as two overlapping circles labelled as follows:

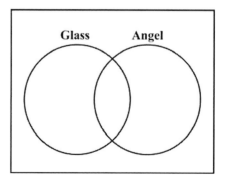

Step 2
Fill in the diagram with the given information.

It is given that 5 ornaments are glass angels, and 10 ornaments are angels but not glass.

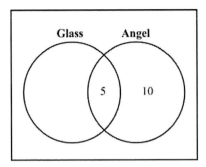

Step 3
Calculate the number of ornaments that are glass but not angels.

Christa has 28 glass ornaments, and 5 of them are also angels.
$28 - 5 = 23$

Therefore, she has 23 glass ornaments that are not angels.

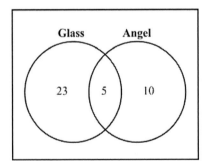

Step 4
Calculate the number of ornaments that are neither glass nor angels.

Add up the numbers on the Venn diagram to determine the number of ornaments that are glass or angels.
$23 + 5 + 10 = 38$

Calculate the difference between the number of ornaments in the universal set and the number of ornaments that are neither glass nor angels.
$47 - 38 = 9$

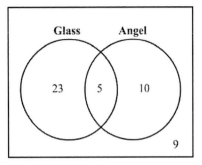

3. **Step 1**
Draw the diagram.

Students had the choice of dinner in a restaurant, a hotel, or the gym. Draw a rectangle to represent the universal set of 77 respondents, as well as three overlapping circles labelled as follows:

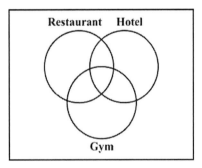

Step 2
Fill in the regions for students who checked off all or none of the options.

There were 18 students who liked all three options, so the number 18 goes in the centre region, where all three circles overlap. There were 3 students who did not check off any options, so the number 3 goes inside the rectangle but outside of all three circles.

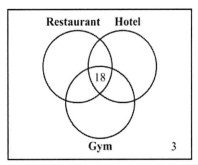

Step 3
Fill in the regions where two circles overlap.

There were 23 students who checked off restaurant or gym. Of these, 18 students chose all three options, so 23 – 18 = 5 students selected only restaurant and gym.

There were 33 students who checked off restaurant or hotel. Of these, 18 students chose all three options, so 33 – 18 = 15 students selected only restaurant and hotel.

There were 26 students who checked off hotel or gym. Of these, 18 students chose all three options, so 26 – 18 = 8 students selected only hotel and gym.

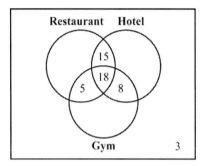

Step 4
Fill in the regions representing students who chose only one option.

There were 47 students who checked off restaurant. Of these, 5 + 18 + 15 = 38 students selected at least one other option, so 47 – 38 = 9 students selected only restaurant.

There were 58 students who checked off hotel. Of these, 15 + 18 + 8 = 41 students selected at least one other option, so 58 – 41 = 17 students selected only hotel.

There were 33 students who checked off gym. Of these, 5 + 18 + 8 = 31 students selected at least one other option, so 33 – 31 = 2 students selected only gym.

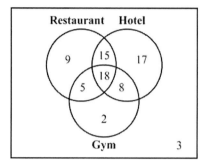

Step 5
Check your answer.

Calculate the number of elements in the universal set.
$9 + 15 + 17 + 5 + 18 + 8 + 2 + 3 = 77$

Therefore, the size of the universal set is equal to the number of students who responded to the survey, and the Venn diagram is correct.

5. a) The elements contained in set B are found in the shaded circle.

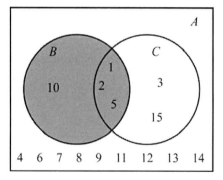

$B = \{1, 2, 5, 10\}$

b) The phrase "NOT C" corresponds to C', as illustrated by the shaded region.

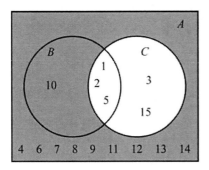

$C' = \{4, 6, 7, 8, 9, 10, 11, 12, 13, 14\}$

c) The phrase "B AND NOT C" corresponds to $B \cap C'$, as illustrated by the shaded region.

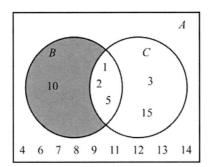

$B \cap C' = \{10\}$

d) The phrase "B OR NOT C" corresponds to $B \cup C'$, as illustrated by the shaded region.

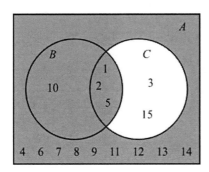

$B \cup C' = \{1, 2, 4, 5, 6, 7, 8, 9, 10, 11, 12, 13, 14\}$

e) The phrase "NOT B AND NOT C" corresponds to $B' \cap C'$, as illustrated by the shaded region.

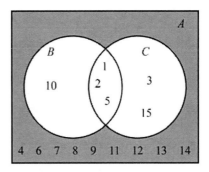

$B' \cap C' = \{4, 6, 7, 8, 9, 11, 12, 13, 14\}$

f) The phrase "NOT (NOT B)" corresponds to $(B')'$. This set contains all of the elements that are not in the complement of B. In other words, it is identical to B.

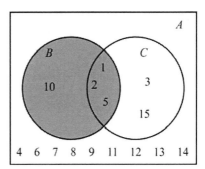

$(B')' = B = \{1, 2, 5, 10\}$

g) The phrase "B AND C" corresponds to $B \cap C$, as illustrated by the shaded region.

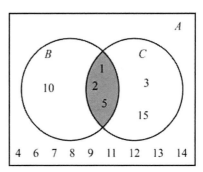

$B \cap C = \{1, 2, 5\}$

h) The phrase "NOT (B AND C)" corresponds to $(B \cap C)'$. It contains all of the elements that are not found in $B \cap C$, as illustrated by the shaded region.

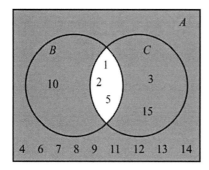

$(B \cap C)' = \{3, 4, 6, 7, 8, 9, 10, 11, 12, 13, 14, 15\}$

i) The phrase "B OR C" corresponds to $B \cup C$, as illustrated by the shaded region.

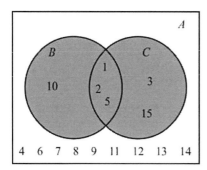

$B \cup C = \{1, 2, 3, 5, 10, 15\}$

j) The phrase "NOT (B OR C)" corresponds to $(B \cup C)'$. It contains all of the elements that are not found in $B \cup C$, as illustrated by the shaded region.

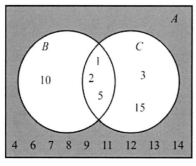

$(B \cup C)' = \{4, 6, 7, 8, 9, 11, 12, 13, 14\}$

7. Calculate the sum of the number of students who attended only the morning session and the number of students who attended both sessions.
$46 + 32 = 78$

Therefore, 78 students attended the morning session.

Practice Test

ANSWERS AND SOLUTIONS

1. The complement of set B can be defined as all the elements that are not in B but are found in the universal set, U. Therefore, $B' = \{-2, 7, 20\}$.

3. In order to answer questions a and b, you must first define sets A and B.

Step 1
Define set A using roster form.

Make a table showing the elements of A. The column on the left shows possible values of n, which may be integers from 0 to 5, inclusive, and the column on the right shows corresponding values of x.

N	$x = 3n$
0	0
1	3
2	6
3	9
4	12
5	15

Therefore, $A = \{0, 3, 6, 9, 12, 15\}$.

Step 2
Define set B using roster form.

Make a table showing the elements of B.
The column on the left shows possible values of n, which may be integers from -2 to 4, inclusive, and the column on the right shows corresponding values of x.

N	$x = 2n + 1$
-2	-3
-1	-1
0	1
1	3
2	5
3	7
4	9

Therefore, $B = \{-3,\ -1,\ 1,\ 3,\ 5,\ 7,\ 9\}$.

a) Determine $A \cup B$.

Set $A \cup B$ is the union of sets A and B and contains all of the elements that are found in A or B. Elements that appear in both sets are not repeated.

Therefore,
$A \cup B = \{-3,\ -1,\ 0,\ 1,\ 3,\ 5,\ 6,\ 7,\ 9,\ 12,\ 15\}$.

b) Determine $A \cap B$.

Set $A \cap B$ is the intersection of sets A and B and contains all of the elements that are found in both sets. Therefore, $A \cap B = \{3,\ 9\}$.

5. a) This set contains only regular polygons, so set B is contained in U. However, the regular octagon has more than seven sides, so it is not an element of A. $B \not\subset A$

b) This set only contains regular polygons, so set C is contained in U. Also, all of the polygons have fewer than seven sides, so C is a subset of A. $C \subset A$

c) This set contains irregular polygons, so set D does not exist in U. $D \not\subset A$

7. **Step 1**
Calculate the number of gyms that offer only free classes.

Of the 16 gyms that offer free classes, 6 gyms also offer towel service, so $16 - 6 = 10$ gyms offer only free classes.

Step 2
Represent the data using a graphic organizer.

Either a Venn diagram or a Carroll diagram can be used to show the data. A Carroll diagram is shown here.

	Free Classes	No Free Classes
Towel service	6	
No towel service	10	4

Step 3
Calculate the number of gyms that offer towel service.

There are $6 + 10 + 4 = 20$ gyms represented in the Carroll diagram, and 25 gyms were surveyed. This means that 5 gyms offer only towel service.

	Free Classes	No Free Classes
Towel service	6	5
No towel service	10	4

Therefore, $6 + 5 = 11$ gyms offer towel service.

9. a) Of the students surveyed, 18 students said that schoolwork was their only source of stress, and 13 students said that schoolwork and home life were both sources of stress.
$18 + 13 = 31$

Therefore, 31 students said that schoolwork was a source of stress.

b) Students who said that schoolwork or home life was a source of stress may have said that stress came from only schoolwork, only home life, or both schoolwork and home life.
$18 + 10 + 13 = 41$

Therefore, 41 students said that schoolwork or home life was a source of stress.

c) Of the students surveyed, 18 students said that schoolwork was their only source of stress, and 9 students said that neither schoolwork nor home life caused them stress.
$18 + 9 = 27$

Therefore, 27 students said that their home life was not a source of stress.

11. The given diagram shows that x is a subset of y, which is a subset of z.

Step 1
Examine each set, and determine which other set or sets it is a subset of.
- $C = \{$red, white$\}$: The elements red and white are also contained in P and S; therefore, $C \subset P$ and $C \subset S$.
- $I = \{$blue, green, orange, white$\}$: Orange is not an element of any other set, so it cannot be a subset.
- $J = \{$black, green, yellow$\}$: The elements black, green, and yellow are also contained in set S; therefore, $J \subset S$.
- $P = \{$blue, red, white, yellow$\}$: The elements blue, red, white, and yellow are also contained in S; therefore, $P \subset S$.
- $S = \{$black, blue, green, red, white, yellow$\}$: The elements black, blue, green, red, white, and yellow are not all contained in any other single set, so it cannot be a subset.

Step 2
Determine which sets are represented by x, y, and z.

Set S is the only set that has more than one subset, so z must represent S.

Sets C, J, and P are all subsets of S. The only one of these sets that contains another subset is P, because C is a subset of P. Therefore, y represents P, and x represents C.

13. Calculate the total of all of the regions of the Venn diagram.
$219 + 19 + 81 + 38 + 11 + 23 + 43 + 1842 = 2\ 276$

Therefore, the database has 2 276 searchable records.

15. a) The shaded region in the diagram represents the intersection of French and Nationalism. Therefore, to obtain the results in this section, Tamia should search *French* AND *nationalism*.

b) The shaded region represents the intersection of French and Nationalism but excludes results that include Québec. Therefore, to obtain the results in this section, Tamia should search (*French* AND *nationalism*) NOT *Québec*.

PROBABILITY

Lesson 1—Odds and Probability

CLASS EXERCISES
ANSWERS AND SOLUTIONS

1. a) **Step 1**
   Make a list of equally probable outcomes for each event:
   - Drawing a marble: {purple1, purple2, orange}
   - Rolling the die: {1, 2, 3, 4, 5, 6}

   Step 2
   Use a graphic organizer to represent the sample space.

   If a tree diagram is used, the outcomes for drawing a marble will be on the left, and each of those outcomes will have six branches leading to the outcomes of rolling the die. If the outcomes for rolling the die are listed first, the outcomes will still be the same.

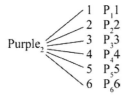

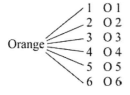

   If a table is used, the outcomes for drawing a marble could be the column headings, and the outcomes for rolling the die could be the row headings. If the columns and rows are reversed, the list of outcomes will still be the same.

	Purple₁	Purple₂	Orange
1	$P_1 1$	$P_2 1$	O1
2	$P_1 2$	$P_2 2$	O 2
3	$P_1 3$	$P_2 3$	O 3
4	$P_1 4$	$P_2 4$	O 4
5	$P_1 5$	$P_2 5$	O 5
6	$P_1 6$	$P_2 6$	O 6

Step 3
List the possible outcomes.

$S = \{P_1 1, P_1 2, P_1 3, P_1 4, P_1 5, P_1 6, P_2 1, P_2 2, P_2 3, P_2 4, P_2 5, P_2 6, O1, O2, O3, O4, O5, O6\}$

b) The draws $P_1 5$ and $P_2 5$ are both favourable, so there are 2 favourable outcomes out of a total of 18 equally probable outcomes. Therefore, the probability of drawing a purple marble and then rolling 5 is $\frac{2}{18}$, or $\frac{1}{9}$.

2. a) The number 4 is on 2 spaces on the spinner, so there are 2 favourable outcomes. There are 6 spaces with numbers other than 4, so there are 6 unfavourable outcomes. Therefore, the odds in favour of spinning 4 are 2:6. This can be reduced to 1:3.

   b) The spinner has 5 spaces with numbers other than 3, so there are 5 unfavourable outcomes. There are 3 spaces showing the number 3, so there are 3 favourable outcomes. Therefore, the odds against spinning 3 are 5:3.

3. a) The odds in favour of an event are the ratio of favourable to unfavourable outcomes. For every 3 favourable outcomes, there are 7 unfavourable outcomes.

   This means that for every 3 favourable outcomes, there are a total of $3 + 7 = 10$ possible outcomes. Therefore, the probability of drawing a blue marble is $\frac{3}{10}$.

b) According to the probability statement, for every 4 marbles in the bag, 1 of the marbles is red.

This means that $4 - 1 = 3$ marbles are not red. Therefore, the odds in favour of drawing a red marble are 1:3.

c) Oliver is most likely assuming that because the probability of drawing a blue marble is $\frac{3}{10}$ and the probability of drawing a red marble is $\frac{1}{4}$, there were 10 marbles in the bag in part a) and only 4 marbles in the bag in part b).

This is incorrect because probability and odds statements express ratios rather than actual amounts. For example, if a bag containing 20 marbles had 6 blue marbles and 5 red marbles, then $\frac{6}{20} = \frac{3}{10}$ of the marbles would be blue, and $\frac{5}{20} = \frac{1}{4}$ of them would be red.

PRACTICE EXERCISES
ANSWERS AND SOLUTIONS

1. On a standard six-sided die, there are a total of 6 possible outcomes. The multiples of 3 are 3 and 6, so there are 2 favourable outcomes. Therefore, the probability of rolling a multiple of 3 is $\frac{2}{6}$, or $\frac{1}{3}$.

3. **Step 1**
Calculate the odds in favour of rolling red.

On this four-sided die, there is one red side, so there is 1 favourable outcome. There are 3 sides that are not red, so there are 3 unfavourable outcomes. Therefore, the odds in favour of rolling red are 1:3.

Step 2
Calculate the odds against rolling red by reversing the order of the terms.

The odds against rolling red are 3:1.

5. **Step 1**
Calculate the odds in favour of drawing a red marble.

The bag contains 3 red marbles, so there are 3 favourable outcomes. There are 12 marbles that are not red, so there are 12 unfavourable outcomes. Therefore, the odds in favour of drawing a red marble are 3:12, or 1:4.

Step 2
Calculate the odds against drawing a red marble by reversing the order of the terms.

The odds against drawing a red marble are 4:1.

7. The section of the spinner with a circle takes up exactly half of the spinner, so it is equally likely to spin a circle or to spin a shape other than a circle. Therefore, for every 1 favourable outcome, there is 1 unfavourable outcome, and the odds of spinning a circle are 1:1.

9. **Step 1**
Identify the possible outcomes for each school:
- Nakiskaw High School: {Grade 10, Grade 11, Grade 12}
- Middleside High School: {Grade 10, Grade 11, Grade 12}

Step 2
Use a table to represent the sample space.

List the outcomes for Nakiskaw at the top of the table and the outcomes for Middleside along the left.

		Nakiskaw		
		10	**11**	**12**
Middleside	**10**	10,10	11,10	12,10
	11	10,11	11,11	12,11
	12	10,12	11,12	12,12

Step 3
Count the number of outcomes.

There are 9 ways to select two students who will lead the committee.

 Copyright Protected

11. Step 1
Identify the equally probable outcomes for each separate event:

- Drawing a marble: {green, yellow$_1$, yellow$_2$, red$_1$, red$_2$}
- Tossing the coin: {heads, tails}

Step 2
Use a tree diagram to represent the possible outcomes.

List the outcomes for drawing the marble on the left. Each of these outcomes will have two branches leading to the outcomes of tossing the coin.

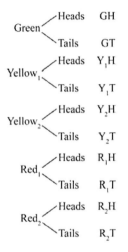

Step 3
Count the number of outcomes.

The sample space contains 10 equally probable outcomes.

13. If the odds in favour of an event are 2:7, then there are 2 favourable outcomes for every 7 unfavourable outcomes. This means that there are 2 + 7 = 9 total outcomes for every 2 favourable outcomes. Therefore, the probability of winning a door prize is $\dfrac{2}{9}$.

15. If the probability of rolling a sum of 6 is $\dfrac{5}{36}$, then there are 5 favourable outcomes for every 36 total outcomes. This means that there are 36 − 5 = 31 unfavourable outcomes for every 5 favourable outcomes. Therefore, the odds in favour of rolling a sum of six are 5:31.

Lesson 2—Mutually Exclusive and Non-Mutually Exclusive Events

CLASS EXERCISES
ANSWERS AND SOLUTIONS

1. a) There is no card showing both a circle and a square, so these events are mutually exclusive.

b) There are two cards that are triangles and black. Therefore, these events are non-mutually exclusive.

c) There is no card showing a shape that is both grey and white, so these events are mutually exclusive.

d) There is no card showing a grey circle, so these events are mutually exclusive.

2. a) The sample space of events A and B are the numbers from 1 to 10. Favourable outcomes for A are the numbers 2, 4, 6, 8, and 10, and favourable outcomes for B are the numbers 5 and 10. Because the number 10 is a favourable outcome for both events, A and B are non-mutually exclusive, and the circles in the diagram should overlap.

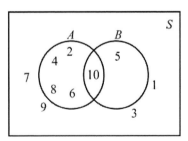

b) The event B' is the set of outcomes that are not elements of B. Therefore, $B' = \{1,\ 2,\ 3,\ 4,\ 6,\ 7,\ 8,\ 9\}$.

c) The event $(A \text{ or } B)'$ is the set of outcomes that are not elements of $(A \text{ or } B)$. Therefore, $(A \text{ or } B)' = \{1,\ 3,\ 7,\ 9\}$.

3. a) Call the probability of drawing a red marble $P(R)$ and the probability of drawing a yellow marble $P(Y)$. Drawing a red marble and drawing a yellow marble are mutually exclusive events, so apply the formula

$$P(R \cup Y) = P(R) + P(Y)$$

$$P(R \cup Y) = P(R) + P(Y)$$
$$P(R \cup Y) = 0.35 + 0.45$$
$$P(R \cup Y) = 0.8$$

Therefore, the probability of drawing a red or yellow marble is 0.8.

b) Call the probability of drawing a red marble $P(R)$ and the probability of drawing a white marble $P(W)$. Drawing a red marble and drawing a white marble are mutually exclusive events, so apply the formula

$$P(R \cup W) = P(R) + P(W).$$

$$P(R \cup W) = P(R) + P(W)$$
$$0.5 = 0.35 + P(W)$$
$$0.15 = P(W)$$

Therefore, the probability of drawing a white marble is 0.15.

4. a) Since some of the chocolates have chocolate and nuts, these are non-mutually exclusive events. Apply the formula

$$P(C \cup D) = P(C) + P(D) - P(C \cap D).$$

$$P(C \cup D) = P(C) + P(D) - P(C \cap D)$$
$$P(C \cup D) = \frac{1}{4} + \frac{1}{2} - \frac{1}{12}$$
$$P(C \cup D) = \frac{3}{12} + \frac{6}{12} - \frac{1}{12}$$
$$P(C \cup D) = \frac{8}{12}$$
$$P(C \cup D) = \frac{2}{3}$$

Therefore, the probability of choosing a chocolate with caramel or dark chocolate is $\frac{2}{3}$.

b) Since some of the chocolates have dark chocolate and nuts, these are non-mutually exclusive events. Apply the formula $P(D \cup N) = P(D) + P(N) - P(D \cap N)$.

$$P(D \cup N) = P(D) + P(N) - P(D \cap N)$$
$$\frac{2}{3} = \frac{1}{2} + \frac{1}{3} - P(D \cap N)$$
$$\frac{4}{6} = \frac{3}{6} + \frac{2}{6} - P(D \cap N)$$
$$P(D \cap N) = \frac{1}{6}$$

Therefore, the probability of choosing a chocolate with dark chocolate and nuts is $\frac{1}{6}$.

PRACTICE EXERCISES
ANSWERS AND SOLUTIONS

1. a) It is impossible land on a space that is both white and grey, so these events are mutually exclusive. They are not complementary, because it is possible to land on black spaces, which are neither white nor grey.

b) The numbers 12, 26, and 42 are all multiples of 2 and multiples of 3. Because the two events have common outcomes, they are non-mutually exclusive.

c) There is no white space on the spinner that has a perfect square, so these events are mutually exclusive. They are not complementary, because it is possible to land on spaces that are neither white nor a perfect square.

d) There is no black space on the spinner that has an even number, so these events are mutually exclusive. They are also complementary, because every space that does not have an even number is black, and every space that is not black has an even number.

e) The number 14 contains the digit 4, and it is on a grey space. Because these two events have a common outcome, they are non-mutually exclusive.

3. The event A' is the set of outcomes that are not elements of A. Therefore, $A' = \{2, 3.$
5, 6, 7, 8 10, 11, 12, 13, 14, 15, 17, 18, 19, 20\}.

5. The sample space of events C and D are the numbers from 1 to 20. Favourable outcomes for C are the numbers 2, 3, 5, 7, 11, 13, 17, and 19, and favourable outcomes for D are the numbers 1, 3, 5, 7, 9, 11, 13, 15, 17, and 19. Because the numbers 3, 5, 7, 11, 13, 17, and 19 are favourable outcomes for both events, C and D are non-mutually exclusive, and the circles in the diagram should overlap.

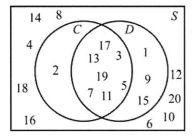

7. The event $(C \cup D)'$ is the set of outcomes that are not elements of either C or D. Therefore,
$$(C \cup D)' = \{4,\ 6,\ 8,\ 10,\ 12,\ 14,\ 16,\ 18,\ 20\}.$$

9. There are no shapes that are both trapezoids and triangles, so these are mutually exclusive events. Use the formula $P(A \cup B) = P(A) + P(B)$.

If event A is drawing a triangle, and event B is drawing a trapezoid, then $P(A) = 0.08$, and $P(A \cup B) = 0.40$.
$$P(A \cup B) = P(A) + P(B)$$
$$0.40 = 0.08 + P(B)$$
$$0.32 = P(B)$$

Therefore, the probability of drawing a trapezoid is 0.32.

11. Step 1
Calculate the probability of drawing a square or a triangle.

There are no shapes that are both squares and triangles, so these are mutually exclusive events. Use the formula $P(A \cup B) = P(A) + P(B)$.

If event A is drawing a square, and event B is drawing a triangle, then $P(A) = 0.20$, and $P(B) = 0.08$.
$$P(A \cup B) = P(A) + P(B)$$
$$P(A \cup B) = 0.20 + 0.08$$
$$P(A \cup B) = 0.28$$

Step 2
Calculate the probability of not drawing a square or a triangle.

Not drawing a square or a triangle is the complement of drawing a square or a triangle. Substitute $P(A \cup B) = 0.28$ into the formula
$$1 = P(A \cup B) + P(A \cup B)',$$ and solve for $P(A \cup B)'$.
$$1 = P(A \cup B) + P(A \cup B)'$$
$$1 = 0.28 + P(A \cup B)'$$
$$0.72 = P(A \cup B)'$$

Therefore, the probability of not drawing a square or a triangle is 0.72.

13. Step 1
Determine which formula to use.

Some of the marbles are small and blue, so these are non-mutually exclusive events. Use the formula $P(B \cup S) = P(B) + P(S) - P(B \cap S)$.

Step 2
Apply the formula.

Substitute the values $P(B) = \dfrac{5}{9}$, $P(B \cap S) = \dfrac{1}{9}$, and $P(B \cup S) = \dfrac{11}{18}$ into the formula, and solve for $P(S)$.
$$P(B \cup S) = P(B) + P(S) - P(B \cap S)$$
$$\frac{11}{18} = \frac{5}{9} + P(S) - \frac{1}{9}$$
$$\frac{11}{18} = \frac{10}{18} + P(S) - \frac{2}{18}$$
$$\frac{3}{18} = P(S)$$
$$\frac{1}{6} = P(S)$$

Therefore, the probability of drawing a small marble is $\dfrac{1}{6}$.

15. Step 1

Calculate the probability that a student selected at random does homework at home or at the library.

There are students who do homework both at home and at the library, so these are non-mutually exclusive events. Use the formula $P(A \cup B) = P(A) + P(B) - P(A \cap B)$.

If event A is selecting a student who does homework at home, and event B is selecting a student who does homework at the library, then $P(A) = 0.77$, $P(B) = 0.36$, and $P(A \cap B) = 0.25$.

$$P(A \cup B) = P(A) + P(B) - P(A \cap B)$$
$$P(A \cup B) = 0.77 + 0.36 - 0.25$$
$$P(A \cup B) = 0.88$$

Step 2

Calculate the probability that a student selected at random does not do homework at home or at the library.

Selecting a student who does not study at home or at the library is complementary to selecting a student who does study at one of these two locations. This means that the probability of selecting a student who does not do homework at home or at the library is equal to $P(A \cup B)'$.

The sum of the probabilities of an event and its complement are always equal to 1, so substitute $P(A \cup B) = 0.88$ into the formula $1 = P(A \cup B) + P(A \cup B)'$, and solve for $P(A \cup B)'$.

$$1 = P(A \cup B) + P(A \cup B)'$$
$$1 = 0.88 + P(A \cup B)'$$
$$0.12 = P(A \cup B)'$$

Therefore, the probability that a student selected at random does not study at home or at school is 12%.

Lesson 3—Dependent and Independent Events

CLASS EXERCISES
ANSWERS AND SOLUTIONS

1. a) If a black card were drawn the first time, then the number of favourable outcomes for the second draw would be one fewer than if a red card had been drawn. Therefore, the result of the first draw affects the probability for the second draw, and A and B are dependent.

b) The result of rolling the die will not have any effect on the spinner. Therefore, A and B are independent.

c) The result of the first die roll will not have any effect on the sample space for the second die roll. Therefore A and B are independent.

d) If a boy is selected the first time, then the number of favourable outcomes for selecting a boy the second time is one fewer than if a girl had been chosen. Therefore, the result of the first choice affects the sample space for the second choice, and A and B are dependent.

2. a) Call the probability of spinning 1 $P(1)$ and the probability of spinning 2 $P(2)$. Since spinning 1 and then spinning 2 are independent events, apply the formula $P(1 \cap 2) = P(1) \times P(2)$.

$$P(1 \cap 2) = P(1) \times P(2)$$
$$P(1 \cap 2) = 0.13 \times 0.36$$
$$P(1 \cap 2) = 0.0468$$

Therefore, the probability of spinning 1 and then 2 is 0.0468.

b) Call the probability of spinning 2 $P(2)$ and the probability of spinning 3 $P(3)$. Spinning 2 and then 3 are independent events, so apply the formula $P(2 \cap 3) = P(2) \times P(3)$.

$$P(2 \cap 3) = P(2) \times P(3)$$
$$0.1044 = 0.36 \times P(3)$$
$$0.29 = P(3)$$

Therefore, the probability of spinning 3 is 0.29.

3. Step 1

Determine which formula to use.

Number the dice 1 and 2. Event *M1* is rolling a multiple of 3 on the first die, event *M2* is rolling a multiple of 3 on the second die, event *F1* is rolling 4 on the first die, and event *F2* is rolling 4 on the second die. There are two ways to roll 4 and a multiple of 3: (*M1* and *F2*) or (*F1* and *M2*). Find the probability of each possibility, and then add them together.

When two dice are rolled, the outcome of one roll has no effect on the probability of the second roll, so these are independent events. Use the formula

$P(M \cap F) = \left[P(M_1) \times P(F_2)\right] + \left[P(F_1) \times P(M_2)\right]$.

Step 2

Calculate each separate probability.

Both dice are the same, so the probabilities will be the same for each of them. There are 2 multiples of 3, so $P(M_1) = P(M_2) = \dfrac{2}{6} = \dfrac{1}{3}$ and

$P(F_1) = P(F_2) = \dfrac{1}{6}$.

Step 3

Apply the formula

$P(M \cap F) = \left[P(M_1) \times P(F_2)\right] + \left[P(F_1) \times P(M_2)\right]$.

$P(M \cap F) = \left[P(M_1) \times P(F_2)\right] + \left[P(F_1) \times P(M_2)\right]$

$P(M \cap F) = \left[\dfrac{1}{3} \times \dfrac{1}{6}\right] + \left[\dfrac{1}{6} \times \dfrac{1}{3}\right]$

$P(M \cap F) = \dfrac{1}{18} + \dfrac{1}{18}$

$P(M \cap F) = \dfrac{2}{18}$

$P(M \cap F) = \dfrac{1}{9}$

Therefore, the probability of rolling 4 and a multiple of 3 is $\dfrac{1}{9}$.

4. Since the first card is not replaced before the second card is drawn, the sample space for the second event is different from the sample space for the first event, and the events are dependent. Use the formula $P(A \cap B) = P(A) \times P(B \mid A)$.

Step 1

Determine the probability of each event.

There are 52 cards in a standard deck, of which 13 are hearts and 13 are diamonds. If event *R* is drawing a red card in on the first draw, then

$P(R) = \dfrac{26}{52} = \dfrac{1}{2}$.

If event *S* is drawing a spade on the second draw, then $P(S \mid R)$ is the probability of drawing a spade on the second draw if a red card was drawn on the first draw. There are 13 spades in a standard deck, and after the first draw, there are 51 cards remaining. Therefore, $P(S \mid R) = \dfrac{13}{51}$.

Step 2

Apply the formula $P(R \cap S) = P(R) \times P(S \mid R)$.

$P(R \cap S) = P(R) \times P(S \mid R)$

$P(R \cap S) = \dfrac{1}{2} \times \dfrac{13}{51}$

$P(R \cap S) = \dfrac{13}{102}$

Therefore, the probability of drawing a red card and then a spade is $\dfrac{13}{102}$.

5. Step 1

Determine which formula to use.

There are two ways that cards can be flipped: the vowel could be flipped first, and the consonant could be flipped second; or the consonant could be flipped first, and the vowel could be flipped second. Find the probability of each possibility, and add them together.

Event *V1* is drawing a vowel on the first draw, event *V2* is drawing a vowel on the second draw, event *C1* is drawing a consonant on the first draw, and event *C2* is drawing a consonant on the second draw.

Since the second card is flipped without returning the first one, the sample space for the second event is different from the sample space for the first event, and the events are dependent. Use the formula

$P(V \cap C) = \left[P(V_1) \times P(C_2 \mid V_1)\right] + \left[P(C_1) \times P(V_2 \mid C_1)\right]$.

Step 2
Calculate each separate probability.

There are 7 cards to start with, of which 2 are vowels and 5 are consonants. Therefore,

$$P(V_1) = \frac{2}{7} \text{ and } P(C_1) = \frac{5}{7}.$$

If a vowel is drawn first, then there will be 6 letters left, of which 5 are consonants. Therefore,

$$P(C_2 \mid V_1) = \frac{5}{6}.$$

If a consonant is drawn first, then there will be 6 letters left, of which 2 are vowels. Therefore,

$$P(V_2 \mid C_1) = \frac{2}{6} = \frac{1}{3}.$$

Step 3
Apply the formula
$$P(V \cap C) = \left[P(V_1) \times P(C_2 \mid V_1) \right] + \left[P(C_1) \times P(V_2 \mid C_1) \right].$$
$$P(V \cap C) = \left[P(V_1) \times P(C_2 \mid V_1) \right] + \left[P(C_1) \times P(V_2 \mid C_1) \right]$$
$$P(V \cap C) = \left(\frac{2}{7} \times \frac{5}{6} \right) + \left(\frac{5}{7} + \frac{1}{3} \right)$$
$$P(V \cap C) = \frac{5}{21} + \frac{5}{21}$$
$$P(V \cap C) = \frac{10}{21}$$

Therefore, the probability that Stephan will flip over a vowel and a consonant is $\frac{10}{21}$.

PRACTICE EXERCISES
ANSWERS AND SOLUTIONS

---

1. **a)** Because the first tile is replaced before the second tile is drawn, the result of the first draw does not affect the sample space for the second draw. Therefore, the events are independent.

b) When the first tile is drawn and not replaced, the sample space for the second draw contains one fewer tile. Therefore, the result of the first draw affects the sample space for the second draw, and the events are dependent.

c) Even though the tile drawn from the first bag is not replaced before the second tile is drawn, the sample space for the second draw is not changed, because the second tile is drawn from a different bag. Therefore, the events are independent.

d) When two tiles are drawn simultaneously from a single bag, they should be treated as though one was drawn first and the other was drawn without replacing the first when calculating the probability. Therefore, the events are dependent.

e) Because the two tiles are drawn from different bags, the result of one draw has no effect on the sample space for the other. Therefore, the events are independent.

3. **Step 1**
Determine which formula to use.

Call the probability of rolling 1 on the first roll $P(A)$ and the probability of rolling 3 on the second roll $P(B)$. The result of the first die roll does not affect the probability of the second roll, so the events are independent. Use the formula
$$P(A \cap B) = P(A) \times P(B).$$

Step 2
Apply the formula $P(A \cap B) = P(A) \times P(B)$.
$$P(A \cap B) = P(A) \times P(B)$$
$$\frac{1}{36} = \frac{1}{12} \times P(B)$$
$$\frac{\left(\frac{1}{36} \right)}{\left(\frac{1}{12} \right)} = P(B)$$
$$\frac{1}{3} = P(B)$$

Therefore, the probability of rolling 3 is $\frac{1}{3}$.

5. Before the first marble is drawn, there are 9 marbles in the bag, and 2 of them are red. After a purple marble is drawn, there will be 8 marbles in the bag, of which 2 are red. Therefore,

$$P(R \mid P) = \frac{2}{8} = \frac{1}{4}.$$

 Copyright Protected

7. Before the first marble is drawn, there are 9 marbles in the bag, and 2 of them are red. After a red marble is drawn, there will be 8 marbles in the bag, of which only 1 is red. Therefore,

$$P\left(R_2 \mid R_1\right) = \frac{1}{8}.$$

9. **Step 1**
Determine which formula to use.

Because the first slip is replaced before the second slip is drawn, the sample space for the two events is exactly the same. The events are independent, so use the formula $P\left(A \cap B\right) = P\left(A\right) \times P\left(B\right)$.

Step 2
Calculate each separate probability.

For each draw, there are 12 even numbers and 5 multiples of 5 out of a total of 25 numbers in the bag. If A is drawing an even number, and B is drawing a multiple of 5, then $P\left(A\right) = \frac{12}{25}$ and

$$P\left(B\right) = \frac{5}{25} = \frac{1}{5}.$$

Step 3
Apply the formula $P\left(A \cap B\right) = P\left(A\right) \times P\left(B\right)$.

$$P\left(A \cap B\right) = P\left(A\right) \times P\left(B\right)$$
$$P\left(A \cap B\right) = \frac{12}{25} \times \frac{1}{5}$$
$$P\left(A \cap B\right) = \frac{12}{125}$$

Therefore, the probability of drawing an even number and then a multiple of 5 is $\frac{12}{125}$.

11. **Step 1**
Determine which formula to use.

There are two ways to draw an odd number and an even number: the even number can be drawn first, and the odd number can be drawn second; or the odd number can be drawn first, and the even number can be drawn second. Find the probability of each possibility, and then add them together.

Event *E1* is drawing an even number on the first draw, event *E2* is drawing an even number on the second draw, event *O1* is drawing an odd number on the first draw, and event *O2* is drawing an odd number on the second draw.

Since the second slip is drawn without returning the first one, the sample space for the second event is different from the sample space for the first event, and the events are dependent. Use the formula
$$P\left(E \cap O\right) = \left[P\left(E_1\right) \times P\left(O_2 \mid E_1\right)\right] + \left[P\left(O_1\right) \times P\left(E_2 \mid O_1\right)\right].$$

Step 2
Calculate each separate probability.

For the first draw, there are 12 even numbers and 13 odd numbers out of a total of 25 numbers in the bag. Therefore, $P\left(E_1\right) = \frac{12}{25}$ and $P\left(O_1\right) = \frac{13}{25}$.

If an even number is drawn first, then there will be 24 slips left, of which 13 are odd numbers. Therefore, $P\left(O_2 \mid E_1\right) = \frac{13}{24}$.

If an odd number is drawn first, then there will be 24 slips left, of which 12 are even numbers. Therefore, $P\left(E_2 \mid O_1\right) = \frac{12}{24} = \frac{1}{2}$.

Step 3
Apply the formula
$$P\left(E \cap O\right) = \left[P\left(E_1\right) \times P\left(O_2 \mid E_1\right)\right] + \left[P\left(O_1\right) \times P\left(E_2 \mid O_1\right)\right].$$
$$P\left(E \cap O\right) = \left[P\left(E_1\right) \times P\left(O_2 \mid E_1\right)\right] + \left[P\left(O_1\right) \times P\left(E_2 \mid O_1\right)\right]$$
$$P\left(E \cap O\right) = \left(\frac{12}{25} \times \frac{13}{24}\right) + \left(\frac{13}{25} \times \frac{1}{2}\right)$$
$$P\left(E \cap O\right) = \frac{13}{50} + \frac{13}{50}$$
$$P\left(E \cap O\right) = \frac{26}{50}$$
$$P\left(E \cap O\right) = \frac{13}{25}$$

Therefore, the probability of drawing an even number and an odd number is $\frac{13}{25}$.

PRACTICE TEST

ANSWERS AND SOLUTIONS

1. The sample space contains all of the possible outcomes. Use subscripted numbers to differentiate results that are the same, such as the letters that are repeated.

The sample space for this experiment is {M, A, T, H}.

3. There are 3 outcomes that are not a vowel and 1 outcome that is a vowel. Therefore, the odds against drawing a vowel are 3:1.

5. Not spinning green is the complement of spinning green. The sum of the probabilities of complementary events is always 1, so apply the formula $1 = P(G) + P(G')$.

$$1 = P(G) + P(G')$$
$$1 = 0.2 + P(G')$$
$$0.8 = P(G')$$

Therefore, the probability of not spinning green is 0.8.

Note: It is also possible to determine the probability of not spinning green by dividing the number of spaces that are not green by the total number of spaces. This is $\frac{4}{5}$, or 0.8.

7. Step 1
Use Aiden's method. A two-way table of this experiment is as follows:

		First spin									
		1	**2_1**	**2_2**	**3_1**	**3_2**	**3_3**	**3_4**	**3_5**	**3_6**	**3_7**
Second spin	**1**	1,1	2,1	2,1	3,1	3,1	3,1	3,1	3,1	3,1	3,1
	2_1	1,2	2,2	2,2	3,2	3,2	3,2	3,2	3,2	3,2	3,2
	2_2	1,2	2,2	2,2	3,2	3,2	3,2	3,2	3,2	3,2	3,2
	3_1	1,3	2,3	2,3	3,3	3,3	3,3	3,3	3,3	3,3	3,3
	3_2	1,3	2,3	2,3	3,3	3,3	3,3	3,3	3,3	3,3	3,3
	3_3	1,3	2,3	2,3	3,3	3,3	3,3	3,3	3,3	3,3	3,3
	3_4	1,3	2,3	2,3	3,3	3,3	3,3	3,3	3,3	3,3	3,3
	3_5	1,3	2,3	2,3	3,3	3,3	3,3	3,3	3,3	3,3	3,3
	3_6	1,3	2,3	2,3	3,3	3,3	3,3	3,3	3,3	3,3	3,3
	3_7	1,3	2,3	2,3	3,3	3,3	3,3	3,3	3,3	3,3	3,3

The table shows a total of 100 possible outcomes. The 14 shaded outcomes are all favourable. According to the probability formula, the probability of spinning 3 and then 2 is $\frac{14}{100}$, or 14%.

Step 2
Use Victor's method. The probability of two independent events can be determined using the formula $P(A \text{ and } B) = P(A) \times P(B)$. If A is spinning 3 on the first spin and B is spinning 2 on the second spin, then A and B are independent events, and the formula can be used.

Copyright Protected

There are 10 equal-sized spaces on the spinner, of which 2 are 2s and 7 are 3s. Therefore, $P(A) = \dfrac{7}{10}$ and $P(B) = \dfrac{2}{10}$.

$$P(A \text{ and } B) = P(A) \times P(B)$$

$$P(A \text{ and } B) = \frac{7}{10} \times \frac{2}{10}$$

$$P(A \text{ and } B) = \frac{14}{100}$$

Victor's method also shows that the probability of spinning 3 and then 2 is $\dfrac{14}{100}$, or 14%.

9. The probability of winning a prize at Cluck-King is $\dfrac{1}{7}$, so there is 1 favourable outcome for every 7 total outcomes. This means that there are $7 - 1 = 6$ unfavourable outcomes for every favourable outcome. Therefore, the odds in favour of winning a prize at Cluck-King are 1:6.

11. Call the probability that the flight will be delayed $P(D)$. If the flight is not delayed, then it must be early or on time; therefore, the probability that a flight will be early or on time is $P(D)'$.

The probability that a flight is delayed is 30%, so substitute 0.30 for $P(D)$ in the equation $P(D) + P(D') = 1$.

$$P(D) + P(D') = 1$$
$$0.30 + P(D') = 1$$
$$P(D') = 0.70$$

Therefore, the probability that Carlene's friend's flight will be early or on time is 70%.

13. **Step 1**
List the favourable outcomes for each event:
A—Odd numbers between 1 and 10 are 1, 3, 5, 7, and 9.

B—Perfect squares between 1 and 10 are 1, 4, and 9.

Step 2
Organize the information using a Venn diagram.

The two events share outcomes, so these are non-mutually exclusive events, and the circles in the diagram should overlap. The sample space, S, contains all of the possible outcomes of rolling the die.

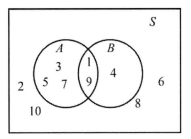

The event $A \cup B$ is rolling an odd number or rolling a perfect square. All of the favourable outcomes for this event are found in the shaded area of the Venn diagram.

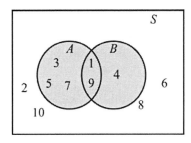

The event $A \cup B$ contains 6 outcomes, and the experiment has a total of 10 outcomes.

Therefore, $P(A \cup B) = \dfrac{6}{10} = \dfrac{3}{5}$.

15. **Step 1**
Determine the size of the sample space.

The sample space contains all of the students whose results are shown in the Venn diagram. Calculate the total of the numbers in each region of the diagram.
$$30 + 50 + 28 + 12 = 120$$

Therefore, the sample space contains 120 students.

Step 2
Calculate $P(C)$.

Of the 120 students, $30 + 50 = 80$ students are enrolled in a computer course. Therefore, $P(C) = \dfrac{80}{120} = \dfrac{2}{3}$, and Amber's calculation is correct.

Step 3
Calculate $P(D')$.

Of the 120 students, $30 + 12 = 42$ students are not enrolled in a data management course. Therefore, $P(D') = \dfrac{42}{120} = \dfrac{7}{20}$, and Amber's calculation is correct.

Step 4
Calculate $P(C \cap D)$.

The probability $P(C \cap D)$ is the likelihood that a student chosen at random is enrolled in both a computer course and a data management course. Of the 120 students, 50 students are enrolled in both courses. Therefore, $P(C \cap D) = \dfrac{50}{120} = \dfrac{5}{12}$, and Amber's calculation is incorrect.

Step 5
Calculate $P(C \cup D)'$.

The probability $P(C \cup D)'$ is the likelihood that a student chosen at random is not enrolled in either course. Of the 120 students, 12 students are enrolled in neither computer nor data management courses. Therefore, $P(C \cup D)' = \dfrac{12}{120} = \dfrac{1}{10}$, and Amber's calculation is correct.

17. Step 1
Determine which formula to use.

Some of the beads are round and white, so these are non-mutually exclusive events. Use the formula
$P(R \text{ or } W) = P(R) + P(W) - P(R \text{ and } W)$.

Step 2
Apply the formula.

Substitute the values $P(R) = 0.47$, $P(R \text{ or } W) = 0.67$, and $P(R \text{ and } W) = 0.08$ into the formula, and then solve for $P(W)$.
$$P(R \text{ or } W) = P(R) + P(W) - P(R \text{ and } W)$$
$$0.67 = 0.47 + P(W) - 0.08$$
$$0.28 = P(W)$$

Therefore, the probability of drawing a white bead is 0.28.

19. Step 1
Determine which formula to use.

The question states that passing math and passing chemistry are independent events. Event M is passing math, and event C is passing chemistry. To determine the probability of passing math and failing chemistry, use the formula
$P(M \cap C') = P(M) \times P(C')$.

Step 2
Determine $P(C')$.

Passing chemistry and not passing chemistry are complementary events, so the sum of their probabilities is 1. Substitute $P(C) = 0.78$ into the formula $1 = P(C) + P(C')$, and solve for $P(C')$.
$$1 = P(C) + P(C')$$
$$1 = 0.78 + P(C')$$
$$0.22 = P(C')$$

Step 3
Apply the formula.

Substitute $P(M) = 0.82$ and $P(C') = 0.22$ into the formula $P(M \cap C') = P(M) \times P(C')$.
$$P(M \cap C') = P(M) \times P(C')$$
$$P(M \cap C') = 0.82 \times 0.22$$
$$P(M \cap C') = 0.1804$$

Therefore, the probability that Xavier will pass math but not chemistry is about 0.18.

21. Step 1
Determine which formula to use.

It is possible for both boys to score a point, so B and C are non-mutually exclusive events. Use the formula $P(B \cup C) = P(B) + P(C) - P(B \cap C)$.

Step 2
Substitute the values $P(B) = \dfrac{7}{10}$, $P(C) = \dfrac{3}{5}$, and

$P[B \cap C] = \dfrac{21}{50}$ into the formula.

$P(B \cup C) = P(B) + P(C) - P(B \cap C)$

$P(B \cup C) = \dfrac{7}{10} + \dfrac{3}{5} - \dfrac{21}{50}$

$P(B \cup C) = \dfrac{35}{50} + \dfrac{30}{50} - \dfrac{21}{50}$

$P(B \cup C) = \dfrac{44}{50}$

$P(B \cup C) = \dfrac{22}{25}$

Therefore, the probability that at least one of the boys will score a point is $\dfrac{22}{25}$.

23. If *O1* is drawing a letter O on the first draw, and *O2* is drawing a letter O on the second draw, then $P(O2|O1)$ is the probability of drawing a letter O on the second draw if a letter O was already drawn on the first draw.

The word TORONTO has 7 letters, of which 3 are the letter O. After a letter O is drawn, there will be 6 letters remaining, of which 2 are the letter O.

Therefore, $P(O_2 \mid O_1) = \dfrac{2}{6} = \dfrac{1}{3}$.

25. Calculate the probability if the first card is not replaced before the second card is drawn.

From step 1, $P(B_1) = \dfrac{26}{52} = \dfrac{1}{2}$. Once a black card is drawn, 51 cards remain in the deck, of which 25 are black. Therefore $P(B_2 \mid B_1) = \dfrac{25}{51}$.

Substitute these values into the formula
$P(B_1 \cap B_2) = P(B_1) \times P(B_2 \mid B_1)$.

$P(B_1 \cap B_2) = P(B_1) \times P(B_2 \mid B_1)$

$P(B_1 \cap B_2) = \dfrac{1}{2} \times \dfrac{25}{51}$

$P(B_1 \cap B_2) = \dfrac{25}{102}$

Therefore, the probability of drawing two black cards when the first card is not replaced before the second card is drawn is $\dfrac{25}{102}$.

27. There are two ways to draw a queen and a king: the queen could be drawn first and the king second, or the king could be drawn first and the queen second. Find the probability of each possibility, and add them together.

Step 1
Calculate the probability if the first card is replaced before the second card is drawn.

Out of 52 cards in the deck, 4 are queens and 4 are kings, so $P(Q) = \dfrac{4}{52} = \dfrac{1}{13}$ and $P(K) = \dfrac{4}{52} = \dfrac{1}{13}$.

Substitute these values into the formula
$P(Q \cap K) = \left[P(Q_1) \times P(K_2) \right] + \left[P(K_1) \times P(Q_2) \right]$.

$P(Q \cap K) = \left[P(Q_1) \times P(K_2) \right] + \left[P(K_1) \times P(Q_2) \right]$

$P(Q \cap K) = \left[\dfrac{1}{13} \times \dfrac{1}{13} \right] + \left[\dfrac{1}{13} \times \dfrac{1}{13} \right]$

$P(Q \cap K) = \dfrac{1}{169} + \dfrac{1}{169}$

$P(Q \cap K) = \dfrac{2}{169}$

Therefore, the probability of drawing a queen and a king when the first card is replaced before the second card is drawn is $\dfrac{2}{169}$.

Step 2
Calculate the probability if the first card is not replaced before the second card is drawn.

From step 1, $P(Q) = P(K) = \dfrac{4}{52} = \dfrac{1}{13}$. If a queen is drawn first, 51 cards remain in the deck, of which 4 cards are kings. If a king is drawn first, then 51 cards will remain in the deck, of which 4 are queens.

Therefore, $P(K \mid Q) = \dfrac{4}{51}$, and $P(K \mid Q) = \dfrac{4}{51}$.

Substitute these values into the formula

$$P(Q \cap K) = \left[P(Q_1) \times P(K_2 \mid Q_1) \right] \\ + \left[P(K_1) \times P(Q_2 \mid K_1) \right].$$

$$P(Q \cap K) = \left[P(Q_1) \times P(K_2 \mid Q_1) \right] \\ + \left[P(K_1) \times P(Q_2 \mid K_1) \right]$$

$$P(Q \cap K) = \left[\dfrac{1}{13} \times \dfrac{4}{51} \right] + \left[\dfrac{1}{13} \times \dfrac{4}{51} \right]$$

$$P(Q \cap K) = \dfrac{1}{663} + \dfrac{1}{663}$$

$$P(Q \cap K) = \dfrac{2}{663}$$

Therefore, the probability of drawing a queen and a king when the first card is not replaced before the second card is drawn is $\dfrac{2}{663}$.

THE FUNDAMENTAL COUNTING PRINCIPLE, PERMUTATIONS, AND COMBINATIONS

Lesson 1—The Fundamental Counting Principle

CLASS EXERCISES ANSWERS AND SOLUTIONS

1. **a)**

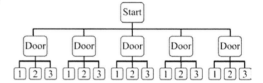

b) The tree diagram shows that the number of different choices is 15.

2. **Step 1**
    List the stages of the task.
    The task is to make a 5-character licence plate that fits the given restrictions. This task has five stages:
    1. Select the first character. There are 21 consonants in the alphabet, so there are 21 choices for the first character.
    2. Select the second character. This letter must be a vowel. There are 5 vowels, so there are 5 choices for the second character.
    3. Select the third character. Since the third character must be a consonant, there are 21 choices for the third character.
    4. Select the fourth character. An odd digit must be selected. Since there are 5 odd digits (1, 3, 5, 7, and 9), there are 5 choices for the fourth character.
    5. Select the fifth character. From the remaining 4 odd digits, there are 4 choices for the fifth character.

Step 2
Determine the number of possible licence plates for this particular province.

Apply the fundamental counting principle. Multiply the number of choices for each character on the licence plate.
$21 \times 5 \times 21 \times 5 \times 4 = 44\,100$

There are 44 100 possible licence plates for this particular province.

PRACTICE EXERCISES
ANSWERS AND SOLUTIONS

1.

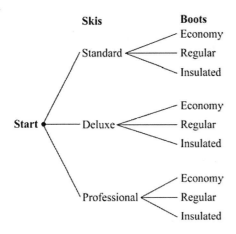

Skis   Boots

Start • — Standard — Economy / Regular / Insulated
— Deluxe — Economy / Regular / Insulated
— Professional — Economy / Regular / Insulated

3. According to the tree diagram, the total number of rental packages possible is 9.

5. **Step 1**
Determine the number of possible assignments for each digit.

The first digit cannot be 0; therefore, there are 9 ways to assign the first digit. For the next 3 digits, repetitions are allowed, which means there are 10 possible assignments for each digit.

Step 2
Apply the fundamental counting principle.
$9 \times 10 \times 10 \times 10 = 9000$

There are 9 000 possible four-digit bank codes in which repetitions are allowed.

7. **Step 1**
Determine the number of possible choices for each digit.

This task involves five stages:
1. Assign the first digit. The five-digit number can begin with a 7 or an 8. Therefore, there are 2 ways to assign the first digit.
2. Assign the second digit. There are 10 digits between 0 and 9. Therefore, there are 10 ways to assign the second digit.
3. Assign the third digit. There are 10 ways to assign the third digit.
4. Assign the fourth digit. There are 10 ways to assign the fourth digit.
5. Assign the fifth digit. The five-digit number has to be even. Any number ending in 0, 2, 4, 6, or 8 is even. Therefore, there are 5 ways to assign the last digit.

Step 2
Determine the number of even five-digit whole numbers that begin with a 7 or an 8.
Apply the fundamental counting principle.
$2 \times 10 \times 10 \times 10 \times 5 = 10\,000$

Therefore, there are 10 000 different even five-digit even numbers that begin with a 7 or an 8.

9. **Step 1**
Determine the number of possible choices for each letter.

This task involves three stages:
1. Assign the first letter. Since the first letter is L, there is 1 way to assign the first letter.
2. Assign the last letter. Since the last letter is P, there is 1 way to assign the third letter.
3. Assign the second digit. Since there are no repetitions, there are 24 ways to assign the second letter.

Step 2
Determine the number of three-letter arrangements that begin with L and end with P if there are no repetitions.

Applying the fundamental counting principle, the number of three-letter arrangements is
$1 \times 24 \times 1 = 24$.

Lesson 2—Factorial Notation

CLASS EXERCISES
ANSWERS AND SOLUTIONS

1. **Step 1**
   Rewrite the factorials as products.
   $$\frac{9!}{3!}$$
   $$=\frac{9\times8\times7\times6\times5\times4\times3\times2\times1}{3\times2\times1}$$

   Step 2
   Cancel out the common factors in the numerator and denominator, and evaluate.
   $$\frac{9\times8\times7\times6\times5\times4\times3\times2\times1}{3\times2\times1}$$
   $$=9\times8\times7\times6\times5\times4$$
   $$=60480$$

   Therefore, $\frac{9!}{3!}=60\,480$.

2. **Step 1**
   Enter the numerator.
   Press $\boxed{2}$ $\boxed{1}$ $\boxed{\text{MATH}}$ $\boxed{\triangleleft}$, and select 4:!.

   Step 2
   Enter the denominator.
   Press $\boxed{\div}$ $\boxed{1}$ $\boxed{6}$ $\boxed{\text{MATH}}$ $\boxed{\triangleleft}$, and select 4:!.

   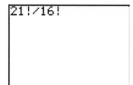

   Step 3
   Press $\boxed{\text{ENTER}}$.

   ```
   21!/16!
           2441880
   ```

3. **Step 1**
   Rewrite the numerator as
   $(n-34)(n-35)(n-36)!$.
   $$\frac{(n-34)!}{(n-36)!}$$
   $$=\frac{(n-34)(n-35)(n-36)!}{(n-36)!}$$

   Step 2
   Cancel out the common factors in the numerator and denominator, and then evaluate.
   $$\frac{(n-34)(n-35)(n-36)!}{(n-36)!}$$
   $$=(n-34)(n-35)$$

   Therefore, the simplified form of $\frac{(n-15)!}{(n-13)!}$ is
   $(n-34)(n-35)$, or $n^2-69n+1190$.

4. **Step 1**
   Divide both sides by $(n-4)!$.
   $$90(n-4)!=(n-2)!$$
   $$90=\frac{(n-2)!}{(n-4)!}$$

   Step 2
   Rewrite as $(n-2)!$ as $(n-2)(n-3)(n-4)!$.
   $$90=\frac{(n-2)!}{(n-4)!}$$
   $$90=\frac{(n-2)(n-3)(n-4)!}{(n-4)!}$$

   Step 3
   Cancel out common factors, and expand.
   $$90=\frac{(n-2)(n-3)(n-4)!}{(n-4)!}$$
   $$90=(n-2)(n-3)$$
   $$90=n^2-5n+6$$

   Step 4
   Bring all terms to one side, and factor.
   $$90=n^2-5n+6$$
   $$0=n^2-5n-84$$
   $$0=(n-12)(n+7)$$

Step 5

Solve for n.

$0 = (n-12)(n+7)$

$n-12 = 0 \qquad n+7 = 0$

$\qquad n = 12 \qquad\quad n = -7$

Since n cannot be a negative integer, the value of n is 12.

PRACTICE EXERCISES
ANSWERS AND SOLUTIONS

---

1. **Step 1**

    Rewrite the denominator as $9 \times 8 \times 7 \times 6!$.

    $$\frac{6!}{9!} = \frac{6!}{9 \times 8 \times 7 \times 6!}$$

    Step 2

    Cancel out the common factors in the numerator and denominator, and then evaluate.

    $$\frac{6!}{9 \times 8 \times 7 \times 6!}$$
    $$= \frac{1}{9 \times 8 \times 7}$$
    $$= \frac{1}{504}$$

    Therefore, $\dfrac{6!}{9!} = \dfrac{1}{504}$.

3. **Step 1**

    Rewrite $26!$ as $26 \times 25 \times 24!$.

    $$\frac{26!}{24!} - 17 = \frac{26 \times 25 \times 24!}{24!} - 17$$

    Step 2

    Cancel out the common factors in the numerator and denominator, and then evaluate.

    $$\frac{26 \times 25 \times 24!}{24!} - 17$$
    $$= (26 \times 25) - 17$$
    $$= 650 - 17$$
    $$= 633$$

    Therefore, $\dfrac{26!}{24!} - 17 = 633$.

5. **Step 1**

    Rewrite the numerator as $(n+1)n!$.

    $$\frac{(n+1)!}{n!} = \frac{(n+1)n!}{n!}$$

    Step 2

    Cancel out the common factors in the numerator and denominator.

    $$\frac{(n+1)n!}{n!} = n+1$$

    Therefore, the simplified form of $\dfrac{(n+1)!}{n!}$ is $n+1$.

7. **Step 1**

    Rewrite the numerator as $(n+1)(n)(n-1)(n-2)!$.

    $$\frac{(n+1)!}{(n-2)!} = \frac{(n+1)(n)(n-1)(n-2)!}{(n-2)!}$$

    Step 2

    Cancel out the common factors in the numerator and denominator.

    $$\frac{(n+1)(n)(n-1)(n-2)!}{(n-2)!}$$
    $$= (n+1)(n)(n-1)$$

    Therefore, $\dfrac{(n+1)!}{(n-2)!} = (n+1)(n)(n-1)$.

9. **Step 1**

    Divide both sides by $(n+7)!$.

    $$(n+9)! = 342(n+7)!$$
    $$\frac{(n+9)!}{(n+7)!} = 342$$

    Step 2

    Rewrite the numerator as $(n+9)(n+8)(n+7)!$.

    $$\frac{(n+9)!}{(n+7)!} = 342$$
    $$\frac{(n+9)(n+8)(n+7)!}{(n+7)!} = 342$$

Step 3

Cancel out the common factors, and expand.

$$\frac{(n+9)(n+8)(n+7)!}{(n+7)!} = 342$$
$$(n+9)(n+8) = 342$$
$$n^2 + 17n + 72 = 342$$

Step 4

Bring all the terms to one side, and factor the trinomial.

$$n^2 + 17n + 72 = 342$$
$$n^2 + 17n - 270 = 0$$
$$(n+27)(n-10) = 0$$

Step 5

Solve for n.

$$(n+27)(n-10) = 0$$

$$n + 27 = 0 \qquad\qquad n - 10 = 0$$
$$n = -27 \qquad\qquad n = 10$$

Since n cannot be a negative integer, $n = 10$.

Lesson 3—Permutations

CLASS EXERCISES
ANSWERS AND SOLUTIONS

1. Since there are 11 different acts for the talent show, and they are going one after another, the order matters. The number of permutations of the 11 acts given in factorial notation is 11!.

2. If you were to determine how many arrangements there are for planting 10 distinct trees, there would be 10! arrangements. However, not all of the trees are distinct.

    If each tree is represented by its first letter (P for pine, E for elm, B for birch, and W for willow), the arrangement consists of 3 P's, 4 E's, 2 B's, and 1 W. For example, one possible order to plant the trees would be EEBWPEPPBE, and another order would be PEPEEEBPBW.

    The number of possible arrangements for planting the trees is $\dfrac{10!}{3!4!2!1!} = 12600$.

3. **Step 1**

    Substitute 12 for n and 5 for r in the formula

    $$_nP_r = \frac{n!}{(n-r)!}.$$

    $$_nP_r = \frac{n!}{(n-r)!}$$
    $$_{12}P_5 = \frac{12!}{(12-5)!}$$
    $$_{12}P_5 = \frac{12!}{7!}$$

    Step 2

    Evaluate $\dfrac{12!}{7!}$.

    Using a calculator, the value of $\dfrac{12!}{7!}$ is 95 040.

    Therefore, $_{12}P_5 = 95040$.

4. There are 6 children, and the number of different seating arrangements of 4 children is required. This problem is a permutation problem. The number of different seating arrangements of 4 children is given by $_6P_4$.

    To evaluate $_6P_4$ using a TI-83 or similar calculator, press $\boxed{6}$ $\boxed{\text{MATH}}$ $\boxed{\triangleleft}$ to access the PRB menu. Select 2: $_nP_r$, and press $\boxed{4}$ $\boxed{\text{ENTER}}$.

    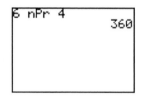

    The result is 360. Therefore, there are 360 different seating arrangements.

5. **Step 1**

    Determine the number of different arrangements with the father in the first place and the mother in the last place.

    There is 1 way to fill the first and last spots. Consider the 2 sons as a one group and the 2 daughters as the second group. Therefore, the number of different arrangements is $(1 \times 2! \times 1) = 2$.

Step 2
Determine how many ways the sons and daughters can arrange themselves within their own groups. The two sons can be arranged within their group in 2!, or 2, ways. The two daughters can be arranged within their group in 2!, or 2, ways.

Step 3
Applying the fundamental counting principle, the total number of arrangements is $2 \times 2 \times 2 = 8$.

6. **Step 1**
Determine the total number of arrangements without restrictions.

Since there are 6 distinct sports cars, the total number of arrangements for the parade is 6! = 720.

Step 2
Determine the number of arrangements with the two cars together.

If the two cars are considered to be one group, then a possible arrangement is as follows:

| Car 1 and Car 2 | 3 | 4 | 5 | 6 |

There are 5 blocks altogether. Therefore, the number of permutations of the 5 groups where the 2 cars are together is $5! \times 2! = 60$.

Step 3
Determine the number of arrangements where the 2 cars are not together.
$720 - 60 = 660$

The number of arrangements is 660.

PRACTICE EXERCISES
ANSWERS AND SOLUTION

1. **Step 1**
Substitute 11 for n and 3 for r in the formula

$_nP_r = \dfrac{n!}{(n-r)!}$.

$_nP_r = \dfrac{n!}{(n-r)!}$

$_{11}P_3 = \dfrac{11!}{(11-3)!}$

$_{11}P_3 = \dfrac{11!}{8!}$

Step 2
Rewrite $\dfrac{11!}{8!}$ as a quotient of products, and then reduce the numerator and denominator.

$_{11}P_3 = \dfrac{11!}{8!}$

$_{11}P_3 = \dfrac{11 \times 10 \times 9 \times 8!}{8!}$

$_{11}P_3 = 11 \times 10 \times 9$

$_{11}P_3 = 990$

3. **Step 1**

Apply the formula $_nP_r = \dfrac{n!}{(n-r)!}$.

In the equation $_{n+1}P_2 = 2$, rewrite $_{n+2}P_2$ as

$\dfrac{(n+1)!}{((n+1)-2)!}$.

$_{n+1}P_2 = 2$

$\dfrac{(n+1)!}{((n+1)-2)!} = 2$

$\dfrac{(n+1)!}{(n-1)!} = 2$

Step 2
Rewrite $(n+1)!$ as $(n+1)n(n-1)!$.

$\dfrac{(n+1)!}{(n-1)!} = 2$

$\dfrac{(n+1)n(n-1)!}{(n-1)!} = 2$

Step 3
Divide out common factors, and solve for n.

$\dfrac{(n+1)n(n-1)!}{(n-1)!} = 2$

$(n+1)n = 2$

$n^2 + n = 2$

$n^2 + n - 2 = 0$

Factor $n^2 + n - 2 = 0$.

$(n-1)(n+2) = 0$

$n - 1 = 0 \qquad n + 2 = 0$

$n = 1 \qquad\quad n = -2$

Since $(n+1) \geq 2$, the value of n is 1.

5. Kyla can listen to 4 CDs in 4! different arrangements in which order matters. Evaluate 4!.

$4!$
$= 4 \times 3 \times 2 \times 1$
$= 2$

Kyla can listen to 4 CDs in 24 different arrangements.

7. Sarah has 9 gifts to give, including 3 identical music books, and 4 identical tuning forks.

Therefore, there are $\dfrac{9!}{3!4!} = 2520$ ways of distributing the gifts.

9. There are 8 competitors, and the number of different outcomes for the top 3 positions in the race is required. Therefore, the number of different arrangements is $_8P_3 = 336$.

Lesson 4—Combinations

CLASS EXERCISES
ANSWERS AND SOLUTIONS

1. The order in which the numbers are selected for a raffle ticket does not matter. In other words, a raffle ticket with the selected numbers 3, 45, 63, 1, and 33 is the same as a raffle ticket with the selected numbers 33, 45, 1, 63, and 3. Therefore, this is a combination problem.

2. The order in which the students are organized in groups of 4 does not matter. Therefore, this is a combination problem.

    Since there are 22 students in Ms. Joseph's gym class, and the group contains 4 students, she can choose a group of 4 in $_{22}C_4$ ways.

    Step 1

    In the formula $_nC_r = \dfrac{n!}{(n-r)!r!}$, substitute 22 for n and 4 for r.

    $_nC_r = \dfrac{n!}{(n-r)!r!}$
    $_{22}C_4 = \dfrac{22!}{(22-4)!4!}$
    $_{22}C_4 = \dfrac{22!}{18!4!}$

Step 2
Determine the value of $_{22}C_4$.

$_{22}C_4 = \dfrac{22!}{18!4!}$
$_{22}C_4 = 7315$

Therefore, Ms. Joseph can organize 7 315 different groups.

3. **Step 1**

    Apply the formula $_nC_r = \dfrac{n!}{(n-r)!r!}$.

    In the equation $_nC_2 = 28$, rewrite $_nC_2$ as

    $\dfrac{n!}{(n-2)!2!}$.

    $_nC_2 = 28$
    $\dfrac{n!}{(n-2)!2!} = 28$

    Step 2
    Rewrite $n!$ as $n(n-1)(n-2)!$.

    $\dfrac{n!}{(n-2)!2!} = 28$
    $\dfrac{(n-1)(n-2)!}{(n-2)!2!} = 28$

    Step 3
    Divide out common factors.
    $\dfrac{n(n-1)(n-2)!}{(n-2)!2!} = 28$
    $\dfrac{n(n-1)}{2!} = 28$

    Step 4
    Solve for n.
    $\dfrac{n(n-1)}{2!} = 28$
    $\dfrac{n^2 - n}{2 \times 1} = 28$
    $n^2 - n = 56$
    $n^2 - n - 56 = 0$
    $(n+7)(n-8) = 0$
    $n + 7 = 0 \qquad n - 8 = 0$
    $n = -7 \qquad n = 8$

    Since $n \geq 2$, the solution is $n = 8$.

4. The order in which the members of the committee are selected does not matter. Therefore, this is a combination problem. Since there are 10 people available for the committee, and 6 members are required, the number of possible committees is $_{10}C_6 = 210$.

5. A hospital team is made of 2 doctors and 5 nurses. There are 3 doctors and 12 nurses to choose from. The order in which the doctors and nurses are chosen does not matter.

Step 1
Determine the number of possible selections of doctors.

A hospital team consists of 2 doctors, and there are 3 doctors to choose from.

Therefore, the number of possible selections of doctors is $_3C_2 = 3$.

Step 2
Determine the number of possible selections of nurses.

A hospital team consists of 5 nurses, and there are 12 nurses to choose from.

Therefore, the number of possible selections of nurses is $_{12}C_5 = 792$.

Step 3
Determine the number of different hospital teams. Applying the fundamental counting principle, the total number of different hospital teams possible is $_3C_2 \times {_{12}C_5} = 3 \times 792 = 2376$.

PRACTICE EXERCISES
ANSWERS AND SOLUTIONS

---

1. In the formula $_nC_r = \dfrac{n!}{(n-r)!r!}$, substitute 7 for n and 5 for r.

Step 1
$$_nC_r = \frac{n!}{(n-r)!r!}$$
$$_7C_5 = \frac{7!}{(7-5)!5!}$$
$$_7C_5 = \frac{7!}{2!5!}$$

Step 2
Evaluate $\dfrac{7!}{2!5!}$.

$$\frac{7!}{2!5!}$$
$$= \frac{7 \times 6 \times 5!}{2!5!}$$
$$= \frac{7 \times 6}{2!}$$
$$= \frac{7 \times 6}{2 \times 1}$$
$$= 21$$

Therefore, $_7C_5 = 21$.

3. Step 1

Apply the formula $_nC_r = \dfrac{n!}{(n-r)!r!}$.

In the equation $_nC_2 = 66$, rewrite $_nC_2$ as $\dfrac{n!}{(n-2)!2!}$.

$$_nC_2 = 66$$
$$\frac{n!}{(n-2)!2!} = 66$$

Step 2
Rewrite $n!$ as $n(n-1)(n-2)!$.

$$\frac{n!}{(n-2)!2!} = 66$$
$$\frac{n(n-1)(n-2)!}{(n-2)!2!} = 66$$

Step 3
Divide out common factors.
$$\frac{n(n-1)(n-2)!}{(n-2)!2!} = 66$$
$$\frac{n(n-1)}{2!} = 66$$

Step 4
Solve for n.

$$\frac{n(n-1)}{2!} = 66$$

$$\frac{n^2 - n}{2 \times 1} = 66$$

$$n^2 - n = 132$$

$$n^2 - n - 132 = 0$$

$$(n-12)(n+11) = 0$$

$$n - 12 = 0 \qquad n + 11 = 0$$

$$n = 12 \qquad n = -11$$

Since $n \geq 2$, the solution is $n = 12$.

5.   A group of 3 people is to be formed from 40 members, and the order does not matter. Therefore, the number of different boards is $_{40}C_3 = 9880$.

7.   There are 6 sculptures that must be selected from 25 sculptures, and the order of selection does not matter. Therefore, the number of different donations is $_{25}C_6 = 177\,100$.

9.   The order that the men and women are chosen for the committee does not matter.

Step 1
Determine the number of selections of 2 women from a group of 4.

The number of selections of 2 women from a group of 4 is $_4C_2 = 6$.

Step 2
Determine the number of selections of 4 men from a group of 5.

The number of selections of 4 men from a group of 5 is $_5C_4 = 5$.

Step 3
Determine the total number of possible committees.

Applying the fundamental counting principle, the number of possible committees with 4 men and 2 women is $6 \times 5 = 30$.

Lesson 5—Solving Probability Problems Involving Permutations and Combinations

CLASS EXERCISES
ANSWERS AND SOLUTIONS

1.   **Step 1**
Determine the number of successful outcomes. There are 3 vowels in the word ABOUT: A, O, and U.

One possible arrangement is as follows:
$\boxed{\text{A, O, U}}$, B, T

The block $\boxed{\text{A, O, U}}$ can be placed in any location of the arrangement. As well, A, O, and U can be placed in any order in the block. Therefore, the number of arrangements in which the vowels are placed together is $3! \times 3!$.

Step 2
Determine an expression for the number of equally likely outcomes.

Since there are 5 distinct letters in the word ABOUT, there are 5! possible arrangements, or outcomes.

Step 3
Determine the probability that the vowels are placed together.

$$P(E) = \frac{S}{N}$$

$$P(\text{A, O, U}) = \frac{3! \times 3!}{5!}$$

$$P(\text{A, O, U}) = \frac{36}{120}$$

$$P(\text{A, O, U}) = \frac{3}{10}$$

Therefore, the probability that the vowels are placed together is $\frac{3}{10}$.

Copyright Protected

2. Step 1
Determine an expression for the number of 3-letter arrangements with no vowels.

Since there are 4 letters in the word PICKLE that are not vowels, the number of letter arrangements with no vowels is given by $_4P_3$.

Step 2
Determine an expression for the total number of 3-letter arrangements.

Since there are 6 letters in the word PICKLE, the total number of 3-letter arrangements is $_6P_3$.

Step 3
Determine the probability that the letter arrangement will have no vowels.

Apply the formula $P(\overline{E}) = \dfrac{S}{N}$.

Let $S = {}_4P_3$ and $N = {}_6P_3$.

$$P(\overline{E}) = \frac{S}{N}$$

$$P(\text{no vowels}) = \frac{_4P_3}{_6P_3}$$

$$P(\text{no vowels}) = \frac{24}{120}$$

$$P(\text{no vowels}) = \frac{1}{5}$$

Step 4
Determine the probability that the 3-letter arrangement has at least one vowel.

$$P(E) = 1 - P(\overline{E})$$

$$P(\text{at least one vowel}) = 1 - P(\text{no vowels})$$

$$P(\text{at least one vowel}) = 1 - \frac{1}{5}$$

$$P(\text{at least one vowel}) = \frac{4}{5}$$

The probability that the 3-letter arrangement has at least one vowel is $\dfrac{4}{5}$.

3. Calculate the probability that Gavin does not pull out a piece of licorice, and subtract that result from 1.

Step 1
Determine an expression for the number of selections in which there are no pieces of licorice. There are $40 + 23 = 63$ pieces of candy to select from that do not include pieces of licorice. Therefore, if Gavin pulls out 2 pieces of candy, the number of selections in which there are no pieces of licorice is given by $_{63}C_2 = 1953$.

Step 2
Determine an expression for the total number of selections.

The total amount of candy is $40 + 23 + 11 = 74$. Since Gavin is selecting 2 pieces of candy from a 74 pieces of candy, the total number of selections is given by $_{74}C_2 = 2701$.

Step 3
Determine the probability that Gavin will not pull a piece of licorice.

Apply the formula $P(\overline{E}) = \dfrac{S}{N}$.

Let $S = {}_{63}C_2$ and $N = {}_{74}C_2$.

$$P(\overline{E}) = \frac{S}{N}$$

$$P(\text{no licorice}) = \frac{_{63}C_2}{_{74}C_2}$$

$$P(\text{no licorice}) = \frac{1953}{2701}$$

Step 4
Determine the probability that Gavin will pull out at least 1 piece of licorice.

$$P(E) = 1 - P(\overline{E})$$

$$P(\text{at least one piece of licorice}) = 1 - \frac{1953}{2701}$$

$$P(\text{at least one piece of licorice}) = \frac{748}{2701}$$

PRACTICE EXERCISES
ANSWERS AND SOLUTIONS

1. **Step 1**
Determine an expression for the number of successful outcomes.

The letters T, O, O, T, and H are required in this specific order. Therefore the number of successful outcomes is 1.

Step 2
Determine an expression for the number of equally likely outcomes.

Since there are 5 letters to arrange that involve 2 T's and 2 O's, the number of equally likely outcomes is $\dfrac{5!}{2!2!}$.

Step 3
Determine the probability that the letters spell TOOTH.

Apply the formula $P(E) = \dfrac{S}{N}$.

Let $S = 1$ and $N = \dfrac{5!}{2!2!}$.

$$P(E) = \frac{S}{N}$$
$$P(\text{TOOTH}) = \frac{1}{\left(\dfrac{5!}{2!2!}\right)}$$
$$P(\text{TOOTH}) = \frac{1}{30}$$
$$P(\text{TOOTH}) \approx 0.03$$

The probability that the letters spell TOOTH is 0.03.

3. **Step 1**
Determine an expression for the number of successful outcomes.

Since a girl needs to be at each end of the row, and the 3 boys can be arranged in any order in middle of the row, the number of successful outcomes is $2! \times 3!$.

Step 2
Determine an expression for the number of equally likely outcomes.

Since there are 5 boys and girls to arrange in a row, the number of equally likely outcomes is $5!$.

Step 3
Determine the probability that the seating arrangement has a girl at each end.

Apply the formula $P(E) = \dfrac{S}{N}$.

Let $S = 2! \times 3!$ and $N = 5!$.

$$P(E) = \frac{S}{N}$$
$$P(\text{girl at each end}) = \frac{2! \times 3!}{5!}$$
$$P(\text{girl at each end}) = \frac{1}{10}$$

Therefore, the probability that the arrangement has a girl at each end is $\dfrac{1}{10}$.

5. **Step 1**
Determine an expressions for the number of successful outcomes.

There is only 1 correct code in which the order of numbers matters. Since the person makes 2 attempts, the number of successful outcomes is $_2P_1$.

Step 2
Determine an expression for the number of equally likely outcomes.

The code has 5 digits with no reputations, and there are 10 possibilities for each digit. Therefore, the number of equally likely outcomes is $_{10}P_5$.

CASTLE ROCK RESEARCH   424   Copyright Protected

Step 3

Determine the probability that the person guesses the code correctly after 2 attempts.

Apply the formula $P(E) = \dfrac{S}{N}$.

Let $S = {}_2P_1$ and $N = {}_{10}P_5$.

$$P(E) = \frac{S}{N}$$

$$P(\text{correct code}) = \frac{{}_2P_1}{{}_{10}P_5}$$

$$P(\text{correct code}) = \frac{2}{30240}$$

$$P(\text{correct code}) = \frac{1}{15120}$$

Therefore, the probability that the person guesses the correct code after 2 attempts is $\dfrac{1}{15\,120}$.

7. To find the probability that at least one calculator has good batteries, consider the complement event. The complement event is that both of the calculators have dead batteries.

The probability that both calculators have bad batteries is $\dfrac{3}{28}$. Therefore, the probability that at least one calculator has good batteries is

$$1 - \frac{3}{28} = \frac{25}{28}.$$

9. **Step 1**

Determine an expression for the number of successful outcomes.

One possible arrangement is as follows:
$R, P_1, P_2, P_3, P_4, P_5, P_6, P_7, D$

Since Rick must be first, and Devon must be last, the first and last positions each have 1 possibility. The middle 7 batters have 7! different orders possible. Therefore, the number of successful outcomes is $1 \times 7! \times 1$ or $7!$.

Step 2

Determine an expression for the number of equally likely outcomes.

Since there are 9 players on the team, and the batting order matters, the number of equally likely outcomes is 9!.

Step 3

Determine the probability that Rick bats first, and Devon bats last.

Apply the formula $P(E) = \dfrac{S}{N}$.

Let $S = 7!$ and $N = 9!$.

$$P(E) = \frac{S}{N}$$

$$P(\text{Rick first and Devon last}) = \frac{7!}{9!}$$

$$P(\text{Rick first and Devon last}) = \frac{1}{72}$$

The probability that Ricks bats first and Devon bats last is $\dfrac{1}{72}$.

Practice Test

ANSWERS AND SOLUTIONS

1. **Step 1**
List the stages of the task.

The task is to form put together an outfit. This task has three stages:
1. Select a top. There are 5 possible choices for the top.
2. Select a skirt. There are 4 possible choices for the skirt.
3. Select a pair of shoes. There are 3 possible choices for the shoes.

Step 2
Determine the number of different outfits Sally can put together.

Apply the fundamental counting principle.
Multiply the number of possible choices for each part of the outfit.
$5 \times 4 \times 3 = 60$

Therefore, Sally can put together 60 different outfits.

3. Since the order in which the vehicles are lined up matters, this is a permutation problem.

   There are 2 identical sports cars, 3 identical sport utility vehicles, and 4 identical trucks. Therefore, the total number of arrangements is given by $\dfrac{9!}{2!3!4!}$.

   $$
   \begin{aligned}
   \frac{9!}{2!3!4!} &= \frac{9 \times 8 \times 7 \times 6 \times 5 \times 4!}{2!3!4!} \\
   &= \frac{9 \times 8 \times 7 \times 6 \times 5}{2!3!} \\
   &= \frac{15\,120}{12} \\
   &= 1260
   \end{aligned}
   $$

   Therefore, the dealership can arrange the 9 vehicles in 1 260 ways.

5. The order in which the ice-cream toppings are chosen does not matter. Therefore, this is a combination problem.

   Since there are 9 different topping choices, the number of 3-topping sundaes a customer can order is $_9C_3 = 84$.

7. The order in which the golfers are placed in groups does not matter. Therefore this is a combination problem.

   Step 1
   List the stages of the task.

   The task is to create 3 groups of golfers from 15 golfers. This task involves three stages:
   1. Select the first group. There are 3 golfers in the first group, and there are 15 golfers to choose from. Therefore, the number of selections for the first group is $_{15}C_3$.
   2. Select the second group. There are 5 golfers in the second group, and there are 12 golfers to choose from. Therefore, the number of selections for the second group is $_{12}C_5$.
   3. Select the third group. There are 7 golfers in the third group and there are 7 golfers to choose from. Therefore, the number of selections for the third group is $_7C_7$.

Step 2
Determine the number of possible divisions of the 15 golfers in 3 groups.

Apply the fundamental counting principle.
$_{15}C_3 \times {}_{12}C_5 \times {}_7C_7 = 360\,360$

The number of possible divisions is 360 360.

9. **Step 1**
Determine the number of successful outcomes. Since Karen and Patricia both make the team, and 6 more girls are chosen from 10 girls, the number of successful outcomes is $_2C_2 \times {}_{10}C_6$.

Step 2
Determine the number of equally likely outcomes. Since there are 12 girls trying out for the team that will consist of 8 players, the number of different selections possible is $_{12}C_8 = 495$.

Step 3
Determine the probability that Karen and Patricia both make the team.

Apply the formula $P(E) = \dfrac{S}{N}$.

$$
\begin{aligned}
P(E) &= \frac{S}{N} \\
P(\text{Karen and Patricia make the team}) &= \frac{{}_2C_2 \times {}_{10}C_6}{{}_{12}C_8} \\
P(\text{Karen and Patricia make the team}) &= \frac{1 \times 210}{495} \\
P(\text{Karen and Patricia make the team}) &= \frac{14}{33}
\end{aligned}
$$

Therefore, the probability that Karen and Patricia both make the team is $\dfrac{14}{33}$.

11. **Step 1**
Determine the number of successful outcomes. One possible arrangement is as follows:
A,N,N,$\boxed{M,O}$,I,A

There are 2 N's and 2A's, and the group $\boxed{M,O}$ can be placed in any location of the arrangement. As well, the letters M and O can be placed in any order within the group. Therefore, the number of successful outcomes is $\dfrac{6!}{2!2!} \times 2!$, or $\dfrac{6!}{2!}$.

Step 2

Determine the number of equally likely outcomes. The number of equally likely outcomes is

$$\frac{7!}{2!2!} = 1260.$$

Step 3

Determine the probability that M and O are together in either order.

Apply the formula $P(E) = \dfrac{S}{N}$.

Let $S = 6! \times 2!$ and $N = 1260$.

$$P(E) = \frac{S}{N}$$

$$P(M \text{ and } O) = \frac{\dfrac{6!}{2!}}{1260}$$

$$P(M \text{ and } O) = \frac{2}{7}$$

The probability that M and O are together in either order is $\dfrac{2}{7}$.

RATIONAL EXPRESSIONS AND EQUATIONS

Lesson 1—Introduction to Rational Expressions and Non-Permissible Values

CLASS EXERCISES
ANSWERS AND SOLUTIONS

1. **a)** The expression $\dfrac{4x^3 + 1}{x}$ is a rational expression, since the numerator and the denominator are polynomials.

   b) The expression $\sqrt{6}p$ is a polynomial, because the radical sign ($\sqrt{}$) does not include the variable. The expression $\dfrac{m - n}{\sqrt{6}p}$ is a rational expression, since the numerator and the denominator are polynomials.

   c) The expression $\dfrac{x^2 + 2\sqrt{x}}{3x - 1}$ is not a rational expression, because there is a variable with a fractional degree ($\sqrt{x}$ is $x^{\frac{1}{2}}$ as a power) in the numerator. Therefore, the numerator is not a polynomial.

   d) The expression $9c^5 + 8^d$ is not a rational expression, because the numerator in $\dfrac{9c^5 + 8^d}{1}$ contains a term with a variable exponent. Therefore, the numerator is not a polynomial.

2. **a)** If $-4x$ in the denominator equals 0, the expression $\dfrac{3x^2}{-4x}$ is undefined. Therefore, the NPV is $x = 0$.

b) If $(2x - 6)$ in the denominator equals 0, the expression $\dfrac{x^2 - 1}{2x - 6}$ is undefined.

$$2x - 6 = 0$$
$$2x = 6$$
$$x = 3$$

Therefore, the NPV is $x = 3$.

3. a) If $(x^2 - 16)$ in the denominator equals 0, the expression $\dfrac{4x}{x^2 - 16}$ is undefined.

$$x^2 - 16 = 0$$
$$x^2 = 16$$
$$x = \pm\sqrt{16}$$
$$x = \pm 4$$

Therefore, the NPVs are $x = 4$ and $x = -4$.

Alternate solution:

$$x^2 - 16 = 0$$
$$(x - 4)(x + 4) = 0$$

$$x - 4 = 0 \qquad \text{or} \qquad x + 4 = 0$$
$$x = 4 \qquad\qquad\qquad x = -4$$

b) If $(a - 6)$ in the denominator equals 0, the expression $\dfrac{a^2 - 9}{a - 6}$ is undefined.

$$a - 6 = 0$$
$$a = 6$$

Therefore, the NPV is $a = 6$.

c) If $(m + 3m)$ in the denominator equals 0, the expression $\dfrac{2m + 1}{m + 3m}$ is undefined.

$$m + 3m = 0$$
$$4m = 0$$
$$m = \frac{0}{4}$$
$$m = 0$$

Therefore, the NPV is $m = 0$.

PRACTICE EXERCISES
ANSWERS AND SOLUTIONS

1. B

The expression $\sqrt{2}x$ is rational because the radical sign ($\sqrt{}$) does not include the variable, and the expression could be written as a fraction, $\dfrac{\sqrt{2}x}{1}$.

The expressions $\dfrac{\sqrt{x}}{y}$, $\dfrac{24}{x^{\frac{3}{2}}}$, and $\sqrt[3]{x} + \sqrt[3]{8}$ each contain terms where the variables have fractional degrees.

3. If $(x - 2)$ or (x) in the denominator equals 0, the expression $\dfrac{(x + 2)(2x)}{3(x - 2)(x)}$ is undefined.

Therefore, $x \neq 0$ and $x \neq 2$.

5. If $(6x^2 - 15x)$ in the denominator equals 0, the expression $\dfrac{x + 6}{6x^2 - 15x}$ is undefined.

$$6x^2 - 15x = 0$$
$$3x(2x - 5) = 0$$

Therefore, $x \neq 0$ and $x \neq \dfrac{5}{2}$.

Lesson 2—Simplifying Rational Expressions

CLASS EXERCISES
ANSWERS AND SOLUTIONS

1. a) Factor the denominator, and reduce by a factor of 3 to simplify the expression.

The NPVs can be identified using the original denominator in factored form.

$$\frac{12x}{3x - 9}$$
$$= \frac{\overset{4}{\cancel{12}}x}{\cancel{3}(x - 3)}$$
$$= \frac{4x}{x - 3}, x \neq 3$$

Copyright Protected

b) Reduce the coefficients in the monomials by a common factor of 8, and use the quotient law of exponents to simplify the expression.

The NPVs can be identified using the original denominator.

$$\frac{8x^3}{48x}$$
$$=\frac{\cancel{8}x^2}{\cancel{48}^6}$$
$$=\frac{x^2}{6}, x \neq 0$$

c) Factor where possible, and eliminate common factors to simplify the expression.

The NPVs can be identified using the original denominator in factored form.

$$\frac{10x^2+2x}{6x^2+4x}$$
$$=\frac{\cancel{2x}(5x+1)}{\cancel{2x}(3x+2)}$$
$$=\frac{5x+1}{3x+2}, x \neq 0, -\frac{2}{3}$$

2. a) Factor where possible, and eliminate common factors to simplify the expression. The NPVs can be identified using the original denominator. The binomial factors in the numerator and denominator are the same even though the terms are written in different orders.

$$\frac{18-4m}{-2m+9}$$
$$=\frac{2(9-2m)}{-2m+9}$$
$$=\frac{2(-2m+9)}{-2m+9}$$
$$=\frac{2(\cancel{9-2m})}{\cancel{-2m+9}}$$
$$=2, m \neq \frac{9}{2}$$

b) Factor where possible, and eliminate common factors to simplify the expression.

The NPVs can be identified using the original denominator in factored form.

$$\frac{x^2-25}{2x^2+10x}$$
$$=\frac{(x-5)(\cancel{x+5})}{2x(\cancel{x+5})}$$
$$=\frac{x-5}{2x}, x \neq 0, -5$$

c) Factor where possible, and eliminate common factors to simplify the expression.

The NPVs can be identified using the original denominator in factored form.

$$\frac{b^2+b}{b+1}$$
$$=\frac{b(\cancel{b+1})}{(\cancel{b+1})}$$
$$=b, b \neq -1$$

PRACTICE EXERCISES
ANSWERS AND SOLUTIONS

1. B
If $(x+1)$ or $(x+3)$ in the denominator equals 0, the expression $\dfrac{(x+1)(x+2)}{(x+1)(x+3)}$ is undefined.

Therefore, the restrictions are $x \neq -1$ and $x \neq -3$.

3. Factor where possible, and eliminate common factors to simplify the expression.

The NPVs can be identified using the original denominator in factored form.

$$\frac{x-2}{x^3-4x}$$
$$=\frac{x-2}{x(x^2-4)}$$
$$=\frac{\cancel{x-2}}{x(x+2)(\cancel{x-2})}$$
$$=\frac{1}{x(x+2)}, x \neq -2, 0, 2$$

5. The strategies are the same for writing equivalent forms of rational numbers and expressions. One method is to multiply the numerator and the denominator by the same value.

Consider the rational number $\dfrac{2}{7}$ and the rational expression $\dfrac{x^2}{2+x}$.

Rational Numbers	Rational Expressions
$\dfrac{2}{7}\left(\dfrac{3}{3}\right)=\dfrac{6}{21}$	$\dfrac{x^2}{2+x}\left(\dfrac{3x}{3x}\right)=\dfrac{3x^3}{6x+3x^2}, x \neq -2, 0$

In these examples, $\dfrac{2}{7}$ is equivalent to $\dfrac{6}{21}$, and

$\dfrac{x^2}{2+x}$ is equivalent to $\dfrac{3x^3}{6x+3x^2}$.

Another method is to simplify the numerator and the denominator by dividing (reducing) by a common factor.

Consider the rational number $\dfrac{8}{36}$ and the rational expression $\dfrac{12x-3}{3x^2}$.

Rational Numbers	Rational Expressions
$\dfrac{8}{36}=\dfrac{(4)(2)}{(4)(9)}$ $=\dfrac{2}{9}$	$\dfrac{12x-3}{3x^2}$ $=\dfrac{3(4x-1)}{3x^2}$ $=\dfrac{4x-1}{x^2}, x \neq 0$

In these examples, $\dfrac{8}{36}$ is equivalent to $\dfrac{2}{9}$,

and $\dfrac{12x-3}{3x^2}$ is equivalent to $\dfrac{4x-1}{x^2}$.

The NPVs must be stated for rational expressions.

7. **Step 1**
Factor the expression where possible, and simplify.
$$\frac{a^2+12a}{2a}=\frac{a(a+12)}{2a}$$

Step 2
Eliminate the common factors, and state any NPVs.
$$\frac{a(a+12)}{2a}=\frac{a+12}{2}, a \neq 0$$

This is in simplest form, since there are no more common factors in the numerator and denominator. You cannot reduce 12 and 2, because 2 is not a factor common to both terms in the numerator. Therefore, the final step is not correct in Marsha's solution.

Lesson 3—Multiplying Rational Expressions

CLASS EXERCISES
ANSWERS AND SOLUTIONS

1. **a)** Simplify the expression first by eliminating common factors, and then multiply.

   The NPVs can be identified using the original denominators.

   $$\frac{x^3 y}{10} \times \frac{2xy}{x^2}$$

   $$=\frac{x^3 y}{10} \times \frac{2xy}{x^2}$$

   $$=\frac{xy}{5} \times \frac{xy}{1}$$

   $$=\frac{x^2 y^2}{5}, x \neq 0$$

b) Since the expression is in factored form already, eliminate common factors, and then multiply.

The NPVs can be identified using the original denominators.

$$\left(\frac{(8)(a)(b)}{(2)(2)}\right)\left(\frac{(4)(c)}{(c)(c)(c)}\right)$$

$$=\left(\frac{(8)(a)(b)}{(\cancel{2})(\cancel{2})}\right)\left(\frac{(\cancel{4})(\cancel{c})}{(\cancel{c})(c)(c)}\right)$$

$$=\frac{8ab}{c^2}, c \neq 0$$

2. Simplify the expressions, and multiply as necessary.

The NPVs can be identified using the original denominators in factored form.

$$\left(\frac{x+3}{x^2-1}\right)\left(\frac{x+1}{x+3}\right)$$

$$=\left(\frac{(x+3)}{(x+1)(x-1)}\right)\left(\frac{x+1}{x+3}\right)$$

$$=\left(\frac{(\cancel{x+3})}{(\cancel{x+1})(x-1)}\right)\left(\frac{\cancel{x+1}}{\cancel{x+3}}\right)$$

$$=\frac{1}{x-1}, x \neq \pm 1, -3$$

3. Simplify the expression, and multiply as necessary. The NPVs can be identified using the original denominators.

$$(2)\left(\frac{x-5}{2x}\right)\left(\frac{x^2-3x}{x-5}\right)$$

$$=\left(\frac{2}{1}\right)\left(\frac{x-5}{2x}\right)\left(\frac{x(x-3)}{x-5}\right)$$

$$=\left(\frac{\cancel{2}}{1}\right)\left(\frac{\cancel{x-5}}{\cancel{2}\cancel{x}}\right)\left(\frac{\cancel{x}(x-3)}{\cancel{x-5}}\right)$$

$$=x-3, x \neq 0, 5$$

Expressions in simplest form can be left in factored form (written as a product of polynomials) rather than actually multiplied out.

PRACTICE EXERCISES
ANSWERS AND SOLUTIONS

1. Simplify the expression, and multiply as necessary. The NPVs can be identified using the original denominators in factored form.

$$\left(\frac{(x+1)^3}{24x}\right)\left(\frac{6(2x)}{2x^2-2}\right)$$

$$=\left(\frac{(\cancel{x+1})(x+1)(x+1)}{\underset{4}{\cancel{24}}\,\cancel{x}}\right)\left(\frac{\cancel{6}(\cancel{2}\,\cancel{x})}{\cancel{2}(x-1)(\cancel{x+1})}\right)$$

$$=\frac{(x+1)(x+1)}{4(x-1)}, x \neq 0, 1, -1$$

3. D

Step 1

Simplify the expression $(-x)\left(\dfrac{x}{3}\right)$.

$$(-x)\left(\frac{x}{3}\right)=-\frac{x^2}{3}$$

The expression $-\dfrac{x^2}{3}$ is not equivalent to $\dfrac{3}{x}$.

Step 2

Simplify the expression $\left(\dfrac{2}{3}\right)\left(\dfrac{6}{x}\right)$.

$$\left(\frac{2}{3}\right)\left(\frac{6}{x}\right)$$

$$=\left(\frac{2}{\underset{1}{\cancel{3}}}\right)\left(\frac{\overset{2}{\cancel{6}}}{x}\right)$$

$$=\frac{4}{x}, x \neq 0$$

The expression $\dfrac{3}{x}$ is not equivalent to $\left(\dfrac{2}{3}\right)\left(\dfrac{6}{x}\right)$.

Step 3

Simplify the expression $\left(\dfrac{3}{3x}\right)(2)$.

$\left(\dfrac{3}{3x}\right)(2)$

$=\left(\dfrac{\cancel{3}}{\cancel{3}x}\right)(2)$

$=\dfrac{2}{x}, x\neq 0$

The expression $\dfrac{3}{x}$ is not equivalent to $\left(\dfrac{3}{3x}\right)(2)$.

Step 4

Simplify the expression $\left(\dfrac{-x}{4x^2}\right)\left(\dfrac{-12x}{x}\right)$.

$\left(\dfrac{-x}{4x^2}\right)\left(\dfrac{-12x}{x}\right)$

$=\left(\dfrac{-\cancel{x}}{\cancel{4}\,x^{1\cancel{2}}}\right)\left(\dfrac{-\overset{3}{\cancel{12}}\,\cancel{x}}{\cancel{x}}\right)$
${}_{1}$

$=\dfrac{3}{x}, x\neq 0$

The expression $\left(\dfrac{-x}{4x^2}\right)\left(\dfrac{-12x}{x}\right)$ is equivalent to $\dfrac{3}{x}$.

5. Answers will vary. The two rational expressions must simplify (after multiplication) to $\dfrac{2}{x}$ and should therefore be more complex than $\dfrac{2}{x}$ (that is, there should be some common factors to eliminate).

One example is $\left(\dfrac{2(x+1)}{x}\right)\left(\dfrac{1}{(x+1)}\right)$, and it is confirmed as follows:

$\left(\dfrac{2(x+1)}{x}\right)\left(\dfrac{1}{(x+1)}\right)$

$=\left(\dfrac{2(\cancel{x+1})}{x}\right)\left(\dfrac{1}{(\cancel{x+1})}\right)$

$=\dfrac{2}{x}$

The restrictions are $x\neq 0$ and $x\neq -1$.

7. **A**

In the given expression, the last factor in the denominator $(x+n-1)$ is 1 less than the last factor in the numerator $(x+n)$, where n is a positive integer greater than 1. As such, after reducing, all the factors in the denominator will be eliminated, and the numerator will remain as $(x+n)$.

There will be $(n-1)$ non-permissible values, and the denominator will be 1.

Lesson 4—Dividing Rational Expressions

CLASS EXERCISES
ANSWERS AND SOLUTIONS

1. Rewrite the quotient as a product using the reciprocal of the second expression.

   Simplify the product, and multiply as necessary.

   $\dfrac{3x}{10}\div\dfrac{12}{30}$

   $=\dfrac{3x}{10}\times\dfrac{30}{12}$

   $=\dfrac{3x}{\cancel{10}}\times\dfrac{\overset{3}{\cancel{30}}}{\underset{4}{\cancel{12}}}$

   $=\dfrac{3x}{4}$

2. **a)** Rewrite the quotient as a product using the reciprocal of the second expression.

   Simplify the product, and multiply as necessary. The NPVs can be identified using the original denominators in the quotient and the new denominator in the product.

   $\dfrac{3(x-8)}{x^2}\div\dfrac{12(x-8)}{x(x+4)}$

   $=\dfrac{3(x-8)}{x^2}\times\dfrac{x(x+4)}{12(x-8)}$

   $=\dfrac{\cancel{3}(\cancel{x-8})}{\cancel{x^2}}\times\dfrac{\cancel{x}(x+4)}{\cancel{12}(\cancel{x-8})}$

   $=\dfrac{x+4}{4x}, x\neq 0,-4,8$

b) Rewrite the quotient as a product using the reciprocal of the second expression.

Simplify the product, and multiply as necessary. The NPVs can be identified using the original denominators in the quotient and the new denominator in the product.

$$\frac{x-5}{2x} \div \frac{x-5}{x^2-3x}$$

$$= \frac{x-5}{2x} \div \frac{x-5}{x(x-3)}$$

$$= \frac{x-5}{2x} \times \frac{x(x-3)}{x-5}$$

$$= \frac{\cancel{x-5}}{2\cancel{x}} \times \frac{\cancel{x}(x-3)}{\cancel{x-5}}$$

$$= \frac{x-3}{2}, x \neq 0, 3, 5$$

c) Rewrite the quotient as a product using the reciprocal of the second expression.

Simplify the product, and multiply as necessary. The NPVs can be identified using the original denominators in the quotient and the new denominator in the product.

$$\frac{x^2-16}{x+4} \div \frac{x^2+2x}{2x+4}$$

$$= \frac{x^2-16}{x+4} \times \frac{2x+4}{x^2+2x}$$

$$= \frac{(x+4)(x-4)}{\cancel{x+4}} \times \frac{2(x+2)}{x(x+2)}$$

$$= \frac{2(x-4)}{x}, x \neq -4, -2, 0$$

PRACTICE EXERCISES
ANSWERS AND SOLUTIONS

1. Rewrite the quotient as a product using the reciprocal of the second expression.

Simplify the product, and multiply as necessary. The NPVs can be identified using the original denominators in the quotient and the new denominator in the product.

The expression $\dfrac{5}{\left(\dfrac{20}{x^2}\right)}$ can be rewritten as $\dfrac{5}{1} \div \dfrac{20}{x^2}$

and then rewritten as the product $\left(\dfrac{5}{1}\right)\left(\dfrac{x^2}{20}\right)$.

This simplifies to $\dfrac{x^2}{4}$, $x \neq 0$.

3. A

One method for solving $\dfrac{x}{3} \div y = \dfrac{2}{x}$ is to investigate what expression must be multiplied by $\dfrac{x}{3}$ to give $\dfrac{2}{x}$. The denominator of $\dfrac{2}{x}$ is x, and the numerator of $\dfrac{x}{3}$ is x, so the unknown expression must have x^2 in the denominator.

$$\left(\frac{x}{3}\right)\left(\frac{}{x^2}\right) = \frac{2}{x}$$

Also, the denominator of $\dfrac{x}{3}$ is 3, and the numerator of $\dfrac{2}{x}$ is 2, so the unknown expression must have 6 in the numerator.

$$\left(\frac{x}{3}\right)\left(\frac{6}{x^2}\right) = \frac{2}{x}$$

The reciprocal of $\dfrac{6}{x^2}$ will give y for the division statement, so $y = \dfrac{x^2}{6}$ in $\dfrac{x}{3} \div y = \dfrac{2}{x}$.

Substitute $y = \dfrac{x^2}{6}$ into the equation $\dfrac{x}{3} \div y = \dfrac{2}{x}$ to verify your response.

$$\frac{x}{3} \div y = \frac{2}{x}$$

$$\frac{x}{3} \div \frac{x^2}{6} = \frac{2}{x}$$

$$\frac{x}{3} \times \frac{6}{x^2} = \frac{2}{x}$$

$$\frac{2}{x} = \frac{2}{x}$$

5. Rewrite the quotient as a product using the reciprocal of the second expression.

   Simplify the product, and multiply as necessary. The NPVs can be identified using the original denominators in the quotient and the new denominator in the product.

   $$\frac{4(1-x)}{x} \div \frac{x-1}{2x}$$
   $$=\left(\frac{4(1-x)}{x}\right)\left(\frac{2x}{x-1}\right)$$
   $$=\left(\frac{-4(-1+x)}{x}\right)\left(\frac{2x}{x-1}\right)$$
   $$=-8, x \neq 0,1$$

Lesson 5—Adding and Subtracting Rational Expressions

CLASS EXERCISES
ANSWERS AND SOLUTIONS

1. **Step 1**
   Simplify each expression where possible.

   The expression $\dfrac{x^2-4}{(x-2)^2}$ can be simplified.

   $$\frac{x^2-4}{(x-2)^2}$$
   $$=\frac{(x-2)(x+2)}{(x-2)(x-2)}$$
   $$=\frac{x+2}{x-2}, x \neq 2$$

   Step 2
   Identify the lowest common denominator (LCD).

   The three denominators of the expressions $\dfrac{2}{5x}$, $\dfrac{3x+1}{2}$, and $\dfrac{x+2}{x-2}$ have no factors in common, so the LCD is $(5x)(2)(x-2)$.

2. **a) Step 1**
   Simplify each expression where possible.

   The expression $\dfrac{6}{10y}$ can be reduced to $\dfrac{3}{5y}$.

   Step 2
   Identify the lowest common denominator (LCD).

   The LCD for the expression $\dfrac{3}{5y} - \dfrac{1}{15y^2}$
   is $15y^2$.

   Step 3

   Write an equivalent expression with the LCD as the denominator.

   $$\frac{3}{5y} - \frac{1}{15y^2}$$
   $$=\frac{3(3y)}{5y(3y)} - \frac{1}{15y^2}$$
   $$=\frac{9y}{15y^2} - \frac{1}{15y^2}, y \neq 0$$

   b) Step 1
   Simplify each expression where possible.

   The expression $\dfrac{x-2x^2}{2x-4x^2}$ can be simplified.

   $$\frac{x-2x^2}{2x-4x^2}$$
   $$=\frac{x(1-2x)}{2x(1-2x)}$$
   $$=\frac{1}{2}, x \neq \frac{1}{2}$$

   Step 2
   Identify the lowest common denominator (LCD).

   The LCD for the expression $\dfrac{x-4}{2x} + \dfrac{1}{2}$ is $2x$.

       Copyright Protected

Step 3
Write an equivalent expression with the LCD as the denominator.

$$\frac{x-4}{2x}+\frac{1}{2}$$
$$=\frac{x-4}{2x}+\frac{1(x)}{2(x)}$$
$$=\frac{x-4}{2x}+\frac{x}{2x}, x\neq 0, \frac{1}{2}$$

You might have noticed that if the x in the numerator and the denominator of

$$\frac{\cancel{x}\left(1-2x\right)}{2\cancel{x}\left(1-2x\right)}$$ had not been eliminated, the

expressions $\dfrac{x-4}{2x}$ and $\dfrac{x}{2x}$ would already

have had a common denominator of $2x$. Noticing details like this is not essential (as shown in the solution) but could certainly save a little time.

3. a) Since the denominator is already common, combine the terms in the numerator, and then simplify if necessary.

Use the original expressions to state any NPVs.

$$\frac{5x^2+1}{x+2}+\frac{1-4x^2}{x+2}$$
$$=\frac{5x^2+1+1-4x^2}{x+2}$$
$$=\frac{x^2+2}{x+2}, x\neq -2$$

b) Since the denominator is already common, combine the terms in the numerator, and then simplify if necessary. Use the original expressions to state any NPVs.

$$\frac{2a}{3a}-\frac{\left(5a-a^2\right)}{3a}$$
$$=\frac{2a-5a+a^2}{3a}$$
$$=\frac{a^2-3a}{3a}$$
$$=\frac{\cancel{a}\left(a-3\right)}{3\cancel{a}}$$
$$=\frac{a-3}{3}, a\neq 0$$

Alternate solution:
Simplify each expression first, and then subtract accordingly.

$$\frac{2a}{3a}-\frac{\left(5a-a^2\right)}{3a}$$
$$=\frac{2\cancel{a}}{3\cancel{a}}-\frac{\cancel{a}\left(5-a\right)}{3\cancel{a}}$$
$$=\frac{2}{3}-\frac{\left(5-a\right)}{3}$$
$$=\frac{2-5+a}{3}$$
$$=\frac{a-3}{3}, a\neq 0$$

c) Step 1
Identify the LCD.

The LCD is $(m-1)(m+3)$.

Step 2
Write equivalent expressions with the new denominator.

$$\frac{m}{m-1}-\frac{m-1}{m+3}$$
$$=\frac{m(m+3)}{(m-1)(m+3)}-\frac{(m-1)(m-1)}{(m-1)(m+3)}$$
$$=\frac{m^2+3m}{(m-1)(m+3)}-\frac{\left(m^2-2m+1\right)}{(m-1)(m+3)}$$

Step 3
Combine like terms in the numerators, keeping the common denominator unchanged.

$$\frac{m^2+3m}{(m-1)(m+3)}-\frac{\left(m^2-2m+1\right)}{(m-1)(m+3)}$$
$$=\frac{m^2+3m-m^2+2m-1}{(m-1)(m+3)}$$
$$=\frac{5m-1}{(m-1)(m+3)}$$

Step 4
Check if the expression can be reduced further, and state the NPVs.

Since the numerator is not factorable, the

expression is $\dfrac{5m-1}{(m-1)(m+3)}$, $m\neq 1, -3$ in

simplest form.

d) Step 1
Simplify each expression where possible.

$$\frac{x}{x-1}-\frac{x}{1-x}$$

$$=\frac{x}{x-1}-\frac{x}{-1(-1+x)}$$

$$=\frac{x}{x-1}+\frac{x}{x-1}$$

Step 2
Identify the lowest common denominator (LCD).

Factoring -1 from the second denominator will make the question a sum with an LCD of $x-1$.

Step 3
Since the denominator is now common, combine the terms in the numerator, and then simplify if necessary. Use the original expressions to state any NPVs.

$$\frac{x}{x-1}+\frac{x}{x-1}$$

$$=\frac{x+x}{x-1}$$

$$=\frac{2x}{x-1}, x\neq 1$$

PRACTICE EXERCISES
ANSWERS AND SOLUTIONS

1. Step 1
Identify the LCD, and write equivalent expressions with the new denominator.

The LCD is $(3x)(4)$. Note that the last term has a denominator of 1.

$$\frac{2}{3x}+\frac{3x}{4}-1$$

$$=\frac{2(4)}{(3x)(4)}+\frac{3x(3x)}{(3x)(4)}-\frac{1(3x)(4)}{(3x)(4)}$$

$$=\frac{8}{(3x)(4)}+\frac{9x^2}{(3x)(4)}-\frac{12x}{(3x)(4)}$$

Step 2
Combine like terms in the numerators, keeping the common denominator unchanged.

$$\frac{8}{(3x)(4)}+\frac{9x^2}{(3x)(4)}-\frac{12x}{(3x)(4)}$$

$$=\frac{9x^2-12x+8}{12x}$$

Step 3
Check if the expression can be reduced further, and state the NPVs.

The expression cannot be factored and simplified any further. Therefore, the expression is
$$\frac{9x^2-12x+8}{12x}, x\neq 0 \text{ in simplest form.}$$

3. Step 1
Simplify each expression where possible.

$$\frac{a-1}{2a+2}-\frac{6}{a}$$

$$=\frac{a-1}{2(a+1)}-\frac{6}{a}$$

The expressions cannot be simplified, but the denominator of the first expression can be factored.

Step 2
Identify the lowest common denominator (LCD).

The LCD will be $(2)(a)(a+1)$.

Step 3
Write an equivalent expression with the LCD as the denominator.

$$\frac{a-1}{2(a+1)}-\frac{6}{a}$$

$$=\frac{a(a-1)}{2a(a+1)}-\frac{6(2(a+1))}{2a(a+1)}$$

$$=\frac{a^2-a}{2a(a+1)}-\frac{6(2a+2)}{2a(a+1)}$$

$$=\frac{a^2-a}{2a(a+1)}-\frac{12a+12}{2a(a+1)}$$

Step 4
Combine like terms in the numerators, keeping the common denominator unchanged.

$$\frac{a^2-a}{2a(a+1)}-\frac{12a+12}{2a(a+1)}$$

$$=\frac{a^2-a-(12a+12)}{2a(a+1)}$$

$$=\frac{a^2-a-12a-12}{2a(a+1)}$$

$$=\frac{a^2-13a-12}{2a(a+1)}$$

Copyright Protected

Step 5

Check if the expression can be reduced further, and state the NPVs.

The expression $\dfrac{a^2-13a-12}{2a(a+1)}$ cannot be factored any further; therefore, the NPVs are $a=-1$ and $a=0$, which can be written beside the expression as $\dfrac{a^2-13a-12}{2a(a+1)}, a \neq -1, 0$.

5. **D**

Step 1

Factor each expression where possible.
$$\frac{9x+27}{x^2-9}+\frac{4x^2+x}{x^2-3x}$$
$$=\frac{9(x+3)}{(x-3)(x+3)}+\frac{x(4x+1)}{x(x-3)}$$

Marc correctly factored each expression in step 1.

Step 2

Simplify each expression where possible.
$$\frac{9(x+3)}{(x-3)(x+3)}+\frac{x(4x+1)}{x(x-3)}$$
$$=\frac{9}{x-3}+\frac{4x+1}{x-3}$$

Marc correctly simplified each expression in step 2.

Step 3

Add the two expressions.
$$\frac{9}{x-3}+\frac{4x+1}{x-3}$$
$$=\frac{9+4x+1}{x-3}$$
$$=\frac{10+4x}{x-3}$$

Marc correctly added the two expressions.

Step 4

State the non-permissible values.

The non-permissible values are $x=-3$, 0, and 3. Marc incorrectly stated the non-permissible values in step 4 because he did not consider the non-permissible values for the original expression.

CLASS EXERCISES
ANSWERS AND SOLUTIONS

1. **a)** **Step 1**

Find the LCM of the denominators, and multiply each term by that LCM.

The LCM will be $(x-1)(x+1)$.
$$\frac{5}{x-1}-\frac{12}{x^2-1}=1$$
$$\frac{5}{x-1}-\frac{12}{(x-1)(x+1)}=1$$
$$(x-1)(x+1)\left[\frac{5}{x-1}-\frac{12}{(x-1)(x+1)}=1\right]$$
$$\frac{5(x-1)(x+1)}{(x-1)}-\frac{12(x-1)(x+1)}{(x-1)(x+1)}=(x-1)(x+1)$$
$$\frac{5(x-1)(x+1)}{(x-1)}-\frac{12(x-1)(x+1)}{(x-1)(x+1)}=x^2-1$$

Step 2

Remove all denominators by eliminating common factors, and then expand where necessary.
$$\frac{5\cancel{(x-1)}(x+1)}{\cancel{(x-1)}}-\frac{12\cancel{(x-1)}\cancel{(x+1)}}{\cancel{(x-1)}\cancel{(x+1)}}=x^2-1$$
$$5(x+1)-12=x^2-1$$
$$5x+5-12=x^2-1$$

Step 3

Gather like terms, and solve the resulting quadratic equation.
$$5x+5-12=x^2-1$$
$$0=x^2-5x+6$$
$$0=(x-2)(x-3)$$
$$0=x-2 \quad \text{or} \quad 0=x-3$$
$$2=x \qquad\qquad 3=x$$

Step 4

State any NPVs for the variable.
The NPVs from the original equation
$$\frac{5}{x-1}-\frac{12}{x^2-1}=1 \text{ are } x=1 \text{ and } x=-1.$$
Therefore, the solutions are $x=2$ and $x=3$.

Step 5
Verify the solution using the original equation.

$x = 2$	$x = 3$
$\dfrac{5}{(2)-1} - \dfrac{12}{(2)^2 - 1}$	$\dfrac{5}{(3)-1} - \dfrac{12}{(3)^2 - 1}$
$= \dfrac{5}{1} - \dfrac{12}{3}$	$= \dfrac{5}{2} - \dfrac{12}{8}$
$= 5 - 4$	$= \dfrac{20 - 12}{8}$
$= 1$	$= \dfrac{8}{8}$
	$= 1$

The solutions $x = 2$ and $x = 3$ have been verified.

b) Step 1
Subtract 3 from both sides of the equation.
$$3 + \frac{2}{3+x} = 5$$
$$\frac{2}{3+x} = 2$$

Step 2
Multiply both sides by $(3 + x)$.
$$\frac{2}{3+x} = 2$$
$$(3+x)\frac{2}{3+x} = (3+x)2$$
$$2 = 6 + 2x$$

Step 3
Solve for x.
$$2 = 6 + 2x$$
$$-4 = 2x$$
$$-2 = x$$

Step 4
State any NPVs for the variable.

The NPV from the original equation
$3 + \dfrac{2}{3+x} = 5$ is $x = -3$.

Step 5
Verify the solution using the original equation.

$x = -2$	
$3 + \dfrac{2}{3+(-2)}$	5
$= 3 + \dfrac{2}{1}$	
$= 5$	

The solution $x = -2$ has been verified.

c) Step 1
With a single expression on either side of the equal sign, cross-multiply to remove the denominators, and then expand where necessary.
$$\frac{2}{x+4} = \frac{5}{3x+12}$$
$$(2)(3x+12) = (5)(x+4)$$
$$6x + 24 = 5x + 20$$

Step 2
Gather like terms, and solve for x.
$$6x + 24 = 5x + 20$$
$$x = -4$$

Step 3
State any NPVs for the variable.

The NPV from the original equation
$\dfrac{2}{x+4} = \dfrac{5}{3x+12}$ is $x = -4$. The solution $x = -4$
is non-permissible, so there are no solutions, and verifying is not necessary.

2. Step 1
Assign a variable to represent the unknown, and set up an equation using the given information.

Let x represent the wind speed. It takes the sailboat the same time to travel 70 km against the wind as it does to travel 130 km with the wind.

The sailboat will travel faster with the wind, so its speed will be $(20 + x)$ km/h.

Similarly, the sailboat will travel slower against the wind, so its speed will be $(20 - x)$ km/h.

 Copyright Protected

Therefore, set up an equation where the two times are equal, $\left(t = \dfrac{d}{s} \right)$.

time with the wind = time against the wind

$$\frac{130 \text{ km}}{(20+x)\text{km/h}} = \frac{70 \text{ km}}{(20-x)\text{km/h}}$$

Step 2
Solve the rational equation.

Cross-multiply, and then solve for x.

$$\frac{130 \text{ km}}{(20+x)\text{km/h}} = \frac{70 \text{ km}}{(20-x)\text{km/h}}$$
$$130(20-x) = 70(20+x)$$
$$2\,600 - 130x = 1\,400 + 70x$$
$$1\,200 = 200x$$
$$6 = x$$

Therefore, the wind speed is 6 km/h.

Step 3
Verify the solution using the original equation.

$x = 6$	
$\dfrac{130}{(20+6)}$ $=\dfrac{130}{26}$ $=5$	$\dfrac{70}{(20-6)}$ $=\dfrac{70}{14}$ $=5$

The solution $x = 6$ has been verified.

PRACTICE EXERCISES
ANSWERS AND SOLUTIONS

1. Step 1
With a single expression on either side of the equal sign, cross-multiply to remove the denominators, and then expand where necessary.

$$\frac{2}{x-1} = \frac{3}{x}$$
$$2(x) = 3(x-1)$$
$$2x = 3x - 3$$

Step 2
Gather like terms, and solve for x.
$$2x = 3x - 3$$
$$3 = x$$

Step 3
State any NPVs for the variable.

The NPVs from the original equation $\dfrac{2}{x-1} = \dfrac{3}{x}$ are $x = 1$ and $x = 0$. Therefore, the solution is $x = 3$.

Step 4
Verify the solution by substituting it into the original equation and simplifying.

$x = 3$	
$\dfrac{2}{3-1}$ $=\dfrac{2}{2}$ $=1$	$\dfrac{3}{x}$ $=\dfrac{3}{3}$ $=1$

The solution $x = 3$ has been verified.

3. Simplify where possible.

$$\frac{x}{x+1} = \frac{-2}{2x+2}$$
$$\frac{x}{x+1} = \frac{\overset{-1}{\cancel{-2}}}{\cancel{2}(x+1)}$$
$$\frac{x}{x+1} = \frac{-1}{x+1}$$

After factoring and eliminating a factor of 2 from the second expression, it is possible to continue solving using the set steps or to solve by observation.

Since both denominators are the same, the numerators must also be equal for the equality to be true. This means that $x = -1$. However, by noting the NPVs, it can be found that $x \neq -1$. Therefore, there is no solution.

5. **B**

Solve by cross-multiplying.

$$\frac{13}{y+1} = 4$$
$$13 = 4(y+1)$$
$$13 = 4y+4$$
$$9 = 4y$$
$$y = \frac{9}{4}$$

The NPV from the original equation $\frac{13}{y+1} = 4$ is

$y \neq -1$. Therefore, the solution is $y = \frac{9}{4}$.

7. **Step 1**

Determine the time taken to travel 528 km by bus.

Recall that $\text{time} = \dfrac{\text{distance}}{\text{speed}}$. If x represents the

average speed of the bus, the time taken to travel

by bus is $\dfrac{528}{x}$ h.

Step 2

Determine the time taken to travel 528 km by airplane.

It is given that the airplane travels at a speed 6 times faster than the bus. Therefore, the time taken

to travel by airplane is $\dfrac{528}{6x}$ h.

Step 3

Determine the equation that represents the difference between the time it takes the bus to travel 528 km and the time it takes the airplane to travel 528 km.

Since the bus takes more time to complete the trip, the time for the airplane flight is subtracted from the time for the bus trip to find a positive value for the difference in time.

Therefore, the equation $\dfrac{528}{x} - \dfrac{528}{6x} = 4$, where

$x \neq 0$, represents the difference between the time it takes the bus to travel 528 km and the time it takes the airplane to travel 528 km.

ANSWERS AND SOLUTIONS

1. **D**

The expression $\dfrac{4}{2x-2}$ simplifies to the expression

$\dfrac{2}{(x-1)}$ through factoring and eliminating a

common factor of 2.

The other expressions reflect some common mistakes in simplifying.

3. **D**

Examine each statement to determine which one is true.

Non-permissible values should always be determined based on the original denominator before simplifying. Therefore, it is not true that a denominator with the factors of $(a)(a-1)$ after simplifying will always have NPVs of $a = 0$ and $a = 1$.

The variable x need not be introduced, so it is false that the expression must have the variable x in the numerator and the factors $(a)(a-1)$ in the denominator.

The variable in the expression $\dfrac{1}{(x)(x-1)}$ is x, so it

is impossible to have NPVs of $a = 0$ and $a = 1$.

To determine the NPVs in the expression

$\dfrac{2}{2a^2 - 2a}$, equate the denominator to 0, and solve

for a.
$$2a - 2a = 0$$
$$2a(a-1) = 0$$

The NPVs are $a = 0$ and $a = 1$, so this statement is true.

Copyright Protected

5. Step 1
Determine the value of x.

If the length of rectangle A is 5 times larger than the length of rectangle B, then $5 = \dfrac{18-x}{x}$.

Solve for x.
$$5 = \frac{18-x}{x}$$
$$5x = 18 - x$$
$$6x = 18$$
$$x = 3$$

Step 2
Determine the width of rectangle B.

The width of rectangle B is given by $w_B = x + 2$.
Let $x = 3$, and solve.
$$w_B = x + 2$$
$$w_B = 3 + 2$$
$$w_B = 5$$

Therefore, the width of rectangle B is 5 units.

7. Step 1
Factor where possible.

The terms in the denominator of the first expression have a common factor of $6y$.
$$\frac{5y}{12y^2 + 6y} + \frac{3y}{10y - 7y}$$
$$= \frac{5y}{6y(2y+1)} + \frac{3y}{10y - 7y}$$

Step 2
Simplify where possible.

The common factor in the numerator and denominator of the first expression is y, and the like terms in the second denominator can be subtracted.
$$\frac{5y}{6y(2y+1)} + \frac{3y}{10y - 7y}$$
$$= \frac{5}{6(2y+1)} + \frac{3y}{3y}$$

To simplify further, divide $3y$ by $3y$ to get 1, or $\dfrac{1}{1}$.
$$\frac{5}{6(2y+1)} + \frac{3y}{3y}$$
$$= \frac{5}{6(2y+1)} + \frac{1}{1}$$

Step 3
Find the LCD.
The LCD is $6(2y+1)$.

Step 4
Express each rational expression with the LCD.
$$\frac{5}{6(2y+1)} + \frac{1}{1}$$
$$= \frac{5}{6(2y+1)} + \frac{1\left[6(2y+1)\right]}{1\left[6(2y+1)\right]}$$
$$= \frac{5}{6(2y+1)} + \frac{6(2y+1)}{6(2y+1)}$$

Step 5
Add the terms in the numerator, keeping the denominator.
$$\frac{5}{6(2y+1)} + \frac{6(2y+1)}{6(2y+1)}$$
$$= \frac{5 + 12y + 6}{6(2y+1)}$$
$$= \frac{12y + 11}{6(2y+1)}$$

Step 6
State all non-permissible values.

The NPVs are $y = -\dfrac{1}{2}$ and $y = 0$.

Step 7
No further simplifying is needed because the numerator and denominator are fully factored and reduced.

When simplified, the expression $\dfrac{5y}{12y^2 + 6y} + \dfrac{3y}{10y - 7y}$ becomes $\dfrac{12y + 11}{6(2y+1)}$, where $y \neq 0, -\dfrac{1}{2}$.

9. Step 1

Determine an expression that represents the length of the original poster board.

Let w represent width and l_1 represent the length of the original poster board. The area of the poster board is $12\,\mathrm{m}^2$. Therefore, by applying the area formula, $\text{area} = \text{length} \times \text{width}$, it follows that $12 = w \times l_1$. When l_1 is isolated, this equation becomes $\dfrac{12}{w} = l_1$.

Step 2

Determine an expression that represents the length of the modified poster board.

Let l_2 represent the length of the modified board. When Michelle modifies the poster board, she decides to increase the width of board by 1 m. Therefore, if l_2 represents the length of the modified board, then it follows that $12 = (w+1) \times l_2$. When l_2 is isolated, this equation becomes $\dfrac{12}{w+1} = l_2$.

Step 3

Set up a rational equation in terms of w. In order to maintain the same area, Michelle will have to decrease the length of the poster board by 2 m. This is represented as $l_1 - 2 = l_2$.

Replace l_1 with $\dfrac{12}{w}$ and l_2 with $\dfrac{12}{w+1}$.

$$l_1 - 2 = l_2$$
$$\frac{12}{w} - 2 = \frac{12}{w+1}$$

This equation can be used to solve for w.

Step 4

Solve for w.

The lowest common denominator is $w(w+1)$.

$$\frac{12}{w} - 2 = \frac{12}{w+1}$$
$$w(w+1)\left[\frac{12}{w} - 2\right] = w(w+1)\left[\frac{12}{w+1}\right]$$
$$12(w+1) - 2w(w+1) = 12w$$
$$12w + 12 - 2w^2 - 2w = 12w$$
$$-2w^2 - 2w + 12 = 0$$
$$w^2 + 2w - 12 = 0$$
$$(w+6)(w-4) = 0$$

The possible values for width are –6 and 4. Since width cannot be a negative value, the solution –6 is rejected. Therefore, the width of the original poster board is 4 m.

LOGARITHMIC AND EXPONENTIAL FUNCTIONS

Lesson 1—Defining Logarithms

CLASS EXERCISES
ANSWERS AND SOLUTIONS

1. The expression $\log_9 81$ is equal to the value of x, which makes the statement $9^x = 81$ true.
    Since $9^2 = 81$, then $2\log_9 81 = 2(2) = 4$.

2. The exponential form of $\log_6 216 = 3$ is $216 = 6^3$.

3. **a) Step 1**
    Divide both sides by 150.

    $$30\,000 = 150(2)^{\frac{m}{40}}$$
    $$200 = 2^{\frac{m}{40}}$$

    Step 2
    Convert the exponential equation into a logarithmic equation.

    Apply the property that if $y = a^x$, then $x = \log_a y$. The logarithmic form of

    $30\,000 = 150(2)^{\frac{m}{40}}$ is $\dfrac{m}{40} = \log_2 200$.

    b) Apply the property that if $x = \log_a y$,
    then $y = a^x$. The exponential form of
    $4a = \log_2 (b - 10)$ is $b - 10 = 2^{4a}$.

4. **a) Step 1**
    Let $\log_2\left(\dfrac{1}{64}\right) = x$. Rewrite $\log_2\left(\dfrac{1}{64}\right) = x$ in exponential form.

    The exponential form of $\log_2\left(\dfrac{1}{64}\right) = x$ is

    $$2^x = \frac{1}{64}.$$

Step 2
Solve the exponential equation $2^x = \dfrac{1}{64}$.

$$2^x = \frac{1}{64}$$
$$2^x = 64^{-1}$$
$$2^x = \left(2^6\right)^{-1}$$
$$2^x = 2^{-6}$$

The value of x is –6. Therefore,
$$\log_2\left(\frac{1}{64}\right) = -6.$$

b) If $\log_3 81 = x$ and $\log_3\left(\dfrac{1}{27}\right) = y$,

determine $x + y$.

Step 1
Determine the value of x.

The exponential form of $\log_3 81 = x$ is
$3^x = 81$.

Since $3^4 = 81$, the value of x is 4.

Step 2
Determine the value of y.

The exponential form of $\log_3\left(\dfrac{1}{27}\right) = y$ is

$$3^y = \frac{1}{27}.$$

Since $3^{-3} = \dfrac{1}{27}$, the value of y is –3.

Step 3
Determine the value of $\log_3 81 + \log_3\left(\dfrac{1}{27}\right)$.

Find the value of $x + y$.
$$x + y = 4 + (-3)$$
$$x + y = 1$$

Therefore, $\log_3 81 + \log_3\left(\dfrac{1}{27}\right) = 1$.

5. Let $\log\left(\dfrac{1}{1000}\right) = x$. The exponential form of

$\log\left(\dfrac{1}{1000}\right) = x$ is $10^x = \dfrac{1}{1000}$.

Since $10^{-3} = \dfrac{1}{1000}$, the value of x is –3.

Therefore, $\log\left(\dfrac{1}{1000}\right) = -3$.

6. Use a TI-83 or similar calculator to evaluate $\log 1782$.

Press $\boxed{\text{LOG}}\boxed{1}\boxed{7}\boxed{8}\boxed{2}\boxed{)}\boxed{\text{ENTER}}$.

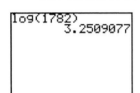

Rounded to the nearest thousandth, the value of $\log 1782$ is 3.251.

PRACTICE EXERCISES
ANSWERS AND SOLUTIONS

1. The logarithmic form of $6^2 = 36$ is $2 = \log_6 36$.

3. The logarithmic form of $5^x = y - 11$ is $x = \log_5(y - 11)$.

5. The logarithmic form of $10^{\log(0.001)} = x$ is $\log(0.001) = \log_{10} x$ or $\log(0.001) = \log x$.

7. The exponential form of $-5 = \log_{\left(\frac{1}{4}\right)} 1024$ is $\left(\dfrac{1}{4}\right)^{-5} = 1024$.

9. The exponential form of $\log(x + 9) = 108$ is $10^{108} = x + 9$.

11. Let $\log_5 25 = x$. The exponential form of $\log_5 25 = x$ is $5^x = 25$.

Since $5^2 = 25$, the value of x is 2.

Therefore, $\log_5 25 = 2$.

13. Let $4\log_6\left(\dfrac{1}{6}\right) = x$.

Step 1

Evaluate $\log_6\left(\dfrac{1}{6}\right)$.

The expression $\log_6\left(\dfrac{1}{6}\right)$ is equal to the value of x that makes $6^x = \dfrac{1}{6}$ true.

$6^x = \dfrac{1}{6}$
$6^x = 6^{-1}$
$x = -1$

Step 2

Substitute –1 for $\log_6\left(\dfrac{1}{6}\right)$ in the expression $4\log_6\left(\dfrac{1}{6}\right)$, then evaluate.

$4\log_6\left(\dfrac{1}{6}\right)$
$= 4(-1)$
$= -4$

15. If $\log_5 1 = x$ and $\log_5\left(\dfrac{1}{125}\right) = y$, determine $x + y$.

Step 1
Determine the value of x.

The exponential form of $\log_5 1 = x$ is $5^x = 1$.
Since $5^0 = 1$, the value of x is 0.

Step 2
Determine the value of y.

The exponential form of $\log_5\left(\dfrac{1}{125}\right) = y$

is $5^y = \dfrac{1}{125}$.

 Copyright Protected

Since $5^{-3} = \dfrac{1}{125}$, the value of y is -3.

Step 3

Determine the value of $\log_5 1 + \log_5 \left(\dfrac{1}{125} \right)$.

Find the value of $x + y$.
$x + y = 0 + (-3)$
$x + y = -3$

Therefore, $\log_5 1 + \log_5 \left(\dfrac{1}{125} \right) = -3$.

17. Use a TI-83 or similar calculator to evaluate $\log 5887$.

Press $\boxed{\text{LOG}}\,\boxed{5}\,\boxed{8}\,\boxed{8}\,\boxed{7}\,\boxed{)}\,\boxed{\text{ENTER}}$.

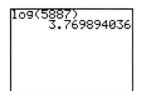

Rounded to the nearest thousandth, the value of $\log 5887$ is 3.770.

Lesson 2—The Laws of Logarithms

CLASS EXERCISES
ANSWERS AND SOLUTIONS

1. **Step 1**
   Write the logarithm of the product $(25 \times a)$ as the logarithm of 25 plus the logarithm of a.
   $\log_5 (25a) = \log_5 25 + \log_5 a$

   Step 2
   Evaluate each logarithm, and add the results.
   $\log_5 25 + \log_5 a$
   $= 2 + \log_5 a$

   No further simplification is possible, so
   $\log_5 25a = 2 + \log_5 a$.

2. Write the sum of the logarithm of $(x+1)$ and the logarithm of $(x-3)$ as the logarithm of the product $(x+1)(x-3)$.
   $\log(x+1) + \log(x-3) = \log \left[(x+1)(x-3) \right]$

3. **Step 1**
   Apply the product law of logarithms.
   $\log_3 = (27 \times 9 \times m) = \log_3 27 + \log_3 9 + \log_3 m$

   Step 2
   Evaluate, and simplify.
   $\log_3 27 \times \log_3 9 \times \log_3 m$
   $= 3 + 2 + \log_3 m$
   $= 5 + \log_3 m$

   Since $\log_3 m = x$, the expression equivalent to $\log_3 (27 \times 9 \times m)$ is $5 + x$.

4. **Step 1**
   Write the logarithm of the quotient $\left(\dfrac{36}{m} \right)$ as the logarithm of 36 minus the logarithm of m.
   $\log_6 \left(\dfrac{36}{m} \right) = \log_6 36 - \log_6 m$

   Step 2
   Evaluate $\log_6 36$.
   $\log_6 36 - \log_6 m$
   $= 2 - \log_6 m$

   Since $\log_6 m = x$, the expression equivalent to $\log_6 \left(\dfrac{36}{m} \right)$ is $2 - x$.

5. **Step 1**
   Write the difference between the logarithm of $72x^2$ and the logarithm of $9x$ as the logarithm of the quotient $\left(\dfrac{72x^2}{9x} \right)$.
   $\log_2 (72x^2) - \log_2 (9x) = \log_2 \left(\dfrac{72x^2}{9x} \right)$

Step 2
Simplify.
$$\log_2\left(\frac{72x^2}{9x}\right)$$
$$= \log_2(8x)$$

Therefore, $\log_2(72x^2) - \log_2(9x) = \log_2(8x)$.

6. **Step 1**
Apply the power law of logarithms.
$$\log_3(81)^{5-k}$$
$$= (5-k)\log_3 81$$

Step 2
Evaluate $\log_3 81$.
$$(5-k)\log_3 81$$
$$= (5-k)4$$

Therefore, $\log_3(81^{5-k})$ is equivalent to the expression $(5-k)4$.

7. **Step 1**
Apply the power law of logarithms to the middle term in the expression, and simplify.
$$\log 100 + 3\log 10 - \log 10\,000$$
$$= \log 100 + \log(10^3) - \log 10\,000$$
$$= \log 100 + \log 1000 - \log 10\,000$$

Step 2
Apply the product law to the first two terms in the expression, and simplify.
$$\log 100 + \log 1000 - \log 10\,000$$
$$= \log 100 + \log 1000 - \log 10\,000$$
$$= \log(100 \times 1000) - \log 10\,000$$
$$= \log 100\,000 - \log 10\,000$$

Step 3
Apply the quotient law of logarithms, and simplify.
$$\log 100\,000 - \log 10\,000$$
$$= \log\left(\frac{100\,000}{10\,000}\right)$$
$$= \log 10$$

Step 4
Evaluate $\log 10$.
$$\log 10 = 1$$

Therefore, $\log 100 + 3\log 10 - \log 10\,000 = 1$.

8. **Step 1**
Apply the power law of logarithms to the first term of the expression.
$$3\log_8 y - \log_8(y^4) + \log_8 x$$
$$= \log_8(y^3) - \log_8(y^4) + \log_8 x$$

Step 2
Apply the quotient law to the first two terms.
$$\log_8(y^3) - \log_8(y^4) + \log_8 x$$
$$= \log_8\left(\frac{y^3}{y^4}\right) + \log_8 x$$
$$= \log_8(y^{-1}) + \log_8 x$$

Step 3
Apply the product law.
$$\log_8(y^{-1}) + \log_8 x$$
$$= \log_8(y^{-1}x)$$
$$= \log_8\left(\frac{x}{y}\right)$$

9. **Step 1**
Apply the power law of logarithms to the first term.
$$3\log_5 4 - \log_5 17$$
$$= \log_5 4^3 - \log_5 17$$
$$= \log_5 64 - \log_5 17$$

Step 2
Apply the quotient law of logarithms.
$$\log_5 64 - \log_5 17 = \log_5\left(\frac{64}{17}\right)$$

Step 3
Apply the change of base formula using base 10 so that a calculator can be used.
$$\log_5\left(\frac{64}{17}\right) = \frac{\log\left(\frac{64}{17}\right)}{\log 5}$$

Step 4
Use a TI-83 or similar calculator to evaluate
$$\frac{\log\left(\frac{64}{17}\right)}{\log 5}.$$
$$\frac{\log\left(\frac{64}{17}\right)}{\log 5} \approx 0.8$$

Copyright Protected

10. To rewrite the expression as a single logarithm with base 2, both terms need to be in base 2.

Step 1

Express $\log_8 (5x)$ with a base of 2.

Apply the change of base formula.

$3\log_2 x + 9\log_8 (5x)$

$= 3\log_2 x + 9\left[\dfrac{\log_2 (5x)}{\log_2 8}\right]$

Step 2

Evaluate $\log_2 8$.

$3\log_2 x + 9\left[\dfrac{\log_2 (5x)}{\log_2 8}\right]$

$= 3\log_2 x + 9\left[\dfrac{\log_2 (5x)}{3}\right]$

$= 3\log_2 x + 3\log_2 (5x)$

Step 3

Factor out 3, and apply the product law of logarithms.

$3\log_2 x + 3\log_2 (5x)$

$= 3\left(\log_2 x + \log_2 (5x)\right)$

$= 3\log_2 \left(x(5x)\right)$

$= 3\log_2 \left(5x^2\right)$

Step 4

Apply the power law of logarithms to express $3\log_2 \left(5x^2\right)$ in the form $\log_2 a$.

$3\log_2 \left(5x^2\right)$

$= \log_2 \left(5x^2\right)^3$

$= \log_2 \left(125x^6\right)$

PRACTICE EXERCISES
ANSWERS AND SOLUTIONS

---

1. **Step 1**

Apply the product law of logarithms.

$\log_3 (9 \times 27)$

$= \log_3 9 + \log_3 27$

Step 2

Evaluate each logarithm, and add the results.

$\log_3 9 + \log_3 27$

$= 2 + 3$

$= 5$

3. **Step 1**

Apply the quotient law of logarithms.

$\log_9 \left(\dfrac{\sqrt[3]{729}}{81}\right)$

$= \log_9 \left(\sqrt[3]{729}\right) - \log_9 81$

Step 2

Evaluate each logarithm, and subtract the results.

$\log_9 \left(\sqrt[3]{729}\right) - \log_9 81$

$= \log_9 9 - \log_9 81$

$= 1 - 2$

$= -1$

Therefore, $\log_9 \left(\dfrac{\sqrt[3]{729}}{81}\right) = -1$.

5. **Step 1**

Apply the quotient law of logarithms.

$\log_3 6 - \log_3 54$

$= \log_3 \left(\dfrac{6}{54}\right)$

$= \log_3 \left(\dfrac{1}{9}\right)$

Step 2

Evaluate $\log_3 \left(\dfrac{1}{9}\right)$.

$\log_3 \left(\dfrac{1}{9}\right)$

$= \log_3 \left(\dfrac{1}{3^2}\right)$

$= \log_3 \left(3^{-2}\right)$

$= -2$

Therefore, $\log_3 6 - \log_3 54 = -2$.

7. **Step 1**

Apply the power law of logarithms.

$\log_4 \left(64^{10}\right)$

$= 10\log_4 64$

Step 2

Evaluate $10\log_4 64$.

$10\log_4 64$

$= 10(3)$

$= 30$

Therefore, $\log_4 \left(64^{10}\right) = 30$.

9. **Step 1**
Apply the product law to the first two terms of the expression.
$\log 5 + \log 4 - \log 200$
$= \log (5 \times 4) - \log 200$
$= \log 20 - \log 200$

Step 2
Apply the quotient law.
$\log 20 - \log 200$
$= \log \left(\dfrac{20}{200} \right)$

Step 3
Evaluate $\log \left(\dfrac{20}{200} \right)$.

$\log \left(\dfrac{20}{200} \right)$
$= \log \left(\dfrac{1}{10} \right)$
$= \log \left(10^{-1} \right)$
$= -1$

Therefore, $\log 5 + \log 4 - \log 200 = -1$.

11. **Step 1**
Apply the power rule of logarithms to all terms of the expression.
$2 \log_{\sqrt{3}} 6 - 2 \log_{\sqrt{3}} 2 - 5 \log_{\sqrt{3}} 1$
$= \log_{\sqrt{3}} \left(6^2 \right) - \log_{\sqrt{3}} \left(2^2 \right) - \log_{\sqrt{3}} \left(1^5 \right)$
$= \log_{\sqrt{3}} 36 - \log_{\sqrt{3}} 4 - \log_{\sqrt{3}} 1$
$= \log_{\sqrt{3}} 36 - \log_{\sqrt{3}} 4 - 0$
$= \log_{\sqrt{3}} 36 - \log_{\sqrt{3}} 4$

Step 2
Apply the quotient law of logarithms.
$\log_{\sqrt{3}} 36 - \log_{\sqrt{3}} 4$
$= \log_{\sqrt{3}} \left(\dfrac{36}{4} \right)$
$= \log_{\sqrt{3}} 9$

Step 3
Evaluate $\log_{\sqrt{3}} 9$.

Rewrite the expression in base 10, and evaluate using a calculator.
$\log_{\sqrt{3}} 9$
$= \dfrac{\log 9}{\log \sqrt{3}}$
$= 4$

Therefore, $2 \log_{\sqrt{3}} 6 - 2 \log_{\sqrt{3}} 2 - 5 \log_{\sqrt{3}} 1 = 4$.

13. **Step 1**
Apply the power law of logarithms to the first term.
$3 \log_2 x + 2 \log_2 (5x)$
$= \log_2 \left(x^3 \right) + \log_2 \left((5x)^2 \right)$

Step 2
Apply the product law of logarithms.
$\log_2 \left(x^3 \right) + \log_2 \left[(5x)^2 \right]$
$= \log_2 \left[x^3 (5x)^2 \right]$
$= \log_2 \left(25x^5 \right)$

Therefore, $3 \log_2 x + 2 \log_2 (5x) = \log_2 \left(25x^5 \right)$.

15. **Step 1**
Apply the power law of logarithms to the last two terms of the expression.
$\log_x a + 3 \log_x b - 2 \log_x a$
$= \log_x a + \log_x \left(b^3 \right) - \log_x \left(a^2 \right)$

Step 2
Apply the product law of logarithms to the first two terms of the expression.
$\log_x a + \log_x \left(b^3 \right) - \log_x \left(a^2 \right)$
$= \log_x \left(ab^3 \right) - \log_x \left(a^2 \right)$

 Copyright Protected

Step 3
Apply the quotient law of logarithms.

$\log_x\left(ab^3\right) - \log_x\left(a^2\right)$

$= \log_x\left(\dfrac{ab^3}{a^2}\right)$

$= \log_x\left(\dfrac{b^3}{a}\right)$

Therefore, $\log_x a + 3\log_x b - 2\log_x a = \log_x\left(\dfrac{b^3}{a}\right)$.

17. Step 1

It is given that $\log_b 9 = m$, so rewrite $\log_b\left(\dfrac{1}{81}\right)$ so

that it includes $\log_b 9$.

$\log_b\left(\dfrac{1}{81}\right)$

$= \log_b\left(\dfrac{1}{9^2}\right)$

$= \log_b\left(9^{-2}\right)$

Step 2
Apply the power law of logarithms.

$\log_b\left(9^{-2}\right)$

$= -2\log_b 9$

Step 3
Substitute m for $\log_b 9$.

$-2\log_b 9 = -2m$

Therefore, the expression $\log_b\left(\dfrac{1}{81}\right)$ in terms of

m is $-2m$.

Lesson 3—Solving Exponential Equations

CLASS EXERCISES
ANSWERS AND SOLUTIONS

1. Since the bases on each side of the equation are equal, the exponents on each side of the equation must also be equal. Equate the exponents, and solve for x.

$-8 - 9p = 1$
$-9p = 9$
$p = -1$

The value of p is -1.

2. a) **Step 1**
Write the equation so that the powers have the same base.

Since both sides can be written as powers with base 5, replace 125 with 5^3 and $\dfrac{1}{25}$ with 5^{-2}.

$125 = \left(\dfrac{1}{25}\right)^{x+9}$

$5^3 = \left(5^{-2}\right)^{x+9}$

Step 2
Simplify the equation using the laws of exponents.

Apply the power law of exponents to the right side of the equation.

$5^3 = \left(5^{-2}\right)^{x+9}$
$5^3 = 5^{-2x-18}$

Step 3
Apply the property that if $b^x = b^y$, where $b \neq 0$ and $b \neq 1$, then $x = y$.

Both sides of the equation have the same base, so equate the exponents.
$3 = -2x - 18$

Step 4
Solve for *x*.
$$3 = -2x - 18$$
$$21 = -2x$$
$$-\frac{21}{2} = x$$

Therefore, the value of *x* is $-\frac{21}{2}$.

b) **Step 1**
Write the equation so that the powers have the same base.

Replace 8 with 2^3.
$$2^{3x+27} = 8$$
$$2^{3x+27} = 2^3$$

Step 2
Apply the property that if $b^x = b^y$, where $b \neq 0$ and $b \neq 1$, then $x = y$.

Both sides of the equation have the same base, so equate the exponents.
$$3x + 27 = 3$$
$$3x = -24$$
$$x = -\frac{24}{3}$$
$$x = -8$$

Therefore, the value of *x* is –8.

3. **Step 1**
Isolate the power.
$$80^{2x} - 4 = 5$$
$$80^{2x} = 9$$

Step 2
Write the equation in logarithmic form.
$$80^{2x} = 9$$
$$\log_{80} 9 = 2x$$

Step 3
Apply the change of base formula to the expression $\log_{80} 9$.
$$\log_{80} 9 = 2x$$
$$\frac{\log 9}{\log 80} = 2x$$

Step 4
Isolate *x*.

Divide both sides by 2.
$$\frac{\log 9}{\log 80} = 2x$$
$$\frac{\log 9}{2 \log 80} = x$$

Step 5
Find an approximate solution using a calculator.
$$x = \frac{\log 9}{2 \log 80}$$
$$x \approx 0.251$$

Therefore, the value of *x* is approximately 0.251.

4. **Step 1**
Take the common logarithm of each side of the equation.
$$2^x = 5^{x-3}$$
$$\log(2^x) = \log(5^{x-3})$$

Step 2
Apply the power law of logarithms.
$$\log(2^x) = \log(5^{x-3})$$
$$x \log 2 = (x-3) \log 5$$

Step 3
Apply the distributive property.
$$x \log 2 = (x-3) \log 5$$
$$x \log 2 = x \log 5 - 3 \log 5$$

Step 4
Isolate *x*.
$$x \log 2 = x \log 5 - 3 \log 5$$
$$x \log 2 - x \log 5 = -3 \log 5$$
$$x(\log 2 - \log 5) = -3 \log 5$$
$$x = \frac{-3 \log 5}{\log 2 - \log 5}$$

Step 5
Using a calculator, determine the solution, correct to the nearest thousandth.
$$x = \frac{-3 \log 5}{\log 2 - \log 5}$$
$$x \approx 5.269$$

Therefore, the value of *x* is approximately 5.269.

Copyright Protected

PRACTICE EXERCISES
ANSWERS AND SOLUTIONS

1. **Step 1**
Write the equation $4^{2x+1} = 64^{x-5}$ so that the powers have the same base.

Replace 64 with 4^3.
$$4^{2x+1} = 64^{x-5}$$
$$4^{2x+1} = \left(4^3\right)^{x-5}$$

Step 2
Apply the product law of exponents to the right side of the equation.
$$4^{2x+1} = \left(4^3\right)^{x-5}$$
$$4^{2x+1} = 4^{3x-15}$$

Step 3
Apply the power law to the right side of the equation.
$$4^{2x-1} = \left(4^3\right)^{x-5}$$
$$4^{2x-1} = 4^{3x-15}$$

Step 4
Solve for x.

Both sides of the equation have the same base, so equate the exponents, and solve for x.
$$2x-1 = 3x-15$$
$$2x-3x = -15+1$$
$$-x = -14$$
$$x = 14$$

Therefore, the value of x is 14.

3. The equation $6^{12x-7} - 2 = 4$ can be rewritten as $6^{12x-7} = 6$. Since the bases on each side of the equation are equal, the exponents on each side of the equation must also be equal. Equate the exponents, and solve for x.
$$2x-7 = 1$$
$$2x = 8$$
$$x = 4$$

Therefore, the value of x in the equation is 4.

5. **Step 1**
Take the common logarithm of each side of the equation.
$$8^{6x-5} = 9^{11x}$$
$$\log\left(8^{6x-5}\right) = \log\left(9^{11x}\right)$$

Step 2
Apply the power law of logarithms.
$$\log\left(8^{6x-5}\right) = \log\left(9^{11x}\right)$$
$$\left(6x-5\right)\log 8 = 11x\log 9$$

Step 3
Apply the distributive property.
$$\left(6x-5\right)\log 8 = 11x\log 9$$
$$6x\log 8 - 5\log 8 = 11x\log 9$$

Step 4
Subtract $6x\log 8$ from both sides of the equation.
$$6x\log 8 - 5\log 8 = 11x\log 9$$
$$-5\log 8 = 11x\log 9 - 6x\log 8$$

Step 5
Factor out x on the right side of the equation.
$$-5\log 8 = 11x\log 9 - 6x\log 8$$
$$-5\log 8 = x\left(11\log 9 - 6\log 8\right)$$

Step 6
Divide both sides by $\left(11\log 9 - 6\log 8\right)$.
$$-5\log 8 = x\left(11\log 9 - 6\log 8\right)$$
$$\frac{-5\log 8}{11\log 9 - 6\log 8} = x$$

Step 7
Find an approximate solution using a calculator.
$$x = \frac{-5\log 8}{11\log 9 - 6\log 8}$$
$$x \approx -0.89$$

Therefore, the value of x is approximately –0.89.

7. **Step 1**
Isolate the power.
$$13 = 125^{4x-1} - 7$$
$$20 = 125^{4x-1}$$

Step 2
Write the equation in logarithmic form.
$$\log_{125} 20 = 4x-1$$

Step 3
Isolate x.
$$\log_{125} 20 = 4x - 1$$
$$\log_{125} 20 + 1 = 4x$$
$$\frac{\log_{125} 20 + 1}{4} = x$$

Step 4
Apply the change of base formula to $\log_{125} 20$ using base 10.
$$\frac{\log_{125} 20 + 1}{4} = x$$
$$\frac{\left(\dfrac{\log 20}{\log 125}\right) + 1}{4} = x$$

Step 5
Find an approximate solution using a calculator.
$$\frac{\left(\dfrac{\log 20}{\log 125}\right) + 1}{4} = x$$
$$x \approx 0.41$$

Therefore, the value of x is approximately 0.41.

9. **Step 1**
Graph each side of the equation $7^{x-4} = 6^{6-x}$.

Press $\boxed{Y=}$, enter the equation as two separate functions, $Y_1 = 7^\wedge(X-4)$ and $Y_1 = 6^\wedge(6-X)$, and press $\boxed{\text{GRAPH}}$. An appropriate window setting is $x:[-2,10,1]$ and $y:[-2, 15, 1]$.

The resulting graph is shown.

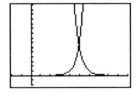

Step 2
Find the point of intersection.

Press $\boxed{\text{2nd}}$ $\boxed{\text{TRACE}}$, and select 5:intersect. When asked for a first curve, position the cursor just left or right of the first intersection point, and press $\boxed{\text{ENTER}}$.

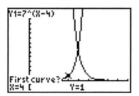

When asked for a second curve, position the cursor just left or right of the first intersection point, and press $\boxed{\text{ENTER}}$.

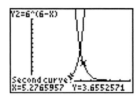

At the "Guess?" prompt, press $\boxed{\text{ENTER}}$.

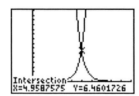

The point of intersection is approximately (4.96, 6.46). The solution is equal to the x-coordinate of the point of intersection. Therefore, the value of x in the equation $7^{x-4} = 6^{6-x}$ is approximately 4.96.

Alternate solution: You can solve the equation $7^{x-4} = 6^{6-x}$ by bringing all the terms to one side of the equation and graphing the corresponding function $y = 7^{x-4} - 6^{6-x}$ using a TI-83 or similar graphing calculator. The zero feature on the calculator will give the x-intercept of the graph, which is the solution to the equation $7^{x-4} = 6^{6-x}$.

Lesson 4—Solving Problems Involving Exponential Functions

CLASS EXERCISES
ANSWERS AND SOLUTIONS

1. **Step 1**
Identify the variables whose values are given in the problem with respect to the function $N_t = N_0 \times R^{\frac{t}{p}}$.

When $t = 0$, there are 32 spiders $\left(N_0 = 32\right)$.

Since the doubling period is required, the growth rate is $R = 2$. After 5 weeks, the spider population is 32 768.

Therefore, in 5 weeks, the spider population will double $\dfrac{5}{p}$ times.

Step 2
Substitute the values $N_0 = 32$, $R = 2$, and $t = 5$ into the function $N_t = N_0 \times R^{\frac{t}{p}}$.

$$N_t = N_0 \times R^{\frac{t}{p}}$$
$$32\ 768 = 32(2)^{\frac{5}{p}}$$

Step 3
Solve for p.

$$32\ 768 = 32(2)^{\frac{5}{p}}$$
$$1\ 024 = 2^{\frac{5}{p}}$$
$$\log 1024 = \log 2^{\frac{5}{p}}$$
$$\log 1024 = \frac{5}{p}\log 2$$
$$p = \frac{5\log 2}{\log 1024}$$
$$p = 0.5$$

Therefore, it takes half a week for the species of spiders to double.

2. **Step 1**
Identify the variables whose values are given in the problem with respect to the function
$$A(t) = A_0 \times R^{\frac{t}{p}} .$$

The car was originally worth \$45 000, so $A_0 = 45\ 000$. The value of the car depreciates at a rate of 8.5%, so the decay rate is $R = (1 - 0.085) = 0.915$. Since the value of the car depreciates every year, $p = 1$.

Substitute the values $A_0 = 45\ 000$, $R = 0.915$, an $p = 1$ into the function $A(t) = A_0 \times R^{\frac{t}{p}}$.

$$A(t) = A_0 \times R^{\frac{t}{p}}$$
$$A(t) = 45\ 000(0.915)^{\frac{t}{1}}$$
$$A(t) = 45\ 000(0.915)^{t}$$

The function $A(t) = 45\ 000(0.915)^{t}$ represents the value of the car after t years.

Step 2
Determine the value of the car after 18 years. The elapsed time is 18 years, so solve for $A(18)$.

$$A(t) = 45\ 000(0.915)^{t}$$
$$A(18) = 45\ 000(0.915)^{18}$$
$$A(18) = 9\ 094.780186$$

After 18 years, the value of the car is \$9 095.

3. **a)** The initial population of ducks is given by the y-intercept of the graph or when $t = 0$. From the graph, when $t = 0$, the value of $P(t)$ is 42. Therefore, the number of ducks that were introduced to the pond is 42.

b) The year 1995 corresponds to when $t = 5$. The value of $P(t)$ when $t = 5$ is 157. Therefore, the population of ducks in 1995 was 157.

c) Since the initial population was 42, determine when $P(t) = 42(2) = 84$. From the graph, $P(t) = 84$ between the values $t = 2$ and $t = 3$. Therefore, the duck population doubled in 1992.

4. a) Step 1
Enter the data values into a TI-83 or similar calculator.

Start by clearing any lists already present. Press $\boxed{\text{2nd}}$ $\boxed{+}$, select 4:ClrAllLists, and press $\boxed{\text{ENTER}}$. Press $\boxed{\text{STAT}}$, and select 1:Edit…. Enter the time values into list L_1 and the bacteria count into list L_2.

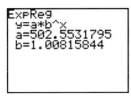

Step 2
Perform the exponential regression.

Press $\boxed{\text{STAT}}$ $\boxed{\triangleright}$ to highlight CALC. Select 0:ExpReg, and press $\boxed{\text{ENTER}}$ to obtain the following window.

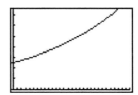

Step 3
Determine the exponential regression function. Substitute the values of a and b into the exponential function $y = ab^x$.

$y = ab^x$
$y = (502.5531795)(1.00815844)^x$

The exponential regression function that best approximates the growth of bacteria is
$B(t) = (502.5531795)(1.00815844)^t$.

Step 4
Graph the exponential function on a TI-83 or similar calculator.

Press $\boxed{\text{Y=}}$, and input the unrounded exponential regression function by pressing $\boxed{\text{VARS}}$, $\boxed{5}$, $\boxed{\triangleright}$, $\boxed{\triangleright}$, and selecting 1:RegEQ.

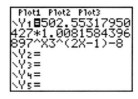

Use the window settings x: [−2, 150, 5] and y: [−10, 1500, 200]. Press $\boxed{\text{GRAPH}}$ to obtain the following window.

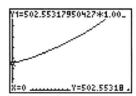

b) The initial number of bacteria corresponds to the y-intercept on the graph of the exponential regression function. Press $\boxed{\text{2nd}}$ $\boxed{\text{TRACE}}$, and select 1:value. Press $\boxed{0}$, then press $\boxed{\text{ENTER}}$ to obtain the following window.

The y-intercept is located at approximately (0, 502.55). Therefore, the initial number of bacteria is approximately 503.

c) In 2 hours, there are 120 minutes. Therefore, use the graph to find the value of $B(t)$ when $t = 120$.

Press 2nd TRACE , and select 1:value. Press 1 2 0 , then press ENTER to obtain the following window.

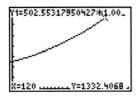

The value of y when $x = 120$ is approximately 1 332.41. Therefore, the bacteria count after 2 hrs is approximately 1 332.

PRACTICE EXERCISES
ANSWERS AND SOLUTIONS

1. Step 1
Identify the variables whose values are given in the problem with respect to the function $N_t = N_0 \times R^{\frac{t}{p}}$.

When $t = 0$, the population is 1 800 $(N_0 = 1\ 800)$. If the population of mice increases 15% each year, then the growth rate is $R = 1.15$. It takes 1 year for the population to increase 15%, so the period is $p = 1$.

Step 2
Substitute the values $N_0 = 1\ 800$, $R = 1.15$, and

$p = 1$ into the function $N_t = N_0 \times R^{\frac{t}{p}}$.

$$N_t = N_0 \times R^{\frac{t}{p}}$$
$$N_t = 1\ 800 \times (1.15)^{\frac{t}{1}}$$
$$N_t = 1\ 800 \times (1.15)^t$$

The function that models the population after t years is $N_t = 1\ 800 \times (1.15)^t$.

3. Step 1
In the function $N_t = 1\ 800 \times (1.15)^t$, let $N_t = 1\ 800 \times 2 = 3\ 600$.

$$N_t = 1\ 800 \times (1.15)^t$$
$$3\ 600 = 1\ 800 \times (1.15)^t$$
$$2 = (1.15)^t$$

Step 2
Solve the equation $2 = (1.15)^t$.

$$2 = (1.15)^t$$
$$\log 2 = \log(1.15)^t$$
$$\frac{\log 2}{\log 1.15} = t$$
$$t \approx 4.959 \text{ years}$$

Step 3
Determine the number of months for the population of mice to double.

Since there are 12 months in one year, it will take approximately $4.959 \times 12 \approx 60\ \text{months}$ for the population of mice to double.

5. Step 1
Determine the value of t.

The variable t is the number of years, so the value of t is $2002 - 1989 = 13\ \text{years}$.

Step 2
Determine the value of the stock on January 1, 2002.

Evaluate $V(13)$.
$$V(t) = 25\ 000(1.065)^t$$
$$V(13) = 25\ 000(1.065)^{13}$$
$$V(13) = 25\ 000(2.267487497)$$
$$V(13) = 56\ 687.18743$$

Therefore, the value of the stock on January 1, 2002, is $56 687.19.

7. The initial mass of the compound corresponds to the y-intercept on the given graph. The y-intercept on the graph is (0, 100). Therefore, the initial mass of radioactive compound was 100 g.

9. The initial mass was 100 g; therefore, $M_0 = 100$.

The growth rate is $R = \dfrac{1}{2}$.

It takes 20 days for the mass of the radioactive substance to decrease to half its initial mass. Therefore, the period is $p = 20$.

Substitute the values $M_0 = 100$, $R = \dfrac{1}{2}$,

and $p = 20$ into the function $M(t) = M_0 \times R^{\frac{t}{p}}$.

$$M(t) = M_0 \times R^{\frac{t}{p}}$$
$$M(t) = 100\left(\frac{1}{2}\right)^{\frac{t}{20}}$$

The function that represents the mass, $M(t)$, of the radioactive compound after t days is

$$M(t) = 100\left(\frac{1}{2}\right)^{\frac{t}{20}}.$$

Lesson 5—Solving Problems Involving Logarithmic Functions

CLASS EXERCISES
ANSWERS AND SOLUTIONS

1. In the formula $\dfrac{L_1}{L_2} = 10^{\left(\frac{dB_1 - dB_2}{10}\right)}$, let $dB_1 = 98$ and $dB_2 = 20$, then solve.

$$\frac{L_1}{L_2} = 10^{\left(\frac{dB_1 - dB_2}{10}\right)}$$
$$\frac{L_1}{L_2} = 10^{\left(\frac{98 - 20}{10}\right)}$$
$$\frac{L_1}{L_2} = 10^{\left(\frac{78}{10}\right)}$$
$$\frac{L_1}{L_2} = 10^{7.8}$$
$$\frac{L_1}{L_2} = 63\,095\,734.45$$

Therefore, an orchestra is 63 095 734 times louder than a whisper.

2. **Step 1**

In the formula $\dfrac{I_1}{I_2} = 10^{m_1 - m_2}$, let $\dfrac{I_1}{I_2} = 102$ and $m_1 = 5.8$.

$$\frac{I_1}{I_2} = 10^{m_1 - m_2}$$
$$102 = 10^{5.8 - m_2}$$

Step 2

Convert the resulting equation to logarithmic form, and solve for m_2.

$$102 = 10^{5.8 - m_2}$$
$$\log 102 = 5.8 - m_2$$
$$m_2 = 5.8 - \log 102$$
$$m_2 \approx 3.79$$

The magnitude of the earthquake in City N was approximately 3.8.

3. **Step 1**

In the formula $\dfrac{\left[H^+\right]_{\text{acidic solution}}}{\left[H^+\right]_{\text{pure water}}} = 10^{pH_{\text{pure water}} - pH_{\text{acidic solution}}}$,

let $\dfrac{\left[H^+\right]_{\text{acidic solution}}}{\left[H^+\right]_{\text{pure water}}} = 50$ and $pH_{\text{pure water}} = 7$.

$$\frac{\left[H^+\right]_{\text{acidic solution}}}{\left[H^+\right]_{\text{pure water}}} = 10^{pH_{\text{pure water}} - pH_{\text{acidic solution}}}$$
$$50 = 10^{7 - pH_{\text{acidic solution}}}$$

Step 2

Convert the resulting equation to logarithmic form, and solve for $pH_{\text{acidic solution}}$.

$$50 = 10^{7 - pH_{\text{acidic solution}}}$$
$$\log 50 = 7 - pH_{\text{acidic solution}}$$
$$pH_{\text{acidic solution}} = 7 - \log 50$$
$$pH_{\text{acidic solution}} \approx 5.30$$

The pH of the acidic solution is approximately 5.3.

4. **a)** **Step 1**

Enter the *x*-values and *y*-values in lists L_1 and L_2, respectively.

Start by clearing any lists already present. Press $\boxed{\text{2nd}}$ $\boxed{+}$, select 4:ClrAllLists, and press $\boxed{\text{ENTER}}$. Press $\boxed{\text{STAT}}$, and select 1:Edit.... Enter the number of months into list L_1 and the length values into list L_2.

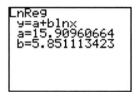

Step 2

Perform the logarithmic regression.

Press $\boxed{\text{STAT}}$ $\boxed{\triangleright}$ to highlight CALC. Select 9:LnReg, and press $\boxed{\text{ENTER}}$ to obtain the following window.

```
LnReg
y=a+blnx
a=15.90960664
b=5.851113423
```

Step 3

Determine the natural logarithmic regression function. Round the *a*- and *b*-values to the nearest hundredth.

Substitute the values of *a* and *b* into the function $y = a + b \ln x$.

$y = a + b \ln x$
$y = 15.91 + 5.85 \ln x$

The natural logarithmic regression function that best approximates the length of the baby boy after birth is $y = 15.91 + 5.85 \ln x$, where y is the length in inches and x is the number of months after birth.

b) In the function $y = 15.91 + 5.85 \ln x$, let $x = 10$, and solve.

$y = 15.91 + 5.85 \ln x$
$y = 15.91 + 5.85 \ln 10$
$y \approx 29.38012279$

Therefore, the length of Miranda's baby after 10 months was 29.4 inches.

PRACTICE EXERCISES
ANSWERS AND SOLUTIONS

1. In the formula $\dfrac{I_1}{I_2} = 10^{m_1 - m_2}$, let $m_1 = 7.8$ and $m_2 = 5.2$, then solve.

$\dfrac{I_1}{I_2} = 10^{m_1 - m_2}$

$\dfrac{I_1}{I_2} = 10^{7.8 - 5.2}$

$\dfrac{I_1}{I_2} = 10^{2.6}$

$\dfrac{I_1}{I_2} \approx 398.107$

Therefore, the earthquake at point *M* is approximately 398 times more intense than the earthquake at point *N*.

3. In the formula $\dfrac{L_1}{L_2} = 10^{\left(\frac{dB_1 - dB_2}{10}\right)}$, let $dB_1 = 120$ and $dB_2 = 50$, then solve.

$\dfrac{L_1}{L_2} = 10^{\left(\frac{dB_1 - dB_2}{10}\right)}$

$\dfrac{L_1}{L_2} = 10^{\left(\frac{120 - 50}{10}\right)}$

$\dfrac{L_1}{L_2} = 10^{\left(\frac{70}{10}\right)}$

$\dfrac{L_1}{L_2} = 10^7$

A rock concert is 10 000 000 or 10^7 times louder than an ordinary conversation.

5. In the formula, $\dfrac{\left[H^+\right]_{\text{battery acid}}}{\left[H^+\right]_{\text{milk}}} = 10^{pH_{\text{milk}} - pH_{\text{battery acid}}}$, let

$pH_{\text{milk}} = 6.7$ and $pH_{\text{battery acid}} = 0.8$, and solve.

$$\dfrac{\left[H^+\right]_{\text{battery acid}}}{\left[H^+\right]_{\text{milk}}} = 10^{pH_{\text{milk}} - pH_{\text{battery acid}}}$$

$$\dfrac{\left[H^+\right]_{\text{battery acid}}}{\left[H^+\right]_{\text{milk}}} = 10^{6.7-0.8}$$

$$\dfrac{\left[H^+\right]_{\text{battery acid}}}{\left[H^+\right]_{\text{milk}}} = 10^{5.9}$$

$$\dfrac{\left[H^+\right]_{\text{battery acid}}}{\left[H^+\right]_{\text{milk}}} \approx 794\ 328.234$$

Therefore, battery acid is approximately 794 328.2 times more acidic than milk.

7. Step 1

In the formula $\dfrac{I_1}{I_2} = 10^{m_1 - m_2}$, let $\dfrac{I_1}{I_2} = 10$ and

$m_1 = 8.8$.

$$\dfrac{I_1}{I_2} = 10^{m_1 - m_2}$$
$$10 = 10^{8.8 - m_2}$$

Step 2

Convert the resulting equation to logarithmic form, and solve for m_2.

$$10 = 10^{8.8 - m_2}$$
$$\log 10 = 8.8 - m_2$$
$$m_2 = 8.8 - \log 10$$
$$m_2 = 7.8$$

The magnitude of earthquake Z is 7.8.

9. In 3 hours, there are 180 minutes. Therefore, use the graph to find the value of y when $x = 180$.

Press 2nd TRACE , and select 1:value.
Press 1 8 0 , then press ENTER to obtain the following window.

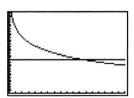

The value of y when $x = 180$ is approximately 21.779. Therefore, the concentration of insulin after 3 hours was approximately 21.8 mu/L.

Practice Test

ANSWERS AND SOLUTIONS

1. Let $\log_3 81 = x$. The exponential form of $\log_3 81 = x$ is $3^x = 81$. Since $3^4 = 81$, $\log_3 81 = 4$.

3. Apply the change of base formula, then evaluate.
$$\dfrac{\log_2 81}{\log_2 9}$$
$$= \log_9 81$$
$$= 2$$

5. Step 1
Write the expression $3\log_7 11$ using base 10.
$$3\log_7 11$$
$$= 3\left(\dfrac{\log 11}{\log 7}\right)$$

Step 2
Evaluate $3\left(\dfrac{\log 11}{\log 7}\right)$ using a calculator.
$$3\left(\dfrac{\log 11}{\log 7}\right)$$
$$\approx 3.696$$

Therefore, $3\log_7 11 = 3.7$.

7. Step 1
Apply the power law of logarithms.
$$\log_8 4608 - 2\log_8 3$$
$$= \log_8 4608 - \log_8 \left(3^2\right)$$
$$= \log_8 4608 - \log_8 9$$

Step 2
Apply the quotient law of logarithms.
$$\log_8 4608 - \log_8 9$$
$$= \log_8 \left(\dfrac{4608}{9}\right)$$
$$= \log_8 512$$

Step 3
Evaluate $\log_8 512$.

$\log_8 512$
$= \dfrac{\log 512}{\log 8}$
$= 3$

Therefore, $\log_8 4608 - 2\log_8 3 = 3$.

9. **Step 1**
Apply the power law of logarithms.
$3\log_7 (5m) - 9\log_7 m$
$= \log_7 \left[(5m)^3 \right] - \log_7 \left(m^9 \right)$

Step 2
Apply the quotient law of logarithms.
$= \log_7 \left[(5m)^3 \right] - \log_7 \left(m^9 \right)$
$= \log_7 \left[\dfrac{(5m)^3}{m^9} \right]$
$= \log_7 \left[\dfrac{5^3 m^3}{m^9} \right]$
$= \log_7 \left(\dfrac{125}{m^6} \right)$

Therefore, $3\log_7 (5m) - 9\log_7 m = \log_7 \left(\dfrac{125}{m^6} \right)$.

11. **Step 1**
Apply the power law of logarithms.
$4\log_5 m - \log_5 n + \dfrac{1}{2}\log_5 p$
$= \log_5 \left(m^4 \right) - \log_5 n + \log_5 \left(p^{\frac{1}{2}} \right)$

Step 2
Apply the quotient law to the first two terms of the expression.
$\log_5 \left(m^4 \right) - \log_5 n + \log_5 \left(p^{\frac{1}{2}} \right)$
$= \log_5 \left(\dfrac{m^4}{n} \right) + \log_5 \left(p^{\frac{1}{2}} \right)$

Step 3
Apply the product law of logarithms.
$\log_5 \left(\dfrac{m^4}{n} \right) + \log_5 \left(p^{\frac{1}{2}} \right)$
$= \log_5 \left(\dfrac{m^4 p^{\frac{1}{2}}}{n} \right)$

Therefore,
$4\log_5 m - \log_5 n + \dfrac{1}{2}\log_5 p = \log_5 \left(\dfrac{m^4 p^{\frac{1}{2}}}{n} \right)$.

13. **Step 1**
Apply the power law of logarithms to the second term.
$\log_6 2A + 3\log_6 B - \log_6 A$
$= \log_6 2A + \log_6 B^3 - \log_6 A$

Step 2
Apply the product law of logarithms to the first two terms.
$\log_6 2A + \log_6 B^3 - \log_6 A$
$= \log_6 2AB^3 - \log_6 A$

Step 3
Apply the quotient law of logarithms.
$\log_6 2AB^3 - \log_6 A$
$= \log_6 \left(\dfrac{2AB^3}{A} \right)$
$= \log_6 \left(2B^3 \right)$

Therefore, $\log_6 2A + 3\log_6 B - \log_6 A = \log_6 \left(2B^3 \right)$.

15. **Step 1**
Apply the power law of logarithms to the first two terms.
$4\log_5 K - \left(2\log_5 K + \log_5 M \right)$
$= \log_5 K^4 - \left(\log_5 K^2 + \log_5 M \right)$

Step 2
Apply the product law of logarithms to the last two terms.
$\log_5 K^4 - \left(\log_5 K^2 + \log_5 M \right)$
$= \log_5 K^4 - \log_5 K^2 M$

Step 3
Apply the quotient law of logarithms.
$\log_5 K^4 - \log_5 K^2 M$
$= \log_5 \left(\dfrac{K^4}{K^2 M} \right)$
$= \log_5 \left(\dfrac{K^2}{M} \right)$

Therefore,
$4\log_5 K - (2\log_5 K + \log_5 M) = \log_5 \left(\dfrac{K^2}{M} \right).$

17. **Step 1**
Add 2 to both sides of the equation.
$7^{13x+4} - 2 = 47$
$7^{13x+4} = 49$

Step 2
Write the equation so that the powers have the same base.
$7^{13x+4} = 49$
$7^{13x+4} = 7^2$

Step 3
Equate the exponents, and solve for x.
$13x + 4 = 2$
$13x = -2$
$x = -\dfrac{2}{13}$

The value of x is $-\dfrac{2}{13}$.

19. **Step 1**
Write the equation so that the powers have the same base.
$\left(\dfrac{125}{8} \right)^{2x} = \left(\dfrac{4}{25} \right)^{x+5}$
$\left(\left(\dfrac{5}{2} \right)^3 \right)^{2x} = \left(\left(\dfrac{2}{5} \right)^2 \right)^{x+5}$
$\left(\left(\dfrac{5}{2} \right)^3 \right)^{2x} = \left(\left(\dfrac{5}{2} \right)^{-2} \right)^{x+5}$

Step 2
Apply the power law to both sides of the equation.
$\left(\left(\dfrac{5}{2} \right)^3 \right)^{2x} = \left(\left(\dfrac{5}{2} \right)^{-2} \right)^{x+5}$
$\left(\dfrac{5}{2} \right)^{6x} = \left(\dfrac{5}{2} \right)^{-2x-10}$

Step 3
Equate the exponents, and solve for x.
$6x = -2x - 10$
$8x = -10$
$x = -\dfrac{10}{8}$
$x = -\dfrac{5}{4}$

Therefore, the value of x is $-\dfrac{5}{4}$.

21. **Step 1**
Isolate the power.
$5^{x+5} - 76 = -12$
$5^{x+5} = 64$

Step 2
Write the equation in logarithmic form.
$5^{x+5} = 64$
$\log_5 64 = x + 5$

Step 3
Rewrite the expression $\log_5 64$ using base 10.
$\log_5 64 = x + 5$
$\dfrac{\log 64}{\log 5} = x + 5$

Step 4
Isolate x.
$\dfrac{\log 64}{\log 5} = x + 5$
$\log_5 64 - 5 = x$

Step 5
Find an approximate solution using a calculator.
$x = \dfrac{\log 64}{\log 5} - 5$
$x \approx -2.4$

Therefore, the value of x is approximately –2.4.

23. Step 1
Take the common logarithm of both sides of the equation.
$$7^{x-2} = 11^{13-x}$$
$$\log 7^{x-2} = \log 11^{13-x}$$

Step 2
Apply the power law of logarithms.
$$\log 7^{x-2} = \log 11^{13-x}$$
$$(x-2)\log 7 = (13-x)\log 11$$

Step 3
Apply the distributive property.
$$(x-2)\log 7 = (13-x)\log 11$$
$$x\log 7 - 2\log 7 = 13\log 11 - x\log 11$$

Step 4
Isolate x.
$$x\log 7 - 2\log 7 = 13\log 11 - x\log 11$$
$$x\log 7 + x\log 11 = 13\log 11 + 2\log 7$$
$$x(\log 7 + \log 11) = 13\log 11 + 2\log 7$$
$$x = \frac{13\log 11 + 2\log 7}{\log 7 + \log 11}$$

Step 5
Find an approximate solution using a calculator.
$$x = \frac{13\log 11 + 2\log 7}{\log 7 + \log 11}$$
$$x \approx 8.07229$$

Therefore, the value of x is approximately 8.1.

25. Step 1
Determine the value of t.

There are 3 years between January 1, 1996, and January 1, 1999. Since t is in months, the value of t is $\left(3\,\text{years} \times \dfrac{12\,\text{months}}{1\,\text{year}}\right) = 36\,\text{months}$.

Step 2
Evaluate N_{36}.
$$N_t = 30\ 000(1.25)^{\frac{t}{6}}$$
$$N_{36} = 30\ 000(1.25)^{\frac{36}{6}}$$
$$N_{36} = 114\ 440.918$$

Therefore, there were approximately 114 441 customers on January 1, 1999.

27. Step 1
Determine the function that represents the population growth of wolves.

Let $W(t)$ represent the population of wolves after time, t, in months.

The initial population of wolves is 56, so $W_0 = 56$.
The population of wolves increased by 25% every 2 months, so $R = 1 + 0.25 = 1.25$ and $p = 2$.

Therefore, the function that represents the population of wolves after t months is
$$W(t) = 56(1.25)^{\frac{t}{2}}.$$

Step 2
Determine the function that represents the population growth of rabbits.

Let $R(t)$ represent the population of rabbits after time, t, in months.

The initial population of rabbits is 42, so $R_0 = 42$.
The population of rabbits increased by 30% every month, so $R = 1 + 0.30 = 1.30$ and $p = 1$.

Therefore, the function that represents the population of rabbits after t months is
$$R(t) = 42(1.30)^t.$$

Step 3
Using a TI-83 calculator, graph the functions
$$W(t) = 56(1.25)^{\frac{t}{2}} \text{ and } R(t) = 42(1.30)^t.$$

Enter each function as $Y_1 = 56(1.25)^{\wedge}(X/2)$ and $Y_2 = 42(1.30)^{\wedge}X$. Press $\boxed{\text{GRAPH}}$.

An appropriate setting is x: [0, 12, 1] and y: [0, 200, 10].

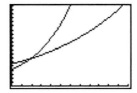

Step 4
Determine the point of intersection.

Press $\boxed{\text{2nd}}$ $\boxed{\text{TRACE}}$, and choose 5:intersect.

For "First curve?", position the cursor just left or right of the intersection point, and press $\boxed{\text{ENTER}}$. For "Second curve?", position the cursor just left or right of the intersection point, and press $\boxed{\text{ENTER}}$. For "Guess?", press $\boxed{\text{ENTER}}$.

The point of intersection is (1.9078011, 69.283615).

Therefore, it took 1.9 months for the populations of wolves and rabbits to become equal.

29. The height of the ledge corresponds to when the number of bounces is 0. On the graph, the height is 7 m when $n = 0$. Therefore, the ledge is 7 m tall.

31. Use the given graph to determine the value of n when $h = 1.5$.

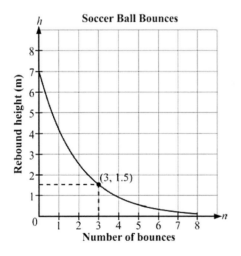

The rebound height of the soccer ball is approximately 1.5 m after 3 bounces.

33. Using the regression function, determine the value of $P(40)$.

$$P(t) = (19\,073.82739)(0.9497983678)^t$$
$$P(40) = (19\,073.82739)(0.9497983678)^{40}$$
$$P(40) \approx 2\,430.4943$$

Therefore, the population of salmon after 40 years will be about 2 430.

35. **Step 1**
Substitute 20 for P_o and 16 for G in the equation $G = 10\log\left(\dfrac{P_o}{P_i}\right)$.

$$G = 10\log\left(\frac{P_o}{P_i}\right)$$
$$16 = 10\log\left(\frac{20}{P_i}\right)$$

Step 2
Divide both sides of the equation by 10.

$$16 = 10\log\left(\frac{20}{P_i}\right)$$
$$\frac{16}{10} = \log\left(\frac{20}{P_i}\right)$$

Step 3
Write the equation $\dfrac{16}{10} = \log\left(\dfrac{20}{P_i}\right)$ in exponential form.

The equation in exponential form is $10^{\frac{16}{10}} = \dfrac{20}{P_i}$.

Step 4
Solve for P_i to the nearest tenth.

$$10^{\frac{16}{10}} = \frac{20}{P_i}$$
$$P_i = \frac{20}{10^{\frac{16}{10}}}$$
$$P_i \approx 0.5$$

The input power is approximately 0.5 W.

37. The formula $\dfrac{I_1}{I_2} = 10^{m_1-m_2}$ can be used to compare an earthquake that has an intensity of I_1 with an earthquake that has an intensity of I_2.

In the formula $\dfrac{I_1}{I_2} = 10^{m_1-m_2}$, let $m_1 = 6.0$ and $m_2 = 3.4$, then solve.

$$\dfrac{I_1}{I_2} = 10^{m_1-m_2}$$

$$\dfrac{I_1}{I_2} = 10^{6.0-3.4}$$

$$\dfrac{I_1}{I_2} = 10^{2.6}$$

$$\dfrac{I_1}{I_2} \approx 398.107$$

Therefore, the earthquake in City P is approximately 398 times more intense than the earthquake in City Q.

39. Using the regression function $L(t) = y = 2.28 + (5.84)\ln t$, determine the value of $L(35)$.

$$L(t) = y = 2.28 + (5.84)\ln t$$

$$L(35) = 2.28 + (5.84)\ln 35$$

$$L(35) \approx 23.04323$$

After 35 weeks, the lizard should be 23.0 cm long.

POLYNOMIAL FUNCTIONS

Lesson 1—Polynomial Functions

ANSWERS AND SOLUTIONS
CLASS EXERCISES

1. a) The function $y = 3x^2 - \sqrt{2}x + 6$ is a polynomial function.

b) The function $f(x) = 32$ is a polynomial function.

c) The function $y = x^4 - 7x^{\frac{1}{2}} - 4$ is not a polynomial function because it has a fraction as an exponent.

d) The function $f(x) = 7x^2 - 6x^5 + \pi$ is a polynomial function.

e) The function $y = 2x^6 - 1.4x^3 - 4x^{-2}$ is not a polynomial function it has a negative exponent on the variable x.

f) The function $y = -x^7 - 5x^4 + \dfrac{2}{x}$ is not a polynomial function because $\dfrac{2}{x} = 2x^{-1}$, and negative exponents are not allowed in polynomial functions.

g) The function $f(x) = (3x-1)(x+2)$ is a polynomial function.

h) The function $g(x) = \dfrac{1}{2}x^3 - 4.\dot{7}x^2 + \dfrac{x}{2}$ is a polynomial function.

i) The function $y = 23x^4 - 3\sqrt{x} - 2x^3$ is not a polynomial function because $\sqrt{x} = x^{\frac{1}{2}}$, and the exponent $\dfrac{1}{2}$ is not a whole number.

j) The function $y = 4x^5 - 3x^m + 6$ is not a polynomial function because it has a variable as an exponent.

k) The function $h = 65t^4 - 3t^5 - 7t$ is a polynomial function.

l) The function $y = 4^x$ is not a polynomial function because it has a variable as an exponent.

2. The leading coefficient is 5.
The degree of the function is 3.
The y-intercept for the graph of the function is –1.

3. Expand (or multiply), collect like terms, and write the function as decreasing powers as follows:
$$f(x) = (3x - 2)(x^2 - 1) - 2(5x - 6) + 1$$
$$f(x) = 3x^3 - 3x - 2x^2 + 2 - 10x + 12 + 1$$
$$f(x) = 3x^3 - 2x^2 - 13x + 15$$

The leading coefficient is 3.
The degree of the function is 3.
The constant term is 15.

4. Substitute –1 for x in the equation.
$$f(x) = 3x + 2$$
$$f(-1) = 3(-1) + 2$$
$$f(-1) = -3 + 2$$
$$f(-1) = -1$$

Since $f(x)$ represents the value of y, the corresponding coordinate point on the graph of $f(x) = 3x + 2$ is $(-1, -1)$.

5. Step 1
Substitute –6 for $g(x)$, and simplify.
$$g(x) = x^2 + 7x + 6$$
$$-6 = x^2 + 7x + 6$$
$$0 = x^2 + 7x + 12$$

Step 2
Factor, and solve the resulting quadratic equation.
$$-6 = x^2 + 7x + 12$$
$$0 = (x + 3)(x + 4)$$

The values of x that satisfy the equation are –3 and –4.

Given that $g(x) = -6$, the possible input values for the function $g(x) = x^2 + 7x + 6$ are $x = -3$ and $x = -4$.

6. Since $f(-1) = 8$, the value of k can be determined as follows:
$$2(-1)^3 + k(-1)^2 + 2(-1) - 4 = 8$$
$$-2 + k - 2 - 4 = 8$$
$$k - 8 = 8$$
$$k = 16$$

PRACTICE EXERCISES
ANSWERS AND SOLUTIONS

1. a) The degree is 3.

b) The leading coefficient is $\sqrt{3}$.

c) The y-intercept is –1.

3. The function $f(x) = \dfrac{3x^2 - 3x + 12}{6}$ can be written as $f(x)\dfrac{1}{2}x^2 - \dfrac{1}{2}x + 2$.

a) The degree is 2.

b) The leading coefficient is $\dfrac{1}{2}$.

c) The y-intercept is 2.

5. The function can be simplified as follows:
$$y = (3x - 2)(x - 1) + (x - 2)^2 - 3$$
$$y = (3x^2 - 5x + 2) + (x^2 - 4x + 4) - 3$$
$$y = 4x^2 - 9x + 3$$

a) The degree is 2.

b) The leading coefficient is 4.

c) The y-intercept is 3.

7. To find the value of $f(-6)$, substitute the value of –6 for x in the function $f(x) = -2(x+3)+5$, and evaluate.

$$f(x) = -2(x+3)+5$$
$$f(x) = -2(-6+3)+5$$
$$f(x) = -2(-3)+5$$
$$f(x) = 6+5$$
$$f(x) = 11$$

9. **Step 1**

Evaluate $f(-2)$ in $f(x) = -20x+5$ by substituting –2 for x.

$$f(x) = -20x+5$$
$$f(-2) = -20(-2)+5$$
$$f(-2) = 40+5$$
$$f(-2) = 45$$

Step 2

Evaluate $f(-5)$ in $f(x) = -20x+5$ by substituting –5 for x.

$$f(x) = -20x+5$$
$$f(-5) = -20(-5)+5$$
$$f(-5) = 100+5$$
$$f(-5) = 105$$

Step 3

Calculate the sum of $f(-2)$ and $f(-5)$.

$$f(-2)+f(-5) = 45+105$$
$$= 150$$

Therefore, the sum of $f(-2)$ and $f(-5)$ is 150.

11. Substitute –2 for x in the given function, and solve for $f(-2)$.

$$f(x) = x^2 - 2x + 5$$
$$f(-2) = (-2)^2 - 2(-2) + 5$$
$$f(-2) = 4 + 4 + 5$$
$$f(-2) = 13$$

Therefore, the value of $f(-2)$ is 13.

13. **Step 1**

Since $g(x) = 13$, substitute 13 for $g(x)$ in the function $g(x) = 10 + \frac{3}{5}x$.

$$g(x) = 10 + \frac{3}{5}x$$
$$13 = 10 + \frac{3}{5}x$$

Step 2

Solve for x.

$$13 = 10 + \frac{3}{5}x$$
$$13 - 10 = \frac{3}{5}x$$
$$3 = \frac{3}{5}x$$
$$3 \times \frac{5}{3} = x$$
$$5 = x$$

Lesson 2—Sketching the Graphs of Polynomial Functions from Factored Form

ANSWERS AND SOLUTIONS
CLASS EXERCISES

1. **Step 1**

Determine the slope and y-intercept of the line defined by the function $f(x) = -\frac{2}{5}x - 1$.

Using the information in the equation, the slope of the line is $a = -\frac{2}{5}$, and the y-intercept is $b = -1$.

Step 2

Given that the slope of the line is $-\frac{2}{5}$ and the line passes through the point $(0, -1)$, determine another point on the line.

Another point on the line will be 2 units down and 5 units to the right of the point $(0, -1)$. This point is $(5, -3)$.

Step 3
Draw a line passing through the points $(0, -1)$ and $(5, -3)$.

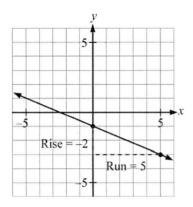

2. Write $f(x) = 2x^2 - 7x - 4$ in factored form to give $f(x) = (2x+1)(x-4)$.

The factored form gives the following information:

The x-intercepts are $-\dfrac{1}{2}$ and 4 (the solutions to $0 = (2x+1)(x-4)$).

The parabola opens upward because $a > 0$.
The y-intercept is -4 because it is the constant term and is the result when $x = 0$.
A sketch of the graph is as shown:

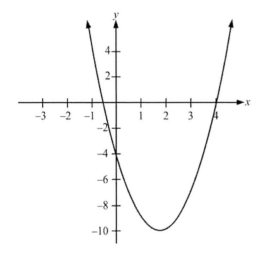

3. From the factored form, it can be seen that the x-intercepts are 2 and -3. The $f(x)$-intercept, or y-intercept, is $f(0) = (0-2)(0+3)^2 = -18$.

The leading coefficient of the function is greater than 0, so the extreme ends of the graph are in quadrants III and I.

Placing the significant points on the graph and drawing a smooth curve through these points gives the following graph:

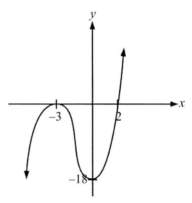

The calculator gives the following graph:

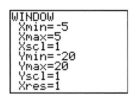

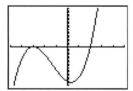

4. From the factored form, it can be seen that the x-intercept is -1. The y-intercept is
$$y = -2(0+1)^3 = -2.$$

The leading coefficient of the function is less than 0, so the extreme ends of the graph are in quadrants IV and II.

The significant points and information are summarized in the following table:

x	$-\infty$	-1	0	$+\infty$
y	$+\infty$	0	-2	$-\infty$

Copyright Protected

Placing the significant points on the graph and drawing a smooth curve through these points gives the following result:

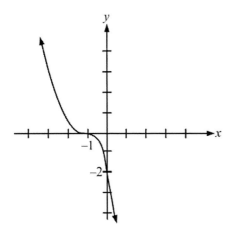

The calculator gives the following graph:

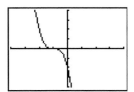

PRACTICE EXERCISES
ANSWERS AND SOLUTIONS

1. $y = 2x + 6$

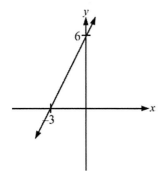

3. $y = -x^2 - 7x$
$= -x(x + 7)$

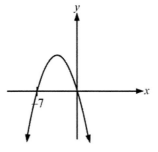

5. $y = -2(x + 2)^2(x - 1)$

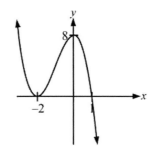

7. $f(x) = (x + 1)^3$

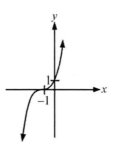

Lesson 3—Solving Problems with Polynomial Functions

CLASS EXERCISES
ANSWERS AND SOLUTIONS

1. a) The ball strikes the ground when the height is 0 m. This is represented by the *x*-intercept of the graph, which is 25. Therefore, the horizontal distance travelled by the ball from the time it was tossed from the cliff to the time it hit the ground is 25 m. Since the base of the cliff is located at a horizontal distance of 5 m, the ball strikes the ground at a distance of $25 - 5 = 20$ m from the base of the cliff.

b) There are two vertical phases the thrown ball experiences. The first phase is the upward path of the ball. The upward vertical flight is from 25 m (location on the top of the cliff) to the maximum height of 45 m. Thus, the vertical distance travelled is $45 - 25 = 20$ m.

The second phase is the downward path of the ball. This flight begins at the maximum height of 45 m and ends when the ball hits the ground at a height of 0 m. Thus, the vertical distance travelled during this phase is $45 - 0 = 45$ m.

Therefore, the total vertical distance travelled over both phases is $20 + 45 = 65$ m.

2. a) Step 1
Enter the quadratic equation
$h(x) = -0.019x^2 + 1.026x + 0.049$ into
$\boxed{Y1=}$ on your graphing calculator.
$Y_1 = -0.019x^2 + 1.026x + 0.049$

Set your window to *x*:[–10, 70, 10], *y*[–10, 20 ,10], and press $\boxed{\text{GRAPH}}$.

Step 2
To find the maximum *y*-value of the graph (which represents the maximum height of the football), press $\boxed{\text{2nd}}$ $\boxed{\text{TRACE}}$ $\boxed{\text{MAXIMUM}}$ to find the maximum *y*-value of 13.9 at an *x*-value of 27.0, as shown in the following screenshot:

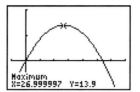

The maximum height of the ball during its flight is 13.9 yd.

b) To find the total horizontal distance the ball travelled, find the second *x*-intercept of the graph, which represents the point where the ball hit the ground. To find this *x*-intercept of the graph, press $\boxed{\text{2nd}}$ $\boxed{\text{TRACE}}$ $\boxed{\text{ZERO}}$. The second *x*-intercept is $x = 54.047716$, as shown on the following screenshot:

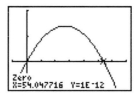

Therefore, the total horizontal distance travelled is 54 yd.

Note: Assume that the ball was kicked at an *x*-value of $x = 0$ on the given graph.

c) The crossbar is located at the 0 yd line, which is 50 yd from where the ball was kicked. Therefore, to find the height of the ball at a horizontal distance of 50, press $\boxed{\text{2nd}}$ $\boxed{\text{TRACE}}$ $\boxed{\text{VALUE}}$, and enter $x = 50$ to find the corresponding *y*-value of $y = 3.849$, as shown in the following screenshot:

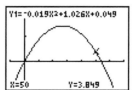

The height of the ball from the ground is 3.849 yd. Since the height of the crossbar is 3 yd, the ball clears the crossbar by a vertical distance of $3.849 - 3 = 0.849$ yd.

Since it clears the crossbar, the field goal is made, and the Edmonton Eskimos win the game.

3. **a)** **Step 1**
Determine the independent and dependent variables.

The independent variable, x, is the width, and the dependent variable, $V(x)$, is the volume of the bin.

Step 2
Draw a diagram.
Let x equal the width of the bin.

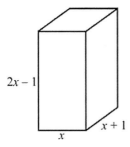

Step 3
Determine a function that models the volume of the storage bin.
$$\text{volume} = \text{length} \times \text{width} \times \text{height}$$
$$V(x) = (x+1)(x)(2x-1)$$

Therefore, the function that represents the volume of the storage bin is
$V(x) = (x)(x+1)(2x-1)$, where x represents the width of the bin.

b) Since the volume of the bin is 7.5 m³,
$7.5 = (x)(x+1)(2x-1)$.

Solve the equation $7.5 = (x)(x+1)(2x-1)$ using a TI-83 or similar calculator.

Step 1
Subtract 7.5 from both sides of the equation.
$$7.5 = (x)(x+1)(2x-1)$$
$$0 = (x)(x+1)(2x-1) - 7.5$$

Step 2
Graph the related function on a TI-83 or similar calculator.

Press $\boxed{Y=}$, and input the equation as $Y_1 = (X)(X+1)(2X-1) - 7.5$.

Use the window settings of x: $[-3, 3, 1]$ and y: $[-10, 10, 1]$, and press $\boxed{\text{GRAPH}}$ to obtain this window.

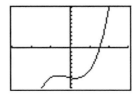

The width, x, corresponds to the positive x-intercept.

Step 3
Determine the zeros of the graph.

Press $\boxed{\text{2nd}}$ $\boxed{\text{TRACE}}$, and select 2:zero.

When asked for a left bound, move the cursor to the left of the first zero, and press $\boxed{\text{ENTER}}$.

When asked for a right bound, move the cursor to the right of the first zero, and press $\boxed{\text{ENTER}}$.

Press $\boxed{\text{ENTER}}$ after the "Guess?" prompt.

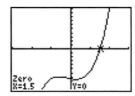

Step 4
Determine the dimensions of the storage bin.

Since the zero of the graph represents the width, the width of the storage bin is 1.5 m, the length is $1.5 + 1 = 2.5$ m, and the height is $2(1.5) - 1 = 2$ m.

4. Step 1

Determine the equation that defines the given data.

Since the *y*-values increase and then decrease, perform a quadratic regression.

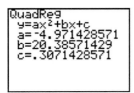

To minimize rounding errors, round the values of the coefficients and the constant value to at least three decimal places.

A possible equation that defines the data is $h = -4.971t^2 + 20.386t + 0.307$, in which *h* is the height of the ball, in metres, and *t* is the time, in seconds.

Step 2

Use the derived equation of the function to solve the given problem. Substitute 2.7 for *t*.

$h = -4.971t^2 + 20.386t + 0.307$

$h = -4.97(2.7)^2 + 20.386(2) + 0.307$

$h \approx 19.11$

At 2.7 s, the ball will be approximate 19.11 m above the ground.

PRACTICE EXERCISES
ANSWERS AND SOLUTIONS

1. a) The given parabola opens downward and has a vertex at (3, 48).

Since the parabola opens downward, the maximum value of the quadratic function represented by the given parabola is equal to the *y*-coordinate of the vertex of the parabola.

Therefore, the maximum height of the baseball is 48 m.

b) At 0 s, the baseball was at its initial height. This corresponds to the ordered pair (0, 1.2) on the parabola.

Therefore, the baseball was hit from an initial height of 1.2 m.

c) The ball remains in the air until it hits the ground. This occurs at the point where the parabola intersects the *x*-axis after reaching its maximum value.

Since the graph intersects the *x*-axis at 6, the ball remains in the air for 6 s.

3. Use a TI-83 or similar calculator to plot the line $y = 12$ and the parabola $y = -2x^2 + 11x - 3$. Then, use the Intersection feature to find the intersection points of the two graphs.

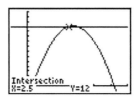

The first intersection point is (2.5, 12).

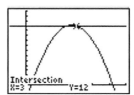

The second intersection point is (3, 12).

The first value of *x* is closest to the moment of the kick, so the first value of *x* is the time taken for the ball to reach a height of 12 m.

Therefore, it took the football 2.5 s to reach a height of 12 yd above the ground.

5. Step 1
Determine the graph of each of the given kinds of equations.

A linear equation can be written in the form $y = ax + b$, and its graph is a straight line.

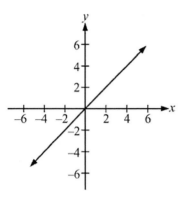

A quadratic equation can be written in the form $y = ax^2 + bx + c$, and its graph is a parabola.

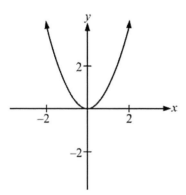

A sinusoidal equation can be written in the form $y = a\sin(bx + c) + d$, and its graph shows periodic data.

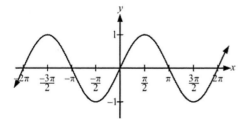

An exponential equation can be written in the form $y = ab^x$, and its graph always has a horizontal asymptote and increases or decreases exponentially.

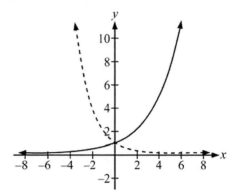

Step 2
Determine which type of equation models the given data most closely.

The points in the scatter plot closely follow the graph of a quadratic equation; therefore, a quadratic regression should be used.

The points do not follow a straight line; therefore, the data does not model a linear function. The data shows no repetition; therefore, it does not model a sinusoidal function. The data does not grow or decay in an exponential matter; therefore, it does not model an exponential function.

7. Use a TI-83 or similar calculator to perform the exponential regression, and solve the regression equation.

Step 1
Enter the time values and distance values in lists L_1 and $L_{2,}$ respectively.

Start by clearing any lists already present. Press $\boxed{\text{2nd}}$ $\boxed{+}$, select 4:ClrAllLists, and press $\boxed{\text{ENTER}}$.

Press $\boxed{\text{STAT}}$, and select 1:Edit… to enter the lists. Enter the times into list L_1 and the distances into list L_2.

L1	L2	L3	1
0	200.5	------	
4	295.7		
8	224.6		
12	110.5		
16	76.5		
20	246.1		
------	------		

L1 = {0,4,8,12,16…

Step 2
Perform the cubic regression.

Press $\boxed{\text{STAT}}$, and then press the right arrow to access the CALC menu. Select 6:CubicReg.

Press $\boxed{\text{ENTER}}$ to run the cubic regression.

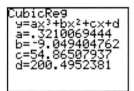

Rounded to the nearest thousandth,
the regression equation is
$D(t) \approx 0.321t^3 - 9.049t^2 + 54.865t + 200.495$.

Step 3
Use the regression equation to find the distance from the sensor after 24 s.

Substitute $t = 24$ into the equation.
$$D(24) \approx 0.321(24)^3 - 9.049(24)^2$$
$$+ 54.865(24) + 200.495$$
$$D(24) \approx 0.321(13824) - 9.049(576)$$
$$+ 54.865(24) + 200.495$$
$$D(24) \approx 4437.504 - 5212.224 + 1316.76$$
$$+ 200.495$$
$$D(24) \approx 742.99$$
$$D(24) \approx 743$$

Practice Test

ANSWERS AND SOLUTIONS

1. The function $f(x) = 2x^4 - \dfrac{3}{x^2} + 4x - 1$ can be expressed as $f(x) = 2x^4 - 3x^{-2} + 4x - 1$. Because the second term of the given function contains a non-whole number exponent, the function is not a polynomial function.

3. The function $f(x)$ is not a polynomial function because it contains a negative exponent and a fractional exponent.

The non-integral coefficient, $\sqrt{3}$, in the function $f(x) = x^2 - \sqrt{3}x^3 + x^{-4} + 5x^{\frac{5}{4}}$ is a real number, and the constant term in the function is not expressed because it is 0. Neither of these characteristics rule out the function as being a polynomial function.

5. Determine the output, $g(x)$, if the input is $\dfrac{1}{3}$.

Substitute $\dfrac{1}{3}$ for x, and solve for $g(x)$.
$$g(x) = 24x - 3$$
$$g\left(\frac{1}{3}\right) = 24\left(\frac{1}{3}\right) - 3$$
$$g\left(\frac{1}{3}\right) = 8 - 3$$
$$g\left(\frac{1}{3}\right) = 5$$

7. **Step 1**
Substitute –2 for $g(x)$, and simplify.
$$g(x) = 2x^2 - 5x - 14$$
$$-2 = 2x^2 - 5x - 14$$
$$0 = 2x^2 - 5x - 12$$

Step 2
Factor and solve the resulting quadratic equation.
$$0 = 2x^2 - 5x - 12$$
$$0 = 2x^2 - 8x + 3x - 12$$
$$0 = 2x(x - 4) + 3(x - 4)$$
$$x = 4, \ -\frac{3}{2}$$

For an output value of $g(x) = -2$, the input values of x are $-\dfrac{3}{2}$ and 4.

9. **Step 1**
Since $f(1) = 2$, substitute 1 for x and 2 for $f(x)$.
$$f(x) = \frac{ax}{4} + \frac{11}{4}$$
$$2 = \frac{a(1)}{4} + \frac{11}{4}$$
$$2 = \frac{a}{4} + \frac{11}{4}$$

Step 2
Solve for a.

$$2 = \frac{a}{4} + \frac{11}{4}$$

$$4(2) = 4\left(\frac{a}{4}\right) + 4\left(\frac{11}{4}\right)$$

$$8 = a + 11$$

$$-3 = a$$

11. $f(x) = -x + 1$

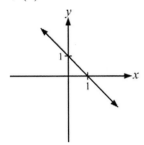

13. $y = (x-2)^2(x+1)$

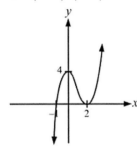

15. The data points form the approximate shape of a parabola opening upward. Therefore, the best model for the daily production costs will be a quadratic function in which the leading coefficient is positive.

It is clear from the given data that production costs will be much greater than 0 when a small number of units are produced. Therefore, it is expected that the C-intercept will be a number much greater than 0.

To determine the C-intercept of each of the given equations, substitute $p = 0$, and calculate the value of C.

Of the given equations, $C = 0.55p^2 - 110p + 9000$ is the best fit for the given data points because it is the only equation with a positive leading coefficient and a C-intercept that is not 0.

17. a) Press the $\boxed{Y=}$ button on your calculator, and enter the equation
$P = 150t^2 - 1\,200t + 14\,900$, $t \geq 0$
in to the Y_1 value as follows:
$Y_1 = 150X^2 - 1\,200X + 14\,900$

Press $\boxed{WINDOW}$, and use settings such as x:[−5, 12 ,2] and y:[7 500, 20 000, 2 500]. Press $\boxed{GRAPH}$.

Use the Minimum feature of your calculator. Press $\boxed{2nd}$ $\boxed{TRACE}$ to access the CALC menu.

Choose 3:minimum from the list. Follow the prompts given by the calculator. Provide a left bound, a right bound, and press $\boxed{ENTER}$ when prompted for a guess.

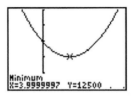

Since the graphing calculator's cursor is at $x \approx 4$, the minimum population will occur at the beginning of $t = 4$, or 2006 + 4 = 2010.

b) Press the $\boxed{Y=}$ button on your calculator, and enter the equation
$P = 150t^2 - 1\,200t + 14\,900$, $t \geq 0$ in to the Y_1 value as follows:
$Y_1 = 150X^2 - 1\,200X + 14\,900$

Enter the line referring to the population of 24 000 into the Y_2 value as follows:
$Y_2 = 24\,000$

Use the Intersection feature of your calculator to find the first positive intersection point between this line and the line of the quadratic function.

Press $\boxed{WINDOW}$, and use settings such as x:[−5, 20 ,2] and y:[7 500, 35 000, 2 500].

Press $\boxed{2nd}$ $\boxed{TRACE}$ to access the CALC menu.

Choose 5:intersect from the list. Follow the prompts given by the calculator. Choose a point near the intersection on the first function (the quadratic function), and a point near the intersection on the second function (the line). Press ENTER when prompted for a guess.

The first positive intersection point occurs when $x = 12.76$, as shown in the given diagram.

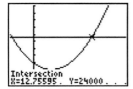

The first year that the population will be more than 24 000 is $2006 + 12.76 = 2018.76$, or 2019.

19. a) The graph of a quadratic equation is one that falls and rises in a smooth curve or rises and falls in a smooth curve.

The trader most likely concluded that the data modelled a quadratic pattern because the data values follow this pattern.

b) Step 1
Enter the data values into the calculator. Start by clearing any lists already present. Press 2nd +, select 4:ClrAllLists, and press ENTER. Press STAT, and select 1:Edit…. Enter the date into list L_1 and the unit stock values into list L_2.

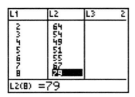

Step 2
Perform the logarithmic regression. Press STAT ▷ to highlight CALC. Select 5:QuadReg, and press ENTER to obtain the following window.

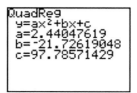

The quadratic regression function that best approximates the given data is $V \approx 2.4t^2 - 21.7t + 97.8$, and the value of c is approximately 97.8.

21. Use the given diagram and the formula
$$\text{volume} = \frac{(\text{width})(\text{height})}{2} \times \text{length} \text{ to determine}$$
the function, $V(x)$.

$$\text{volume} = \frac{(\text{width})(\text{height})}{2} \times \text{length}$$
$$V(x) = \frac{x(0.5+x)}{2} \times 2x$$
$$V(x) = x^2(0.5+x)$$
$$V(x) = 0.5x^2 + x^3$$

Therefore, the function that represents the volume of the tent is $V(x) = 0.5x^2 + x^3$, where x represents the width of the base.

SINUSOIDAL FUNCTIONS

Lesson 1—Graphs of Sinusoidal Functions

ANSWERS AND SOLUTIONS
CLASS EXERCISES

1. **Step 1**
    Determine the period of the graph.

    A maximum occurs at $(-0.5, -3)$ and again at $(5.5, -3)$. These points are $5.5 - (-0.5) = 6$ units apart. Therefore, the period of the graph is 6 units.

    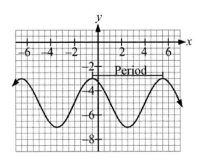

    Step 2
    Determine the horizontal midline axis.

    The horizontal midline axis is $y = \dfrac{-3 + (-7)}{2} = -5$.

    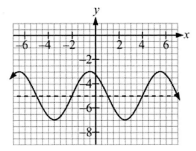

Step 3
Determine the amplitude.

The maximum value is -3, and the minimum value is -7. Therefore, the amplitude is $\dfrac{-3 - (-7)}{2} = 2$ units.

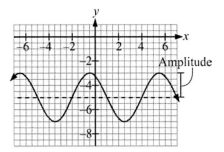

2. **Step 1**
    Determine the period.

    The value of b is 3. Therefore, the period is $\dfrac{2\pi}{b} = \dfrac{2\pi}{3}$.

    Step 2
    Determine the amplitude.

    The value of a is 9. Therefore, the amplitude is 9.

    Step 3
    Determine the horizontal midline axis.

    The value of d is 12. Therefore, the equation of the horizontal midline axis is $y = 12$.

    Step 4
    Determine the range.

    Since the horizontal midline axis is $y = 12$ and the amplitude is 9, the maximum value is $12 + 9 = 21$. Similarly, the minimum value is $12 - 9 = 3$. Therefore, the range is $3 \le y \le 21$.

ANSWERS AND SOLUTIONS
PRACTICE EXERCISES

1. **Step 1**
    Determine the period of the graph.

    A maximum occurs at $(1, 3)$ and again at $(5, 3)$. These points are $5 - 1 = 4$ units apart. Therefore, the period of the graph is 4 units.

Step 2
Determine the amplitude.

The maximum value is 3, and the minimum value is –5. Therefore, the amplitude is $\dfrac{3-(-5)}{2}=4$ units.

Step 3
Determine the horizontal midline axis.

The horizontal midline axis is $y=\dfrac{3+(-5)}{2}=-1$.

Step 4
Determine the range.

The range is $-5\le y\le 3$.

3. **Step 1**
Determine the period of the graph.

A maximum occurs at (0, 5) and again at (4, 5). These points are $4-0=4$ units apart. Therefore, the period of the graph is 4 units.

Step 2
Determine the amplitude.

The maximum value is 5, and the minimum value is –12. Therefore, the amplitude is $\dfrac{5-(-12)}{2}=8.5$ units.

Step 3
Determine the horizontal midline axis.

The horizontal midline axis is $y=\dfrac{5+(-12)}{2}=-3.5$.

Step 4
Determine the range.

The range is $-12\le y\le 5$.

5. **Step 1**
Determine the amplitude.

The value of a is $\dfrac{1}{2}$. Therefore, the amplitude is $\dfrac{1}{2}$.

Step 2
Determine the period.

The value of b is 1. Therefore, the period is $\dfrac{2\pi}{1}=2\pi$.

Step 3
Determine the horizontal midline axis.

The value of d is 8. Therefore, the equation of the horizontal midline axis is $y=8$.

Step 4
Determine the maximum and minimum values.

The horizontal midline axis is $y=8$, and the amplitude is $\dfrac{1}{2}$. Therefore, the maximum value is $8+\dfrac{1}{2}=8.5$. Similarly, the minimum value is $8-\dfrac{1}{2}=7.5$.

7. **Step 1**
Determine the value of a.

The graph has a maximum of 8 and a minimum of 2, so the amplitude is $\dfrac{8-2}{2}=3$. Therefore, the value of a is 3.

Step 2
Determine the value of b.

A maximum occurs at (–6, 8) and again at (2, 8). Therefore, the period is $2-(-6)=8$ rad, and the value of b is calculated as follows:
$$b=\dfrac{2\pi}{\text{period}}$$
$$b=\dfrac{2\pi}{8}$$
$$b=\dfrac{\pi}{4}$$

Step 3
Determine the value of d.

The horizontal midline axis is $y=\dfrac{8+2}{2}=5$.

Therefore, the value of d is 5.

Step 4
Determine the function that represents the graph.
Substitute the values of a, b, and d into the function $y = a\sin(bx) + d$.

$y = a\sin(bx) + d$

$y = 3\sin\left(\dfrac{\pi}{4}x\right) + 5$

The function that represents the graph is
$y = 3\sin\left(\dfrac{\pi}{4}x\right) + 5$.

9. **Step 1**
Determine the value of a.

The graph has a maximum of 9 and a minimum of –15, so the amplitude is $\dfrac{9 - (-15)}{2} = 12$.

Therefore, the value of a is 12.

Step 2
Determine the value of b.

A maximum occurs at (–6, 9) and again at (2, 9). Therefore, the period is $2 - (-6) = 8$ rad, and the value of b is calculated as follows:

$b = \dfrac{2\pi}{\text{period}}$

$b = \dfrac{2\pi}{8}$

$b = \dfrac{\pi}{4}$

Step 3
Determine the value of d.

The horizontal midline axis is $y = \dfrac{9 + (-15)}{2} = -3$.

Therefore, the value of d is –3.

Step 4
Determine the function that represents the graph.
Substitute the values of a, b, and d into the function $y = a\sin(bx) + d$.

$y = a\sin(bx) + d$

$y = 12\sin\left(\dfrac{\pi}{4}x\right) - 3$

The function that represents the graph is
$y = 12\sin\left(\dfrac{\pi}{4}x\right) - 3$.

Lesson 2—Solving Contextual Problems Involving Sinusoidal Functions

CLASS EXERCISES
ANSWERS AND SOLUTIONS

1. **a)** According to the given graph, the maximum height of the rider is 22 m, and the minimum height of the rider is 2 m.

   b) **Step 1**
   Determine the height of the axle.

   The axle of the wheel is the horizontal midline axis of the graph. Thus, the height of the axle is determined as follows:

   $y = \dfrac{\text{maximum} + \text{minimum}}{2}$

   $y = \dfrac{22 + 2}{2}$

   $y = \dfrac{24}{2}$

   $y = 12\,\text{m}$

   Step 2
   Determine how long it takes the rider to reach the height of the axle.

   According to the graph, the time the rider reaches a height of 12 m is 15 s after the ride begins.

   c) One complete revolution is equivalent to the period of the graph. According to the graph, the rider makes one complete revolution in 60 s.

   d) If the time for one revolution increased, then the period of the graph would increase. As a result, the graph would stretch horizontally and look wider, while the amplitude, horizontal midline axis, and range would stay the same.

2. **a)** In the function
   $h(t) = 5.08\sin(0.51t + 2.02) + 6.48$, the value of a (amplitude) is 5.08, and the value of d (horizontal midline axis) is 6.48.

   Therefore, the maximum height of the tide is $5.08 + 6.48 = 11.56$ m.

b) In the function
$h(t) = 5.08\sin(0.51t + 2.02) + 6.48$, the value of b is 0.51. Thus, the period is calculated as follows:

$$\text{period} = \frac{2\pi}{b}$$
$$\text{period} = \frac{2\pi}{0.51}$$
$$\text{period} \approx 12.3$$

The period is approximately 12.3 h.

c) **Step 1**
Determine the height of the tide at 5 h.

Substitute 5 for t in the given function, and solve for $h(t)$.
$$h(t) = 5.08\sin(0.51t + 2.02) + 6.48$$
$$h(5) = 5.08\sin(0.51(5) + 2.02) + 6.48$$
$$h(5) \approx 1.45$$

Step 2
Determine the height of the tide at 2 h.

Substitute 2 for t in the given function, and solve for $h(t)$.
$$h(t) = 5.08\sin(0.51t + 2.02) + 6.48$$
$$h(5) = 5.08\sin(0.51(2) + 2.02) + 6.48$$
$$h(5) \approx 7.00$$

Step 3
Subtract the height at 5 h from the height at 2 h.
$$7.00 - 1.45 = 5.55$$

The tide at 2 h is approximately 5.5 m taller than the tide at 5 h.

3. a) **Step 1**
Determine the value of a.

The value of a (amplitude) is given by the radius of the water wheel. The diameter of the wheel is 2.4 m. Since the radius of the wheel is half the diameter, the radius is $\frac{2.4}{2} = 1.2$.

Therefore, the value of a is 1.2.

Step 2
Determine the value of b.

The value of b is given by the formula $b = \dfrac{2\pi}{\text{period}}$. Since it takes 20 s for the wheel to make half a rotation, it will take $20 \times 2 = 40\,\text{s}$ for the wheel to make one full rotation. Therefore, the value of b is $\dfrac{2\pi}{40} = \dfrac{\pi}{20}$.

Step 3
Determine the value of d.

The value of d represents the horizontal midline axis, or median. The centre of rotation is 1.5 m above ground level. Therefore, the value of d is 1.5 m.

Step 4
Determine the function that models the height of the bucket.
Substitute the values of a, b, and d into the function $h(t) = a\sin(bt) + d$.
$$h(t) = a\sin(bt) + d$$
$$h(t) = 1.2\sin\left(\frac{\pi}{20}t\right) + 1.5$$

Therefore, the function that represents the height of the bucket on the water wheel is
$$h(t) = 1.2\sin\left(\frac{\pi}{20}t\right) + 1.5.$$

b) Using the function $h(t) = 1.2\sin\left(\dfrac{\pi}{20}t\right) + 1.5$, determine the value of $h(9)$.
$$h(t) = 1.2\sin\left(\frac{\pi}{20}t\right) + 1.5$$
$$h(9) = 1.2\sin\left(\frac{\pi}{20}(9)\right) + 1.5$$
$$h(9) \approx 2.7$$

The water bucket is 2.7 m above the ground at 9 s.

4. a) Step 1

Enter the data values into the calculator.

Start by clearing any lists already present. Press $\boxed{2nd}$ $\boxed{+}$, select 4:ClrAllLists, and press $\boxed{ENTER}$. Press $\boxed{STAT}$, and select 1:Edit.... Enter the values for time in L_1 and the values for frequency in L_2. After you have entered all the data values, you should see the following window.

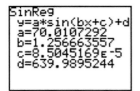

Step 2

Perform the sinusoidal regression. Press $\boxed{STAT}$ $\boxed{\triangleright}$ to highlight CALC. Select C:SinReg, and press $\boxed{ENTER}$ to obtain the following window.

```
SinReg
y=a*sin(bx+c)+d
a=70.0107292
b=1.256663557
c=8.5045169ᴇ-5
d=639.9895244
```

Step 3

Determine the sinusoidal regression function. For the data entered, $a \approx 70.01$, $b \approx 1.26$, $c \approx 0.00$, and $d \approx 639.99$. Therefore, the trigonometric equation of the function that best approximates the data is
$y = 70.01\sin(1.26x) + 639.99$, where y is the frequency of the siren after x seconds.

b) The value of b in the function
$y = 70.01\sin(1.26x) + 639.99$ is 1.26.

Therefore, the period is calculated as follows:

$\text{period} = \dfrac{2\pi}{1.26}$

$\text{period} \approx 4.99$

The period of the siren is approximately 5.0 s.

c) Use the function
$y = 70.01\sin(1.26x + 8.50) + 639.99$ to find the value of y when $x = 12$.

$y = 70.01\sin(1.26x) + 639.99$

$y = 70.01\sin(1.26(12)) + 639.99$

$y \approx 678.8$

Therefore, the frequency of the siren at 12 s is approximately 678.8 Hz.

PRACTICE EXERCISES
ANSWERS AND SOLUTIONS

1. The graph starts to repeat itself when $x = 360°$. Therefore, the period is 360°.

The period of the graph can also be determined by reasoning about the situation. Since the wheel is a circle, and a circle has 360°, the period of the graph must be 360°.

3. Step 1

Determine the measurement of θ after $1\frac{1}{2}$ revolutions.

After making $1\frac{1}{2}$ revolutions, the rock has passed through $360° + \frac{1}{2}(360°) = 540°$.

Step 2

Determine the height of the rock after a 540° rotation.

According to the graph, after a 540° rotation, the height of the rock is 28 cm. Therefore, the height of the rock after $1\frac{1}{2}$ revolutions is 28 cm.

5. The first minimum of the graph is located at (6.3, 2.0). The x-coordinate of this point gives the number of hours after 12:00 A.M. that the first minimum occurs. The value 6.3 h corresponds to 6:18 A.M. Therefore, the tide reaches its first minimum height at 6:18 A.M.

7. Step 1
Determine the maximum height of the piston head.

In the function $h = 5\sin(157.08t) + 15$,

the amplitude is 5, and the horizontal midline axis is $y = 15$. Therefore, the maximum height of the piston head is $15 + 5 = 20\,\text{cm}$.

Step 2
Determine the minimum height of the piston head. The minimum value of the function is determined by subtracting the amplitude from the value of the horizontal midline axis. Therefore, the minimum height of the piston head is $15 - 5 = 10\,\text{cm}$.

9. One cycle takes 0.04 s. The number of cycles made in 1 h, or $60 \times 60 = 3600\,\text{s}$, can be found as follows:

$$\frac{3600\,\text{s}}{x} = \frac{0.04\,\text{s}}{1\,\text{cycle}}$$

$$\frac{(3600\,\text{s})(1\,\text{cycle})}{0.04\,\text{s}} = x$$

$$90\,000\,\text{cycles} = x$$

The piston makes 90 000 complete cycles in one hour.

11. One complete revolution is equivalent to the period for the given function.

In the function $h(t) = 4\sin(0.26t + 4.71) + 6$, the value of b is 0.26. Therefore, the period is calculated as follows:

$$\text{period} = \frac{2\pi}{b}$$
$$\text{period} = \frac{2\pi}{0.26}$$
$$\text{period} \approx 24.17$$

It takes approximately 24 s for the ferris wheel to make one complete revolution.

13. Step 1
Enter the data values into the calculator.

Start by clearing any lists already present. Press 2nd +, select 4:ClrAllLists, and press ENTER. Press STAT, and select 1:Edit.... Enter the values for time in L_1 and the values for pressure in L_2.

After you have entered all the data values, you should obtain the following window.

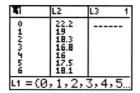

Step 2
Perform the sinusoidal regression.

Press STAT ▷ to highlight CALC. Select C:SinReg, and press ENTER to obtain the following window.

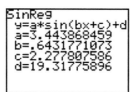

Step 3
Determine the sinusoidal regression function. For the data entered, $a \approx 3.44$, $b \approx 0.64$, $c \approx 2.28$, and $d \approx 19.31$. Therefore, the equation of the trigonometric function that best approximates the data is $y = 3.44\sin(0.64x + 2.28) + 19.31$,

where y is the pressure in PSI over a period of time, x, in hours.

15. Step 1
Determine the period of the function.

In the function $y = 3.44\sin(0.64x + 2.28) + 19.31$, $b = 0.64$, so the period of the function is $\frac{2\pi}{0.64} \approx 9.8$, or approximately 10 h.

Step 2
Make a list of times that Pierre will have good water pressure over the course of two days.

Assume that the first time that the pressure is very good is at midnight. The next time that the water pressure will be high is 10 h later at 10:00 A.M. The following list shows periods of high water pressure over 48 h:

- Day 1
  - 12:00 A.M.
  - 10:00 A.M.
  - 8:00 P.M.

- Day 2
  - 6:00 A.M.
  - 4:00 P.M.

Therefore, the times of day when the pressure is highest varies from day to day.

Note: This solution assumes that the first period of high pressure occurs at midnight. It would be possible to choose a different time of day to represent the first period of high pressure, and the results would be similar.

Practice Test

ANSWERS AND SOLUTIONS

1. **Step 1**
Determine the period.

The value of b is 5. Therefore, the period is $\dfrac{2\pi}{b} = \dfrac{2\pi}{5}$.

Step 2
Determine the amplitude.

The value of a is 3. Therefore, the amplitude is 3.

Step 3
Determine the horizontal midline axis.

The value of d is –2. Therefore, the equation of the horizontal midline axis is $y = -2$.

Step 4
Determine the range.

Since the horizontal midline axis is $y = -2$ and the amplitude is 3, the maximum value is $-2 + 3 = 1$. Similarly, the minimum value is $-2 - 3 = -5$. Therefore, the range is $-5 \le y \le 1$.

3. **Step 1**
Determine the value of a.

The graph has a maximum of 5 and a minimum of –3, so the amplitude is $\dfrac{5-(-3)}{2} = 4$. Therefore, the value of a is 4.

Step 2
Determine the value of b.

A maximum occurs at (0.5, 5) and again at (2.5, 5). Therefore, the period is $2.5 - (0.5) = 2$ units, and the value of b is calculated as follows:

$b = \dfrac{2\pi}{\text{period}}$
$b = \dfrac{2\pi}{2}$
$b = \pi$

Step 3
Determine the value of d.

The horizontal midline axis is $y = \dfrac{5+(-3)}{2} = 1$.
Therefore, the value of d is 1.

Step 4
Determine the function that represents the graph. Substitute the values of a, b, and d into the function $y = a\sin(bx) + d$.

$y = a\sin(bx) + d$
$y = 4\sin(\pi x) + 1$

The function that represents the graph is $y = 4\sin(\pi x) + 1$.

5. **Step 1**
Determine the period.

The value of b is 2. Therefore, the period is $\dfrac{2\pi}{b} = \dfrac{2\pi}{2} = \pi$.

Step 2
Determine the amplitude.

The value of a is 6. Therefore, the amplitude is 6.

Step 3
Determine the horizontal midline axis.

The value of d is 0. Therefore, the equation of the horizontal midline axis is $y = 0$.

Step 4
Determine the maximum and minimum values.

Since the horizontal midline axis is $y = 0$ and the amplitude is 6, the maximum value is $0 + 6 = 6$. Similarly, the minimum value is $0 - 6 = -6$.

Step 5
Sketch the graph.

Use the identified characteristics to sketch a graph of $y = 6\sin(2x)$.

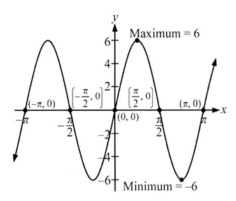

7. The cost of an average bill corresponds to the horizontal midline axis. The value of d is 136, so the horizontal midline axis is $y = 136$, and the average monthly bill is $136.00.

9. May is the fifth month, so substitute 5 for m into the function $f(m) = 59\sin(0.5m + 1.3) + 136$, and solve.
$$f(m) = 59\sin(0.5m + 1.3) + 136$$
$$f(5) = 59\sin(0.5(5) + 1.3) + 136$$
$$f(5) \approx 99.90$$

Therefore, the family can expect to pay $99.90 to heat the house in May.

11. **Step 1**
Determine the amplitude.

The amplitude of the function corresponds to the distance between the shaft of the mechanism and the lowest or highest points of the rotation. This is given in the diagram as 25 cm. Therefore, the amplitude is 25 cm.

Step 2
Determine the horizontal midline axis.

The horizontal midline axis corresponds to the height of the horse when it is exactly between its lowest and highest points. At its lowest point, the seat of a horse is 110 cm from the platform. The horizontal midline axis is 25 cm above this point.
$$110 + 25 = 135$$

Therefore, the horizontal midline axis is $y = 135$ cm.

Step 3
Determine the minimum and maximum.

The minimum is given as 110 cm. The maximum is 25 cm above the horizontal midline axis. Therefore, the maximum is $135 + 25 = 160$ cm.

Step 4
Determine the period.

The mechanism makes 20 complete rotations in 60 s, so it makes one complete rotation in $60 \div 20 = 3$ s. Therefore, the period is 3 s.

The period of the graph is 3 s. If the height of the horse is 110 cm at $t = 0$, then it will return to 110 cm at 3 s and again at 6 s. The horse will be at its maximum height of 160 cm at 1.5 s and again at 4.5 s.

13. **Step 1**
Determine the values of a, b, and d.

The amplitude is 25, so the value of a is 25. The horizontal midline axis is $y = 135$, so the value of d is 135.

The period is 3 s, so $3 = \dfrac{2\pi}{b}$.
$$3 = \frac{2\pi}{b}$$
$$3b = 2\pi$$
$$b = \frac{2\pi}{3}$$

Step 2
Determine the function that represents the height of the horse as a function of time.

Substitute the values of a, b, and d into the function $h = a\sin(bt - \dfrac{\pi}{2}) + d$.
$$h = a\sin(bt - \frac{\pi}{2}) + d$$
$$h = 25\sin(\frac{2\pi}{3}t - \frac{\pi}{2}) + 135$$

The function that represents the height of the seat of the horse is $h = 25\sin(\dfrac{2\pi}{3}t - \dfrac{\pi}{2}) + 135$.

15. Step 1
Calculate the radius of the circle travelled by the rider.

The radius of the circle travelled by the rider corresponds to the amplitude of the function. The graph has a minimum of 0.75 and a maximum of 4.75, so the amplitude is $\dfrac{4.75-0.75}{2}=2$.

Therefore, the circle travelled by the rider has a radius of 2 m.

Step 2
Calculate the radius of the merry-go-round.

At the nearest point, the girl is 0.75 m away from the fence, which is right at the edge of the platform. This means that the horse that the girl is riding must be 0.75 m from the edge.

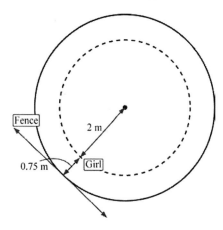

Therefore, the radius of the merry-go-round platform is 2.75 m.

17. Step 1
Enter the data values into the calculator.

Start by clearing any lists already present. Press [2nd] [+], select 4:ClrAllLists, and press [ENTER]. Press [STAT], and select 1:Edit.... Enter the day numbers into list L_1 and the number of daylight hours into list L_2.

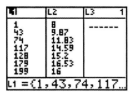

Step 2
Perform the sinusoidal regression.
Press [STAT] [▷] to highlight CALC. Select C:SinReg, and press [ENTER] to obtain the following window.

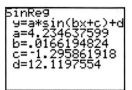

Step 3
Determine the sinusoidal regression function.

For the data entered, $a \approx 4.23$, $b \approx 0.017$, $c \approx -1.30$, and $d \approx 12.12$. Therefore, the sinusoidal function that best approximates the data is $H(d) = 4.23\sin(0.017d - 1.30) + 12.12$, where $H(t)$ is number of hours of daylight with respect to the day number, d, of the year 2011.

The day of year with the greatest number of daylight hours is given by the x-coordinate of the maximum of the function
$H(d) = 4.23\sin(0.017d - 1.30) + 12.12$.

19. Step 1
Graph the functions
$y = 4.23\sin(0.017x - 1.30) + 12.12$ and $y = 12$ on a TI-83 or similar graphing calculator.

Press [Y=], and input the first function as $y = 4.22\sin(0.02x - 1.29) + 12.12$. Press [ENTER], and then input the second function as $y = 12$. Use the window settings of x:[0, 314, 20] and y:[0, 20, 2], and press [GRAPH] to obtain this window.

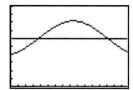

Step 2
Determine the *x*-coordinate at each of the points of intersection.

Press ⎡2nd⎤ ⎡TRACE⎤ , and select 5: intersect. When asked for the first curve, position the cursor to the left of the first point of intersection, and press ⎡ENTER⎤ .

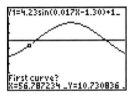

When asked for the second curve, position the cursor to the left of the first point of intersection, and press ⎡ENTER⎤ .

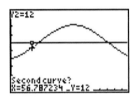

After the "Guess?" prompt, press ⎡ENTER⎤ . The results are the coordinates of the first point of intersection.

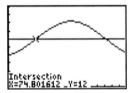

Repeat the process for the second point of intersection. Press ⎡ENTER⎤ ⎡TRACE⎤ , and select 5: intersect. When asked for the first curve, position the cursor to the left of the second point of intersection, and press ⎡ENTER⎤ .When asked for the second curve, position the cursor to the left of the second point of intersection, and press ⎡ENTER⎤ . After the "Guess?" prompt, press ⎡ENTER⎤ . The results are the coordinates of the second point of intersection.

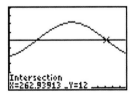

Therefore, when *y* = 12, the *x*-value is either 74.80 or 262.94. Therefore, according to the model, the hours of daylight are equal to the hours of darkness on days 75 and 263 of the year.

These days correspond to March 16, 2011, and September 20, 2011.

21. In the function
$h(t) = 3.15\sin(1.05d + 0.02) + 7.51$, substitute 45 for *t*, and solve for *h(t)*.
$h(t) = 3.15\sin(1.05d + 0.02) + 7.51$
$h(45) = 3.15\sin(1.05(45) + 0.02) + 7.51$
$h(45) \approx 7.05$

Therefore, the tip of the blade after 45 s of rotation is 7.1 m above the ground.

23. The height of the tower corresponds to the horizontal midline axis of the function. This is the value of *d* when the function is written in the form $f(x) = a\sin(bx + c) + d$.

In the function
$h(t) = 3.15\sin(1.05d + 0.02) + 7.51$, the value of *d* is 7.51. Therefore, the tower of the turbine is 7.51 m high.

Student Notes and Problems

APPENDICES

PUZZLE AND GAME GLOSSARY

Backgammon

Backgammon is a game for two players. Each player controls 15 checkers that he or she moves around the board to his or her home board. Once all of the checkers are in the home board, the player may begin removing checkers from the board. The first player to remove all of his or her checkers from the board wins the game.

The board setup, location of the home board, and direction of movement for each player is shown:

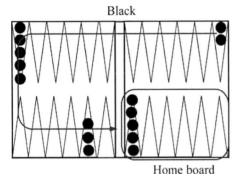

Black

Home board

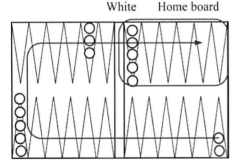

White   Home board

Players start by each rolling one die. The player with the highest roll goes first, moving one checker according to the number shown on one die and the same or a different checker according to the number shown on the other die. Play alternates, with each player rolling two dice and moving one or two checkers. If doubles are rolled, the player must move the number shown four times rather than twice.

No player may land on a spot covered by two or more of the opponent's checkers. If a player lands on a spot covered by one of the opponent's checkers, then the checker that was landed on is moved to the bar in the middle of the board. If a player has any checkers on the bar in the middle, then that player must use one roll to place it in the opponent's home board before moving any other checkers. If a player has no legal moves, then he or she misses a turn.

Once all of a player's checkers are in the home board, that player may begin moving his or her checkers off of the board. The first player to remove all of his or her checkers wins the game. If a player wins before the opponent has removed any of his or her pieces from the board, then this is called a gammon. If the opponent still has checkers on the bar or in the opposing home board, then the win is called a backgammon.

Battleships

Battleships is a game for two players. Each player has a hidden 10-by-10 grid on which the following five ships are placed either horizontally or vertically. (The names of the ships vary in different versions of the rules):

• Aircraft carrier—5 squares
• Battleship—4 squares
• Submarine—3 squares
• Destroyer—3 squares
• Patrol boat—2 squares

The object of the game is to discover the location of the opponent's ships. On his or her turn, each player names the location of a square that is being shot at.
The opponent must name the shot as either a hit or a miss. Once all of the squares of a ship have been hit, the ship's controller announces that it is sunk. The first player to sink all of the opponent's ships wins the game.

Bulls and Cows

In the game of Bulls and Cows, one player (player 1) chooses a secret number with an agreed-upon number of digits (usually between three and six) and no repeating digits. The other player uses logical reasoning to determine the hidden number. Player 2 guesses numbers, and player 1 indicates how many digits were correct. For every digit that is correct and in the correct place, player 1 gives player 2 a bull. For digits that are contained in the number but are incorrectly placed, player 2 gets a cow.

For example, if the hidden number is 1 836, and player 2 guesses 3 865, one bull is given for the digit 8 being in the correct position, and two cows are given for 3 and 6, which are not in the correct positions. Player 2 has no way of knowing which digits are the cows and which digit is the bull.

The object of the game is to determine the secret number in the fewest possible guesses.

Checkers

Checkers is played by two players on an 8-by-8 grid with the following starting setup:

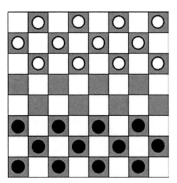

Each player chooses a colour, and on their turn they move one piece at a time. Any piece may slide one space diagonally into an unoccupied square. A piece can capture an opponent's piece by jumping over it diagonally into an unoccupied square. Captured pieces are removed from play. The capturing checker must move again if another capture is possible. Capturing moves must be made whenever possible.

Regular pieces may move forward only. Once a piece reaches the opposite side of the board, it becomes a king. This is usually indicated by stacking an additional checker on top of the kinged checker. A king may move diagonally forward or backward.

The player who captures all of the opponent's checkers or leaves the opponent with no legal moves wins the game.

Kakuro

Kakuro is a logical reasoning game. It is also known as Cross Sums. The goal of Kakuro is to completely fill in a grid so that the sum of the numbers in a row or column adds up to the numbers given in the clue to the left of the row or above the column. Only the numbers 1 through 9 are used, and no number can appear twice in one sum.

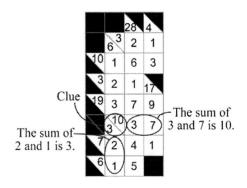

Logic Puzzles

Logic puzzles are logical reasoning games in which a series of clues are used to resolve a given situation. Common situations include matching people's names with their hobby, pet, job, and so on. Grids and tables are both commonly used in the solutions to logic problems.

Consider the following example of a logic problem, together with a grid and a table that may be used to solve it:

Maddy, Isaiah, and Raya are all extremely busy with their hobbies (building model airplanes, stamp collecting, and scrapbooking) and sports (swimming, soccer, and track and field). Determine who enjoys each hobby and sport, given the following information:

- The soccer player enjoys making scrapbooks.
- The swimmer, the model-airplane maker, and Maddy walk to school together every morning.
- Raya is afraid of water.

	Model airplanes	Stamp collecting	Scrapbooking	Swimming	Soccer	Track and field
Maddy						
Isaiah						
Raya						
Swimming						
Soccer						
Track						

Name	Hobby	Sport

The three given clues are sufficient to complete the grid and the table, thereby identifying which student enjoys each hobby and sport.

	Model airplanes	Stamp collecting	Scrapbooking	Swimming	Soccer	Track and field
Maddy	×	×	✓	×	✓	×
Isaiah	×	✓	×	✓	×	×
Raya	✓	×	×	×	×	✓
Swimming	×	✓	×			
Soccer	×	×	✓			
Track	✓	×	×			

Name	Hobby	Sport
Maddy	Scrapbooking	Soccer
Isaiah	Stamp collecting	Swimming
Raya	Model airplanes	Track and field

Minesweeper

Minesweeper is a game for one player. It is a computer game played on a grid containing a specified number of hidden mines, which must be located using logical reasoning.

The game begins with a blank grid. The size of the grid and the number of hidden mines vary depending on the difficulty of the game.

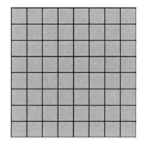

The player clicks on squares to reveal what is underneath. Numbered squares indicate how many mines are vertically, horizontally, or diagonally adjacent. Empty squares have no adjacent mines.

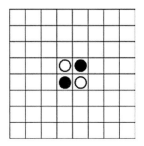

The game is won if the contents of the grid are revealed without clicking on a mine.

Reversi

Reversi is played by two players on an 8-by-8 grid with the following starting setup:

Each piece is identical, with black on one side and white on the other side. On a player's turn, that player places a piece with his or her colour facing up onto the board, capturing one or more of the opponent's pieces. A player captures another player's pieces by surrounding a vertical, horizontal, or diagonal row with his or her own pieces. If a player cannot make a capture, then the turn is missed.

In the following situation, if white plays in the starred square, then a vertical row and a diagonal row of black pieces are surrounded. Black will be forced to flip over all of the pieces in the grey-shaded squares so that the white side faces up.

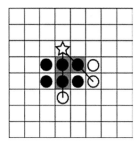

The player whose pieces cover the majority of squares at the end of the game is the winner.

Spokes

Spokes is a logical reasoning game in which a player must determine the location of spokes linking a set of circles. The circles can be arranged in a triangular or rectangular pattern, and the difficulty of the puzzle depends on the number of circles given. Each circle gives the number of spokes that connect that circle to adjacent circles.

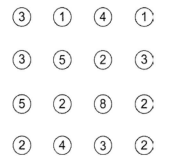

Spokes may connect circles horizontally, vertically, or diagonally, but spokes may never cross each other. The location of all of the spokes can be determined using logical reasoning.

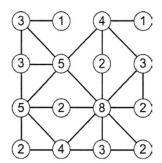

Sudoku

Sudoku is a logical reasoning game played on a grid that is divided into smaller boxes. The size of the grid varies depending on the difficulty of the puzzle, but the most common size is a 9-by-9 grid divided into nine 3-by-3 boxes.

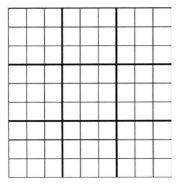

In a 9-by-9 puzzle, the numbers 1 through 9 must be placed on the grid so that no number is repeated in any column, row, or 3-by-3 box. Some numbers are given, and the remainder must be filled in using logical reasoning. In the given puzzle, shaded numbers were given, and the remaining numbers were filled in using logical reasoning.

6	5	3	9	8	1	4	7	2
9	2	4	6	7	5	3	1	8
7	8	1	4	2	3	9	6	5
2	9	6	7	4	8	5	3	1
1	4	7	5	3	6	2	8	9
8	3	5	1	9	2	6	4	7
4	7	2	3	1	9	8	5	6
5	1	9	8	6	4	7	2	3
3	6	8	2	5	7	1	9	4

PUZZLE SOLUTIONS

Lesson 2: Logical Reasoning Games

ELIMINATING POSSIBILITIES
ANSWERS AND SOLUTIONS

Example

1	3	5	6	2	4
4	2	6	5	1	3
2	5	4	1	3	6
6	1	3	4	5	2
5	6	2	3	4	1
3	4	1	2	6	5

Class Exercise 1

Use the total number of cows and bulls given for each guess to determine the digits included in the secret number. Assuming that only one digit was replaced in each guess, the following guidelines can be used:

- If the number of correct digits increases by one, then an incorrect digit was replaced with a correct digit.
- If the number of correct digits decreases by one, then a correct digit was replaced with an incorrect digit.
- If the number of correct digits remains the same, then either a correct digit was replaced with another correct digit or an incorrect digit was replaced with another incorrect digit.

Step 1
Analyze the second guess.

The digit 1 was replaced with 5, and the number of correct digits remained the same, so 1 and 5 are either both correct or both incorrect.

Step 2
Analyze the third guess.

The digit 2 was replaced with 6, and the number of correct digits decreased by one, so 2 is correct, and 6 is incorrect.

   Copyright Protected

Step 3
Analyze the fourth guess.

Two changes were made in the fourth guess. The incorrect 6 was replaced with a correct 2, so the number of correct digits went from two to three.

Also, 3 was replaced with 7, and the number of correct digits remained at three, so 3 and 7 are either both correct or both incorrect.

Step 4
Analyze the fifth guess.

The digit 4 was replaced with 8, and the number of correct digits decreased by one, so 4 is correct, and 8 is incorrect.

Step 5
Analyze the sixth guess.

The digit 5 was replaced with 9, and the number of correct digits decreased by one, so 5 is correct, and 9 is incorrect. Also, based on the second guess, you know that because 5 is correct, 1 is also correct.

Therefore, the correct digits are 2, 4, 5, and 1.

TRIAL AND ERROR
ANSWERS AND SOLUTIONS

Example

2	7	4	1	8	9	3	5	6
8	1	3	5	7	6	4	2	9
5	6	9	3	2	4	1	8	7
1	3	5	8	4	7	6	9	2
9	8	2	6	3	5	7	4	1
7	4	6	2	9	1	5	3	8
6	5	8	9	1	3	2	7	4
3	2	7	4	6	8	9	1	5
4	9	1	7	5	2	8	6	3

Class Exercise 3

5	1	7	4	2	3	8	9	6
2	4	6	8	1	9	7	5	3
8	9	3	6	5	7	4	2	1
4	6	8	2	7	1	9	3	5
3	2	5	9	6	8	1	7	4
1	7	9	5	3	4	6	8	2
9	8	2	3	4	6	5	1	7
6	5	1	7	9	2	3	4	8
7	3	4	1	8	5	2	6	9

SIMPLIFYING THE
ORIGINAL PROBLEM
ANSWERS AND SOLUTIONS

Example

Practice Exercises
2.

3.

4.

2	3	1	3
1	3	4	2
3	3	4	4
2	4	2	2

5.

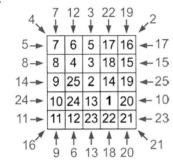

Practice Test

5.

♥	♦	♥	♧
♤	♣	♦	♢
♦	♧	♠	♣
♠	♣	♡	♧

7.

2	3	③	①	4
④	①	3	2	5
①	②	④	2	7
①	③	2	④	8
6	6	7	5	

GLOSSARY

Amplitude   Amplitude is the vertical distance from the horizontal midline axis to any maximum or minimum y-value of a sinusoidal function. The amplitude of $y = a\sin(bx + c) + d$ is $a = \dfrac{\text{maximum} - \text{minimum}}{2}$.

Change of base formula   The change of base formula is $\log_b c = \dfrac{\log_a c}{\log_a b}$, where $a > 0$ and $a \neq 1$. It is used to connect logarithmic expressions with different bases.

Combination   A combination is a selection of objects from a larger set in which the order does not matter. The number of combinations of n objects taken r at a time is $_nC_r = \dfrac{n!}{(n-r)!\,r!}$, where $n \geq r$.

Common logarithm   Any logarithm with a base of 10

Complement   The complement of set A is defined as all elements not included in the set but found within the given universe. This is denoted as A' or $\overline{A}$.

Complementary events   Complementary events are two mutually exclusive events with probabilities that have a sum of 1. The complement, A' or $\overline{A}$, of an event A is the set of all of the outcomes in the sample space that are not elements of A.

Compound event   An event involving two or more simple events

Cubic function   A function of the form $y = ax^3 + bx^2 + cx + d$, where a, b, c, and d are real numbers, and $a \neq 0$

Cubic regression   A technique for finding the best-fitting cubic function for a set of data that appears to follow a cubic pattern

Degree   The degree of a polynomial function is equal to the sum of the multiplicities of its zeros. In general, the degree of a polynomial function of the form $a_n x^n + a_{n-1} x^{n-1} + a_{n-2} x^{n-2} + \ldots + a_2 x^2 + a_1 x + a_0$ is n.

Dependent events   Two events in which the outcome of one event affects the probability of the other event

Disjoint   Sets are disjoint if they have no common elements. This is denoted as $A \cap B = \varnothing$.

Doubling period   The amount of time it takes for a quantity to double

Empty set   The set containing no elements, denoted $\varnothing$ or { }

Event   A subset of a given sample space

Exponential decay   Decrease in number or size at a progressively less rapid rate

Exponential equation   An equation with the variable in the exponent

Exponential function   A function of the form $y = a \cdot b^x$, where a represents either the y-intercept or the initial value, and the b value is always positive and determines the rate of growth or decay

Exponential growth   Increase in number or size at a progressively more rapid rate

Exponential regression   A technique for finding the best-fitting exponential function to represent exponential data

Factorial notation   Factorial notation is shorthand mathematical notation for multiplying descending sequences. In general, $n! = n \times (n-1) \times (n-2) \times ... \times 2 \times 1$.

Fundamental counting principle   If a task is made up of several stages in which there are m ways to accomplish stage 1, n ways to accomplish stage 2, p ways to accomplish stage 3, and so on, then the total ways to accomplish the entire task (stage 1, stage 2, stage 3, and so on) is $m \times n \times p \times ....$

Half-life   The amount of time it takes for half of a given amount of radioactive substance to undergo nuclear decay

Horizontal midline axis   The horizontal midline axis is the line located halfway between the maximum and minimum points of a sinusoidal function.
The horizontal midline axis of $y = a\sin(bx + c) + d$
is $y = d = \dfrac{\text{maximum} + \text{minimum}}{2}$.

Independent events   Two events in which the outcome of one event does not affect the probability of the other event

Intersection   The intersection of sets A and B consists of all elements contained in set A that are also contained in set B. This is denoted as $A \cap B$.

Linear function   Models a straight line with a positive or negative slope and is given by the equation $y = ax + b$, where a represents the slope, and b is the y-intercept

Linear regression   A technique for finding the best-fitting linear function for a set of data that follows a straight line with a positive or negative slope

Logarithmic expression   A technique for finding the best-fitting linear function for a set of data that follows a straight line with a positive or negative slope

Logarithmic function   A logarithmic function is of the form $y = \log_B x$, where $B > 0$, $B \neq 1$, and $x > 0$. If $B > 1$, the function is increasing. If $0 < B < 1$, the function is decreasing.

Logarithmic regression   A technique for finding the best-fitting logarithmic function that represents logarithmic data

Maximum   The y-coordinate of the highest point on the graph of a quadratic or sinusoidal function

Minimum   The y-coordinate of the lowest point on the graph of a quadratic or sinusoidal function

Multiplicity   The number of times that a specific value is a zero for a given function

Mutually exclusive events   Events that do not have any common outcomes

Natural logarithm   A natural logarithm is any logarithm that has a base of e, where e is an irrational number approximately equal to 2.71828. The natural logarithm is denoted as ln.

Non-mutually exclusive events   Events that have at least one common outcome

Non-permissible values   Values of the variable that make the denominator of a rational expression equal to 0

Odds against   The ratio of unfavourable outcomes to favourable outcomes for an event

Odds in favour   The ratio of favourable outcomes to unfavourable outcomes for an event

Period   The period is the length of the shortest repeating section of a periodic function. The period of $y = a\sin(bx + c) + d$ is $\dfrac{2\pi}{b}$.

Periodic function   The graphs of periodic functions repeat the same y-value for some consistent increase in the domain value.

Permutation   The graphs of periodic functions repeat the same y-value for some consistent increase in the domain value.

pH scale   A pH scale is a logarithmic scale used to indicate how acidic or basic a substance is. The scale has a range from 0 to 14, where a pH of 7 is neutral, pH values less than 7 are acidic, and pH values greater than 7 are basic.

Phase shift   A phase shift is the horizontal translation of a sinusoidal graph. If $c \neq 0$ in the function $y = a\sin(bx + c) + d$, a phase shift has occurred.

Polynomial function   A function of the form $a_n x^n + a_{n-1} x^{n-1} + a_{n-2} x^{n-2} + ... + a_2 x^2 + a_1 x + a_0$, where a_0, a_1, a_2, ... a_n are real numbers, and n represents a positive whole number

Power law of logarithms $\log_a(M^n) = n \log_a M$

Probability   Probability is the ratio of favourable outcomes for an event to the total possible outcomes in which all outcomes are equally likely. The probability, $P(E)$, of an event is given by the formula

$$P(E) = \frac{\text{number of favourable outcomes}}{\text{total number of possible outcomes}}.$$

Quadratic function   Models a set of data that follows a parabolic pattern and is given by the equation $y = ax^2 + bx + c$, where a, b, and c are real numbers, and $a \neq 0$, or $y = a(x - p)^2 + q$, where a, p, and q are real numbers, and $a \neq 0$

Quadratic regression   A technique for finding the best-fitting quadratic function for a set of data that appears to follow a parabolic pattern

Quotient law of logarithms

$$\log_a\left(\frac{M}{N}\right) = \log_a M - \log_a N$$

Rational expression   An expression of the form $\dfrac{f(x)}{g(x)}$, where $f(x)$ and $g(x)$ are polynomials, and $g(x) \neq 0$

Richter scale   The Richter scale is the logarithmic scale used to indicate the intensity of earthquakes. The scale has no upper limit, but any earthquake with a magnitude of 2 or less is considered a microearthquake, and earthquakes with a magnitude of 6 or more are considered strong.

Roster form   A list of the elements in a set written between curly brackets, such as {2, 3, 4}

Sample space   The set of possible outcomes in a probability experiment

Set   A collection of distinct objects, such as people, items, or numbers

Set builder notation   Shorthand mathematical notation used to describe a set according to the properties of its elements

Sinusoidal function   A function that can be defined by the equation $y = a\sin(bx + c) + d$, where a, b, c, and d are real numbers, and $a \neq 0$

Sinusoidal regression   The technique for finding the best-fitting sinusoidal function for a set of data that appears to follow a sinusoidal pattern

Subset   Set A is considered a subset of B when set A is completely contained in set B. This is denoted as $A \subset B$.

Union   The union of sets A and B consists of all the elements found in set A or set B. This is denoted as $A \cup B$.

Universal set   A set that is the larger, inclusive set from which elements can be considered

Zero   A zero is a value of x that makes a function equal to 0. The zeros of a function are the x-intercepts of the graph of the function and the roots of the corresponding equation.

Credits

Every effort has been made to provide proper acknowledgement of the original source and to comply with copyright law. However, some attempts to establish original copyright ownership may have been unsuccessful. If copyright ownership can be identified, please notify Castle Rock Research Corp so that appropriate corrective action can be taken.

Some images in this document are from www.clipart.com, copyright © 2012 Getty Images.

NOTES

496 Copyright Protected

Looking for extra practice?

Try

solaro

- Extra practice questions
- Detailed curriculum-aligned lessons
- Available online and on mobile devices

www.solaro.com

BOOK ORDERING INFORMATION

SENIOR HIGH SCHOOL TITLES

Castle Rock Research offers the following resources to support Alberta students. You can order any of these materials online at:

www.castlerockresearch.com/store

SOLARO.com - Study Online		The KEY		SNAP	Prob Solved	Class Notes
$29.95 ea.*		$29.95 ea.*		$29.95 ea.*	$19.95 ea.*	$19.95 ea.*
Biology 30	Mathematics 30-1	Biology 30	Mathematics 30-1	Biology 20	Biology 20	Biology 20
Biology 20	Mathematics 30-2	Biology 20	Mathematics 30-2	Chemistry 30	Chemistry 30	Chemistry 30
Chemistry 30	Mathematics 30-3	Chemistry 30	Mathematics 20-1	Chemistry 20	Chemistry 20	Chemistry 20
Chemistry 20	Mathematics 20-1	Chemistry 20	Mathematics 10 C	Mathematics 30-1	Mathematics 30-1	Mathematics 30-1
Physics 30	Mathematics 20-2	English 30-1	Social Studies 30-1	Mathematics 30-2	Mathematics 30-2	Mathematics 30-2
Physics 20	Mathematics 20-3	English 30-2	Social Studies 30-2	Mathematics 31	Mathematics 31	Mathematics 31
Science 30	Mathematics 20-4	English 20-1	Social Studies 20-1	Mathematics 20-1	Mathematics 20-1	Mathematics 20-1
Science 20	Mathematics 10 C	English 10-1	Social Studies 10-1	Mathematics 10 C	Mathematics 10 C	Mathematics 10 C
Science 10	Mathematics 10-3	Physics 30		Physics 30	Physics 30	Physics 30
English 30-1	Mathematics 10-4	Physics 20		Physics 20	Physics 20	Physics 20
English 30-2	Social Studies 30-1	Science 10		Science 10	Science 10	Science 10
English 20-1	Social Studies 30-2					
English 20-2	Social Studies 20-1					
English 10-1	Social Studies 10-1					
English 10-2						

Prices do not include taxes or shipping.

Study online using **SOLARO,** with access to multiple courses available by either a monthly or an annual subscription.

The KEY Study Guide is specifically designed to assist students in preparing for unit tests, final exams, and provincial examinations.

The **Student Notes and Problems (SNAP) Workbook** contains complete explanations of curriculum concepts, examples, and exercise questions.

The **Problem Solved** contains exercise questions and complete solutions.

The **Class Notes** contains complete explanations of curriculum concepts.

If you would like to order Castle Rock resources for your school, please visit our school ordering page:

www.castlerockresearch.com/school-orders/

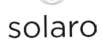